Lab-in-a-Box:
Introductory Experiments
in Electric Circuits

Revised Third Edition

Lab-in-a-Box: Introductory Experiments in Electric Circuits

Revised Third Edition

Robert W. Hendricks

Kathleen Meehan

Virginia Tech

John Wiley & Sons, Inc.

"It is only through refined measurements and careful experimentation that we can have a wider vision. And then we see unexpected things: we see things that are far from what we would guess – far from what we could have imagined. Our imagination is stretched to the utmost, not, as in fiction, to imagine things which are not really there, but just to comprehend those things which *are* there."

— Richard Feynman

Contents

Preface...ix

To the Student xiii

Chapter 1: Introduction 1

Chapter 2: The Scientific Method..7

  2.1 The Scientific Method 8

  2.2 Acquisition of Data...11

  2.3 Analysis of Data...13

  2.4 Presentation of Data...15

  2.5 Preparation of Reports and Papers...18

  2.6 References...19

Chapter 3: Experimental Methods 23

  3.1 Laboratory Safety 23

  3.2 Laboratory Notebooks 27

  3.3 The RSR/VT Analog & Digital Trainer 29

  3.4 Circuit Breadboarding and Wiring 30

  3.5 Digital Multimeter 37

  3.6 Oscilloscope...41

  3.7 Working with Wires and AWG Wire Sizes...44

  3.8 Resistors...48

  3.9 Capacitors 52

  3.10 Inductors 56

  3.11 Trimmer Potentiometers (Trim pots)...59

  3.12 Operational Amplifiers 62

  3.13 Light-Emitting Diodes (LEDs) 65

  3.14 555 Timer...69

  3.15 References...70

Chapter 4: Experiments...75

  Experiment 1: Breadboard Basics...79

  Experiment 2: Component Tolerances 85

  Experiment 3: Ohm's Law...91

  Experiment 4: Kirchhoff's Laws 95

  Experiment 5: Series and Parallel Resistors 99

  Experiment 6: Voltage and Current Dividers 103

  Experiment 7: Delta-Wye Configurations 109

  Experiment 8: Mesh Current and Node Voltage Analysis 113

  Experiment 9: Superposition and Thévenin Equivalent 117

  Experiment 10: Measuring Equivalent Resistances.....................................121

  Experiment 11: An Inverting Amplifier Circuit 129

  Experiment 12: A Non-Inverting Amplifier Circuit.....................................135

Contents

Experiment 13: Current Source (Voltage-to-Current Converter) 141

Experiment 14: Series RC Circuit 149

Experiment 15: Metronome Circuit Using a 555 Timer 157

Experiment 16: A Differentiator Circuit 163

Experiment 17: A Circuit with Two Ideal Differentiators 171

Experiment 18: An Integrator Circuit 179

Experiment 19: Design A Voltmeter 187

Experiment 20: Design a Logic Probe 191

Experiment 21: Design A Traffic Arrow 197

Experiment 22: Introduction to Phasors 203

Experiment 23: Phasor Analysis and Kirchhoff's Current Law 209

Experiment 24: Using Nodal or Mesh Analysis to Solve AC Circuits 213

Experiment 25: Simulated Inductance (The Gyrator) 217

Experiment 26: The Wien-Bridge Oscillator 221

Experiment 27: Complex Power in AC Circuit Analysis 225

Experiment 28: A Three Phase Power Supply 235

Experiment 29: Three-Phase Loads 241

Experiment 30: Transformer Dot Markings and Turns Ratios 247

Experiment 31: Properties of a Real Transformer 251

Experiment 32: Hybrid Couplers 259

Experiment 33: Passive Filters 265

Experiment 34: An Active Filter 271

Experiment 35: Sweeping Passive Filters 275

Experiment 36: Impedance Transmission Parameters 281

Experiment 37: Electromagnetic Interference 291

Experiment 38: Noise and the Instrumentation Amplifier 299

Acknowledgements 305

About the Authors 307

Meet the Developers 309

Appendix A: Parts List 313

Appendix B: Recommended Bibliography 315

Appendix C: Elements of Statistical Analysis of Data 317

Appendix D: MATLAB Codes 327

D.1 Experiment 27–complexpowerlab.m 327

D.2 Experiment 34–networkfunction.m 331

Appendix E: Derived SI Units 333

Appendix F: SI and PSpice Prefixes 333

Photo Credits 335

Preface

Lab-in-a-Box, a concept that originated with the ECE Department at the University of Washington and was generously shared with Virginia Tech, has been developed to assist students enrolled in their first course(s) in electric circuits gain a hands-on experience in experimental research by creating and measuring simple AC and DC circuits. The experiments have been designed to support several textbooks on electric circuits and are easily adapted to both single-semester and two-semester courses. All experimental work can be performed by the student at home or at a study break table using student-owned equipment; no dedicated laboratory space or university-owned equipment is required. Student learning is enhanced through an integrated approach that includes mathematical analysis and computer modeling of the circuits under construction.

Learning Objectives

The Lab-in-a-Box concept has three learning objectives, each of which addresses one or more of the ABET "a–k" objectives. Having successfully completed the experiments described in this text, the student will be able to:

- build a variety of AC and DC circuits on a student-owned analog and digital trainer kit using student-owned tools and components to departmental wiring standards;

- measure and characterize these circuits using a student-owned digital multimeter and oscilloscope; and

- analyze and model circuit performance using modern mathematical tools such as MATLAB and PSpice and compare with the experimental measurements.

An important learning objective of Lab-in-a-Box is to integrate mathematical analysis and, where appropriate, computer simulation, with experimental observation. With this integrated approach, students are shown that careful analysis prior to building a circuit is required to assure that experimental results are both reasonable and as expected. Thus, each experiment includes instructions for a mathematical analysis and, in some cases, a computer simulation of the circuit under consideration. Although several circuit modeling programs are available, we have developed our experiments around Cadence OrCAD PSpice version 9.1 and OrCAD PSpice Demo version 10.0 for three reasons: both are available to students at no cost, many introductory texts include PSpice instructions, and there are several good PSpice tutorial texts available.

Each experiment is designed to be performed as a homework problem or as an exercise in a traditional laboratory setting and should take approximately one to two hours to complete. However, several experiments will take longer. Required components include a powered breadboard, resistors, capacitors, inductors, op amps, transformers, and LEDs. Some measurements are made with a digital multimeter (DMM), while signal traces for time-varying signals (transients and periodic signals) are observed using an oscilloscope. The oscilloscope may be a program that allows the student to convert a PC equipped with a sound card into a simple oscilloscope, a more sophisticated USB device attached to a PC with an accompanying oscilloscope software package, or a true stand-alone oscilloscope. The choice of equipment is, of course, determined by the cost that the instructor and/or curriculum committee deems appropriate for the course(s) involved.

Additional objectives of Lab-in-a-Box include introducing students to the scientific method and teaching them the basic concepts of experimental design, data acquisition, analysis, and reporting of technical results. To this end, students will learn: how to identify electronic components and how to read their specifications; how to wire experiments neatly in order to increase both analysis and debugging efficiency; how to make experimental DC measurements with a digital multimeter (voltage, current, resistance, and capacitance); how to make experimental AC measurements with an oscilloscope; the role of component tolerances in the performance of real circuits; the role of statistical variability of component values and the propagation of errors in the analysis of data; and how to maintain a laboratory notebook and present experimental results.

Features   The pedagogical benefits of Lab-in-a-Box are several:

- The behavior and properties of real devices and components such as wires, resistors, capacitors, inductors, transformers, and LEDs are emphasized. The differences in performance between actual devices and the idealized components discussed in standard textbooks on electric circuits are made real to the student through measurement and observation.

- The relationship between design, analysis, and testing is emphasized. In almost every experiment the student first analyzes the circuit, either analytically or with a computer modeling language such as MATLAB or PSpice, to determine how the circuit should perform. The student then builds and tests the circuit to determine its actual performance. The performance of the as-built circuit is compared with the expected performance and discrepancies are explored in terms of the properties and performance of the components.

- Attention is paid to the accuracy and precision of experimental measurements, as well as to an analysis of the errors associated with many of the experiments.

- The hands-on experience offered by Lab-in-a-Box is enthusiastically endorsed by the great majority of students who have completed courses that use this approach. Students are more excited about their Lab-in-a-Box learning experience than with their experience in the more classical university-operated labs.

- Students particularly enjoy the opportunity to perform the experiments in a location and at a time of their choosing.

- Many students take advantage of the opportunity to explore circuits encountered in other courses by building and testing them using their Lab-in-a-Box components. Some even purchase additional components for such experiments.

Revisions

The revisions to the third edition result from the increasing availability of relatively inexpensive USB oscilloscopes. There are several on the market that have the capability to measure signals on two channels and have an arbitrary function generator integrated into the unit. The frequency range is well beyond the limitations of the sound card used with the software oscilloscope, which has allowed the development of a number of new experiments. Some of these experiments have been included in the present edition. In addition, many of these oscilloscopes have additional functionality that allows students to investigate ac circuits in more depth. In addition, the experiments on inverting and non-inverting amplifiers have been rewritten so that the students use their oscilloscopes earlier and, thus, gain greater familiarity with its operation.

Instructor Resources

To assist instructors who teach Lab-in-a-Box as well as to assist the those who grade the laboratory reports, there is an Instructor's Manual that contains helpful information for designing and setting up a Lab-in-a-Box course and typical experimental results for each experiment. This manual is available to instructors who adopt this book.

Errata

Although every effort has been made to assure that the experimental techniques presented in this text, as well as the experiments themselves, are correct and will perform as expected, errors are bound to occur. Such errors should be reported to the authors at **authors@lab-in-a-box.net**. Corrections and errata will be posted regularly to our website at **http://www.lab-in-a-box.net**.

Robert W. Hendricks
Kathleen Meehan

Blacksburg, Virginia
August 2011

To the Student

Welcome to Lab-in-a-Box, a new concept for laboratory instruction in introductory electric circuits courses. Lab-in-a-Box has been designed to help you gain hands-on experience by having you analyze, build, and measure simple AC and DC circuits. You will be able to perform experimental work at home or at a study break table using equipment that you own. Your learning experience will be enhanced through an integrated approach that includes mathematical analysis and computer modeling of the circuits under construction using computational tools that are industry-standard: MATLAB and Cadence OrCAD PSpice.

Organization

The book is organized with a number of supporting chapters presented before the detailed descriptions of the experiments. First, in Chapter 1 we present a brief introduction to pedagogy and learning styles and an overview of the Lab-in-a-Box lab kit. Then, in Chapter 2 you are introduced to the scientific method including such topics as how science is done, modern criticisms of science, the design of experiments, the acquisition, analysis, and presentation of data, and the preparation of reports. These are topics that are critical for the education of scientists and engineers, but appear to be only rarely covered in current engineering and science programs. Next, in Chapter 3, an introduction to experimental methods of relevance to electrical engineering and in particular to the Lab-in-a-Box experiments is presented. These include such topics as general electrical safety, as well as laboratory safety, preparation of lab notebooks, circuit breadboarding, digital multimeters, oscilloscopes, and various electrical components (wires, resistors, capacitors, inductors, op amps, and LEDs). These topics are presented because they are rarely discussed elsewhere in the engineering curriculum. Finally, the thirty-eight experiments are presented in Chapter 4. Their order of presentation roughly follows the order of presentation of the topics in most introductory electric circuits textbooks.[†] Thus, you can use this text with little difficulty regardless of the text your instructor has chosen for the lecture course.

Although it is recommended that you read Chapters 2 and 3 in their entirety prior to embarking on your experimental work, liberal cross-references to relevant experimental techniques and component information are given both in the references for each experiment and in each experimental procedure. With but few exceptions, all necessary information required to perform and understand each experiment is included in your textbook, the PSpice and MATLAB tutorials, or this book. The tutorials ad other supplemental materials are available at the text website **www.lab-in-a-box.net**.

Format of Experiments

The experiments presented in Chapter 4 follow a standard layout. First, the various developers of the experiment are identified. Brief biographies of each are given in "Meet the Developers" to put a human face on the large team of

---

[†] A list of possible accompanying textbooks is given in Table 18 found in Chapter 4.

students, staff and faculty who have been involved in this project. You will note that the majority of experiments presented in this text were developed by undergraduate students such as yourselves after they had completed a two-semester sequence that covered both DC and AC circuits.

Table 1: Generic components of Lab-in-a-Box

1. A powered breadboard (the RSR/VT analog and digital "ANDY" trainer)
2. A digital multimeter (DMM)
3. A tool kit that includes a wire cutter and stripper, screw drivers, needle-nose pliers, and tweezers
4. A laptop PC with a USB dual channel oscilloscope and arbitrary function generator
5. A resistor kit with 5 each of 73 standard-value, 5% tolerance resistors
6. A wire kit with six spools of different color wire
7. A kit of course-specific components that includes resistors, capacitors, inductors, LEDs, trim pots, op amp chips, 555 timers, audio speaker, and transformers

Following a brief statement of the objectives of the experiment, a graph showing the distribution of completion times for each experiment by typical students and a section on preparation for the experiment are given. A section on background information for the experiment follows. A list of references for outside reading is given as appropriate to set the proper perspective for the experiment. It is important to note that the background does not purport to be a detailed and/or inclusive statement of the underlying theory for the experiment. That is the function of the textbook selected by your instructor to accompany the lecture portion of the course(s). Rather, the background gives only a brief overview of the experiment with the necessary equations quoted without proof or derivation. However, necessary details not found in the textbooks are presented in some detail. These sections are followed by a list of necessary equipment and supplies and a description of the experimental procedure. The experimental procedure includes several subsections. There is almost always a section on mathematical analysis of the circuit under consideration that may include calculations that should be performed using MATLAB, typically a section on PSpice modeling of that circuit, and then an experimental procedure for building and testing the circuit. Laboratory notebooks may be prepared in standard bound laboratory notebooks, in computer-based word processing programs such as Microsoft (MS) Word, or in computational programs such as MATLAB. Templates for each experiment, suitable for preparation of lab notebooks, are provided as MS Excel or Word files for student calculations and experimental results at the text website found at: **http://www.lab-in-a-box.net**.

Materials and Supplies

To perform the experiments described in this book, Lab-in-a-Box requires the generic materials and supplies shown in Table 1. Detailed specifications for each item may be found in Appendix A. Although equivalent components are available from a variety of electronics supply houses, we have developed a "one-stop shopping" arrangement by which all components have been made available from Electronix Express (Electronics Express, 2008). This assures that you can obtain the correct materials, at modest cost, from a single source. Also, we have found that an inexpensive plastic fishing tackle box provides excellent storage for all components. Many such boxes are available at sporting goods shops or even at "big box" stores such as K-Mart or Wal-Mart. We have found the Plano Model 7271 (Plano, 2008), usually available at Wal-Mart for about $25, to be excellent.

Computer Use

Lab-in-a-Box makes extensive use of personal computers. First, MATLAB and/or Excel are used for analyzing and graphing experimental results, while MS Word is used for preparing lab reports. Of course, other programs with similar capabilities and operating on either a PC or on an Apple Mac could be used for such applications. However, the program posted on the text website for the hardware dual-trace oscilloscopes, which have a USB interface, are for installation on PCs. The software for the oscilloscopes has run properly computers with Linux operation systems. The authors have not tested the use of these programs on a Mac operating in PC mode.

Student Resources

Lab-in-a-Box is supported with additional on-line materials that may be found on our website at **http://www.lab-in-a-box.net**. Here you will find Errata Sheets with the most up-to-date corrections and modifications to the text; the User Guide for the ANDY Board, MATLAB files for the codes listed in Appendix D; the Installation and User Guides for the Velleman PCSGU250 Oscilloscope, which is the oscilloscope currently used in our laboratory courses; support files for the DMM; and PDF files describing various PSpice simulations. In addition, you will find templates for each experiment in Excel with the exception of the design experiments where it is expected that you will write a formal lab report at the conclusion of the experiment. These templates reduce the effort required to duplicate the steps in the experimental procedures as you prepare your electronic lab notebooks. All of the templates may be downloaded at no charge.

Bibliography

Throughout this book, but especially in Chapters 2 and 3, we have referred to numerous texts from the fields of science and engineering, history and philosophy of science, statistical analysis, ethics, graphical representation of data, and preparation of reports and documents. Some of these texts are classics. Many are likely to be unknown to you. It is our experience from long years of teaching that several are "must" books for a well-rounded engineer's bookshelf. We have identified those we think are most important with an asterisk in front of the first author's name in the bibliography (references) at the end of each chapter[†] or in

---

[†] See the reference to Gibaldi (2003) at the end of this Section.

the description of the experiment in which they appear, and then have compiled this list into a single *Recommended Library* in Appendix B. Here, we have added comments about each book describing the particular relevance to engineering science and especially electrical and computer engineering. We recommend that you give serious consideration to acquiring some, or all, of these classics for your personal professional library during the course of your college education. Perhaps through these references you may even find topics of interest that will assist you in choosing technical or free electives available in later years of your electrical or computer engineering curriculum.

Internet Citations To provide the most current commercial information regarding parts and component specifications as well as to provide links to educational information that is not found in the archival literature, many citations in this book are given as links to websites. The citations follow the format recommended by the Modern Language Association (Gibalidi, 2003; see Section 9.1). Wherever possible, the first date given in the citation indicates either the "last modified on" date or the copyright date of the document. The second date quoted is the date of most recent access by the authors. If there is no date associated with the document itself, then only the date of our most recent access is given.

As is well-known, such citations are notorious for their instability. We have checked each hyperlink and have verified that each works correctly at the time the manuscript went to press (July 2011) but cannot assure their continued availability in the future. Any hyperlink found to be inoperable or incorrect should be reported to **authors@lab-in-a-box.net**.

Instructor Resources To assist faculty members implement, manage, and grade Lab-in-a-Box courses, we have developed an Instructor's Manual that contains suggested curriculums for both one semester and two semester courses, has hints for supporting students as they perform the experiments, and has typical experimental results for each experiment. This manual is available to those instructors who adopt this book.

Invitation Although each experiment has been carefully designed and tested, errors of both omission and commission are bound to occur. Your comments and corrections are most welcome and may be made directly to **authors@lab-in-a-box.net**.

Finally, you are encouraged to experiment and explore. Feel free to develop new experiments or to modify and expand the existing experiments. Suggestions for modification of the text would be gladly received.

We hope you enjoy working with Lab-in-a-Box and will be delighted to learn of your successes.

Robert W. Hendricks
Kathleen Meehan

References

Electronix Express, (2008). 365 Blair Road, Avenel, New Jersey 07001.
10 November 2008 <http://www.elexp.com>

*Gibaldi, J., (2003). <u>MLA Handbook for Writers of Research Papers</u> (6/E). New
York: Modern Language Association of America. See Section 9.1.

Plano Molding Co., (2008). 431 East South Street, Plano, IL, 60545.
11 November 2008 <http://www.planomolding.com> (See, e.g., the Model 7271
Tackle Box.)

Lab-in-a-Box:
Introductory Experiments
in Electric Circuits

Chapter 1: Introduction

A n introduction to electric circuit theory and analysis lies at the foundation of electrical and computer engineering and is one of the first courses taught in the curriculum. In about half of the programs at major universities this subject is covered in a single-semester course, while in the other half it is presented in a two-semester course. Regardless of duration, in only a few schools is there an accompanying laboratory course. In some cases, such as at Columbia University (Tsividis, 2002), previously in our own department, and elsewhere (Kaplan and White, 2003), introductory circuits experiments have been combined with electronics experiments that accompany follow-on electronics lecture courses. We have found this combined mode to be less than satisfactory as the need for more sophisticated electronics labs is compromised by the time invested in the introductory circuits experiments. The lack of introductory circuits laboratories is, no doubt, a result of the trend towards compression of the curriculum, the large number of students, and the very high cost of equipping and staffing the requisite laboratories.

Learning Styles   It is well documented that students have a wide range of learning styles (Mckeachie et al., 1990; Bransford et al., 2000). Engineering students are no different. Felder and Smith have developed a taxonomy of these learning styles (Felder and Smith, 1988) while Felder has compared this taxonomy to three other common descriptions including the Myers-Briggs Type Indicators (MBTI), the Kolb taxonomy, and the Hermann Brain Dominance Instrument (HBDI) (Felder, 1996). Of particular significance, research on gender and ethnicity differences in learning styles has clearly demonstrated that — at least in the sciences, technology, engineering, and mathematics (STEM) — women are generally more visual learners than are men (Thom, 2001; Margolis and Fisher, 2003). Hands-on experience greatly enhances the learning experience for all students but is generally more important for women and minorities than for white males. Clearly, most people learn by doing (Myers and Jones, 1993; Felder and Brent, 2003). These observations stand in contradiction to the usual methods of teaching introductory circuits courses. The problem thus arises: how may one introduce a hands-on experience in these courses without incurring the very high cost of facilities, equipment and personnel? We believe that we have solved this problem with Lab-in-a-Box. Preliminary assessment of the concept tends to confirm our concept (Hendricks, Lai, and Webb, 2005).

Objectives   The objectives of Lab-in-a-Box are (i) to give the student hands-on experience with wiring and analyzing simple circuits similar to those described in standard circuits textbooks using equipment that is both student owned and completely portable, and (ii) in so doing, to introduce the student to good laboratory practices for building and testing introductory circuits using these tools. Good laboratory practice also includes both safety issues and the proper procedures for keeping a laboratory notebook.

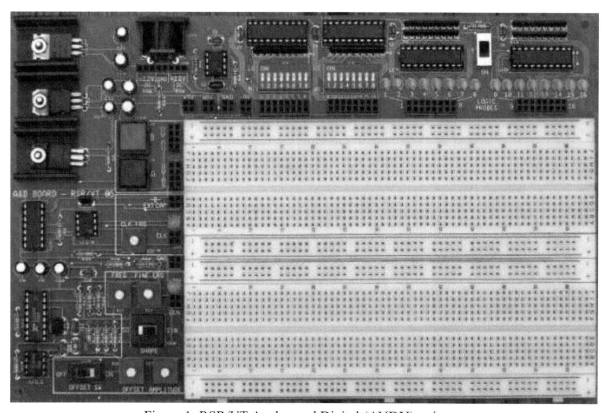

Figure 1: RSR/VT Analog and Digital (ANDY) trainer.

Outline

This chapter provides a brief overview of the equipment, components, and experiments that are the subject of the remainder of the book. In Chapter 2, we present an introduction to the scientific method, the design of experiments, the acquisition, analysis, and the presentation of data. The chapter concludes with an introduction to the preparation of laboratory reports. These are all subjects that are covered only to a limited extent both in high school science classes and in freshman-level introductory chemistry and physics courses. In our combined forty-plus years of pedagogical experience, we have found that many students only poorly understand how science and engineering are done. Our brief introduction in Chapter 2 is an attempt to remedy this deficiency. However, it can only serve as an introduction to a huge body of material in the literature. Thus, we have attempted to include copious references to lead the reader to more elegant and more thorough presentations than are possible in this book.

In Chapter 3 we introduce the student to the three basic tools or instruments used in the course: the RSR/VT Analog and Digital ("ANDY") trainer which is used as the platform for the construction of all projects; a versatile digital multimeter (DMM), which is used for most measurements of non-time- varying signals; and Velleman PCSGU250 oscilloscope package from Velleman, Inc., which is a portable, fully-functional digital hardware oscilloscope. (2005 Velleman)

Figure 2: The MY-64 digital multimeter.

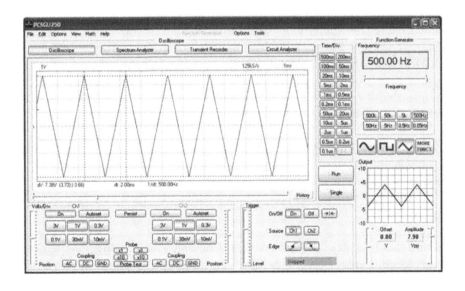

Figure 3: Screenshot from the Velleman oscilloscope software.Needs to be replaced with a photo of the scope.

Chapter 1

Components

The ANDY board, shown in Figure 1, is a logic trainer that also can be used in introductory digital electronics and/or computer engineering courses. The recommended DMM, the model MY-64 from Electronix Express, is shown in Figure 2, while a screenshot from the Velleman PCSGU250 oscilloscope is shown in Figure 3. In this chapter, the student is introduced to the concepts of good wiring procedures and to the standards that are used in all courses in which the ANDY board is used for project development. Be assured that even with simple circuits, when something goes wrong and it is necessary to debug the circuit, the ease with which a neatly wired circuit can be traced (as compared to *spaghetti wiring*) will more than repay you for your effort. Thus, neatness of wiring is taken into consideration when grading all projects in all courses.

Before starting even the most rudimentary circuit experiments, it is necessary to assure that your ANDY board is operating correctly. Thus, there is a defined test and checkout procedure to be followed to test each aspect of the board. This test procedure is given in the ANDY Board User Manual (Lineberry et al., 2006). Once you are sure that you have your platform operating correctly, you will then perform a simple continuity check of the breadboard's wiring diagram to gain familiarity with how the backplane wiring of the unit becomes a part of every circuit you build.

Finally, in Chapter 3, you are introduced to the properties, characteristics, and naming conventions for all of the components used in the experiments described in Chapter 4—wires, resistors, trim pots, capacitors, inductors, op amps, and LEDs. You are introduced to the color coding of resistors and the nomenclature for identifying capacitors, inductors, op amps, trim pots, and LEDs. A tutorial program for learning resistor color codes is available (Chen, 2004). Having mastered these fundamentals, In Chapter 4 you will then embark upon a series of experiments in which you will build increasingly complex circuits that explore and illustrate each of the fundamental circuit analysis techniques that are described in your text.

Safety

Of course, it is imperative that all experiments be performed safely. Thus, we begin Chapter 3 with an introduction to various operations and/or wiring conditions that can lead to unsafe conditions that could cause injury to you or that could damage your equipment. It is essential that these safety precautions be learned and followed carefully.

References

*Bransford, J.D., A.L. Brown, and R.R. Cocking, (2000). How People Learn: Brain, Mind, Experience, and School, Washington, DC: National Academy Press.

Chen, S., (2004). Resistor Color Code: A Teaching-Learning Tool, Version 1.0. (This program is available at the course website found at <**http://www.lab-in-a-box.net**>.)

Felder, R.N., and L.K. Smith (1988). "Learning and Teaching Styles in Engineering." J. Eng. Ed. **78**(7), pp 674–681. (See also a recent update to this paper at <http://www.ncsu.edu/felder-public/Papers/LS-1988.pdf>. 3 June 2010).

Felder, R.N., (1996). "Matters of Style," ASEE Prism **6**(4), pp 18-23. (See also < http://www4.ncsu.edu/unity/lockers/users/f/felder/public/Papers/LS-Prism.htm >. 3 June 2010)

Felder, R.N., and R. Brent, (2003). "Learning by Doing." Chem. Eng. Ed. **37**(4), pp 282–283. (See also <http://www4.ncsu.edu/unity/lockers/users/f/felder/public/Columns/Active.pdf>. 3 June 2010).

Hendricks, R.W., K.M. Lai, and J.B. Webb, (2005). "Lab-in-a-Box: Experiments in Electronic Circuits That Support Introductory Courses for Electrical and Computer Engineers." Proceedings of the ASEE Annual Meeting, Portland, OR, June 12–15, 2005. Available on-line at <http://www.asee.org>. 11 November 2008.

Kaplan, D.N., and C.G. White, (2003). Hands-On Electronics: A Practical Introduction to Analog and Digital Circuits, Cambridge, UK: Cambridge University Press.

Lineberry, R.B., W.C. Headley, and R.W. Hendricks, (2006). "RSR/VT A&D ANDY Board User Manual and Test Procedure." The Bradley Department of Electrical and Computer Engineering, Virginia Polytechnic Institute and State University, Blacksburg, VA 24061. <http://www.ece.vt.edu/tutorials/download/Andy_User_Manual_v22.pdf > 4 June 2010.

Margolis, J., and A. Fisher, (2003). Unlocking the Clubhouse: Women in Computing, Cambridge: MIT Press.

McKeachie, W.J., P.R. Pintrich, Y-G Lin, D.A. Smith, and R. Sharma, (1990). Teaching and Learning in the College Classroom: A Review of the Research Literature (2E), Ann Arbor: University of Michigan.

Myers, C., and T.B. Jones, (1993). Promoting Active Learning: Strategies for the College Classroom, San Francisco: Jossey-Bass.

Thom, M., (2001). Balancing the Equation: Where are Women and Girls in Science, Engineering, and Technology? New York: National Council for Research on Women.

Tsividis, Y., (2002). A First Lab in Circuits and Electronics, New York: John Wiley and Sons.

Velleman, Inc., (2005). "USB-PC SCOPE + GENERATOR (2CH.)" 4 June 2010. <http://www.vellemanusa.com/us/enu/product/view/?id=524708>.

Chapter 2: The Scientific Method

There are numerous steps to be performed in successfully executing a research project. The process begins with the conception of the project and the formation of a hypothesis to be tested. This is followed by the design of an experimental approach and the construction of an apparatus or equipment to test the hypothesis. The process continues with the acquisition and analysis of data to determine if the hypothesis is confirmed or denied. It concludes with the preparation of graphs and charts and ultimately reports, papers, and/or presentations for making the work known to the scientific and engineering community or to society in general. This is often a long and arduous process, with innumerable details to be considered at every step. Each of these topics has been the subject of numerous texts that date over a long period of years, or even centuries. Further, philosophers have long debated the nature of the scientific method and the meaning of scientific truth. Of course, it is neither possible, nor appropriate, to delve into all aspects of this process in an introductory text on experimental methods in electrical engineering. However, it is important that you ultimately consider these issues at some time during your educational journey to becoming and electrical or computer engineer.

In this chapter, we will examine only some of the central aspects of how one performs experimental research. Other topics will be left to more advanced courses. In Section 2.1 we set the stage by discussing the nature of the scientific method. How does one actually go about *doing science*? In Section 2.2 we look at some aspects of the acquisition of data. What are some of the basic measurement tools used in the profession of electrical and computer engineering? In Sections 2.3 and 2.4 we then consider the analysis and presentation of data, respectively. How does one determine the validity of an experimental result? When can data be discarded? What is the most effective manner of representing the results so that others can quickly and correctly understand them? Finally, in section 2.5 the chapter ends with a brief overview of the preparation of reports and papers. Again, there are innumerable ways to present the results, most of which are determined by the audience and the venue of publication. We can only point you towards much of this literature.

The purpose of this chapter is to broadly acquaint you with the basic ideas of how research is carried out and reported. Along the way, we will provide you with considerable detail for methodologies that are important to performing and reporting the experiments presented in this text. In other cases, we will only mention some of the subjects in passing, but will present you with a bibliography of some of the texts and references that we have found to be important to us in our professional careers. We denote these texts with an asterisk before the first author's name and present a cumulative list in Appendix B.

2.1 The Scientific Method

How is science done? The formal creation of a "scientific method" is usually credited to Francis Bacon (1561–1626) who suggested that science must be done by recording and analyzing what was observed in nature. However, Hall (1954) tells us that it took some three hundred years of trial and error to develop the scientific method as we know it today. In the intervening two hundred years (from roughly 1800 to the present day) man has refined and used the scientific method to achieve an astonishing understanding of nature.

Features

The scientific method comprises four steps (Wilson, 1952; Valiela, 2001; Godfrey-Smith, 2003;Wolfs, 2008). These are: to make observations on some natural phenomenon; to develop a hypothesis to explain the observations; to predict new results suggested by the hypothesis; and to make independent measurements of the predictions that either verify or falsify the hypothesis. If the results of the new experiments do not confirm the hypothesis, then the hypothesis must be revised or rejected and the process repeated. According to Hall (1954), modern science:

1. requires consistent protocols and attention to detail when performing an experiment,
2. pertains to the physical world that can be observed and measured,
3. leaves open for future explanation events that are not understood and does not invoke supernatural beings or powers,
4. distinguishes between theories confirmed by multiple evidence, tentative hypotheses, and unsupported speculations, and
5. presents the conclusions drawn from the experiment in a logical manner with supporting information gained from the present and preceding scientific body of knowledge.

There are many theories that have stood the test of time for so long they have become accepted as "laws." In electrical engineering, Ohm's and Kirchhoff's Laws are prime examples. It is the nature of the scientific method that even these laws can be superseded in the light of new measurements. However, it is generally found that these laws are rarely discarded in total, but are only proven to be special cases of more general theories and that they remain valid under special conditions (Valiela, 2001). Perhaps the best example of such a case is Newton's laws being superseded by Einstein physics.

Because scientific progress depends on replication of experimental results by independent observers, impeccable standards for observing, recording, and reporting scientific results are of paramount importance. It is a prime objective of this text to instill in the student an appreciation for learning and practicing such skills. We embark on this task in Chapter 3.

Doing Science

There are several books the objectives of which are to teach students, researchers, and engineers various aspects of good experimental technique. Of those of which we are aware, the texts by Wilson (1952), Valiela (2001), and Boot et al. (2008) are noted. The book by Wilson is old (the section on computational methods predates the computer!) but his methodology is outstanding. The text by Valiela is very modern and, although oriented towards the life sciences, his discussion of the scientific method and of current perceptions and criticisms of science are well worth reading. The text by Booth et al. provides a very practical introduction to doing research.

There are number of steps to performing scientific research, each of which must meet the requirements of the scientific method outlined above. Among these are (Wilson, 1952; Valiela, 2001):

1. choice of problem,
2. literature search,
3. design of the experiment,
4. experimental techniques,
5. acquisition of data,
6. analysis of data,
7. presentation of data, and
8. preparation of reports and papers.

The choice of problem is determined not only by the field of research but also by whether the work is basic research, applied research, or engineering development. In basic research, the driving force for the choice of topic is the desire to understand the workings of nature. In applied research, one attempts to understand those workings of nature necessary to make a desired engineering application possible, while in engineering development, known facts concerning nature are used to develop an application or product that is desired by a customer or consumer, with the words "customer" and "consumer" being used in their broadest sense.

The process outlined above takes many years of study and preparation — perhaps fifteen or more. Before one is really able to do science or to become an engineer where one is responsible for selecting a topic for research or engineering design, one must carefully learn the fundamentals of the topics towards the end of the list above: experimental techniques relevant to the field of specialization; the acquisition, analysis, and presentation of data; and the preparation of reports and papers. In this introductory text, the choice of problem, the associated literature search, and the design of the experiment have already been performed for you by the authors and will not be considered further.[†] You will learn more about these topics later in your undergraduate and/or graduate education. Rather, our purpose here is to help you start to develop your skills in experimental measurement, data acquisition, analysis, and presentation, and in

---

[†] Exceptions to this statement are several introductory design experiments presented in Chapter 4 in which you are given only the specifications for creating a circuit with desired properties. It will be your challenge to determine how to fulfill the stated requirements.

report writing so that you can apply these skills with confidence at the appropriate time.

We begin in Chapter 3 where we will introduce you to various experimental skills: how to use a breadboard to create a prototype circuit; how to use a digital multimeter and a simple oscilloscope to make a variety of electrical measurements; how to identify and understand the nature of the basic components of electric circuits such wires, resistors, capacitors, inductors, operational amplifiers, and LEDs. But, our breadboard and our oscilloscope are not quite as simple as might seem at first glance. The breadboard has built-in power supplies of various voltages, a built-in function generator, and a variable frequency clock. The Velleman oscilloscope has a built-in function generator, as do several other USB-powered dual-trace oscilloscopes, which you will employ in a number of the experiments in the second half of the lab manual. Then, in Chapter 4, we lead you through a series of increasingly complex DC and then AC experiments. In most of these experiments, the objective is to teach you, through hands-on experience, how real devices and circuits behave. In almost every case, prior to building a circuit, you will be asked to model it using either analytical tools you have learned in your mathematics courses, or by using sophisticated industry-standard computer modeling software such as MATLAB and PSpice. However, we make stops along the way to challenge you with simple, but interesting, design experiments that will give you a bit of the flavor of how the development process works.

Criticisms of the Modern Method Of Science

The model of the scientific method presented above is based on inductive logic which is used to infer a more general truth about nature from a particular set of observations. This picture of how science is done is not without controversy and over the centuries many other models have been proposed. For instance, sociological explanations of science (e.g., Merton (1979) or Latour (1988)) concentrate on the institutional arrangements and human value systems required to achieve results capable of communal acceptance by groups of experts. From a philosophical standpoint, other scholars have suggested that the scientific method by itself is insufficient because of the need for the deductive or "abductive" logical steps in addition to induction (Pierce, 1998) or have even questioned whether method has been the most central element in scientific work at all (Feyerabend, 1993). Nonetheless, the scientific method as described earlier in the section remains an excellent initial guide to experimental work.

The discussion above implies, and it is conventionally accepted, that science is a linear, incremental development of ideas. Kuhn (1996) argues that, in the broadest view, this is not how science proceeds. Although science may proceed incrementally for a while, this incremental progress is periodically undermined by revolutions of scientific thought that completely change the way scientists think about their fields. Classical, but modern examples, are of course the discovery of the double helix which completely revolutionized molecular biology, and quantum mechanics, which completely revolutionized physics.

Other criticisms of science have focused on the misuse or misappropriation of supposedly scientific ideas. There have been, for example, political as well as religious intrusions into the scientific process over the years, including both the twentieth and twenty-first centuries, several of which have ended with serious negative repercussions. It is not an appropriate digression to consider these issues in this text, but it is ultimately important that a well-educated engineer have exposure to such topics. To assist you in starting this journey, we recommend a few references that we hope will stimulate your interest and perhaps even whet your appetite for taking elective courses in the history and philosophy of science.

Valiela (2001) provides an excellent introduction to this subject in <u>Doing Science</u>, while Newton (1997) gives a lucid introduction to the nature of scientific truth in his book, <u>The Truth of Science</u>. (This is not to be confused with the also important ethical problem of truth *in* science!) There are many hypotheses of how nature works that have been discarded because they have been proven wrong: they have been falsified. Grant (2006) provides a fascinating description of such problems in his book <u>Discarded Science</u>. His examples span the centuries from ancient to modern times. In the sequel, <u>Corrupted Science</u>, Grant (2007) discusses a number of episodes in which science has been subverted by charlatans, fraudulent scientists, politicians, and theologians. Examples worthy of consideration by everyone include the rejection of Mendelian genetics by Lysenko in the Soviet Union in the 1940's and the rejection of *Judenphysik* by the Nazis in pre-World War II Germany, among others. This book is essential reading for all engineers and scientists. Sagan (1996) presents a lucid account of the increasing influence of pseudoscience in our modern world in <u>The Demon-Haunted World</u>, this despite (or perhaps in reaction to?) our increasingly technological age. And, ever since the time of Francis Bacon and the famous dispute between Galileo and Cardinal Bellarmine regarding the Copernican versus Ptolemeic model of the solar system, there have been clashes between science and religion. The literature on this subject is immeasurable. The very nice little paperback, <u>Science and Theology: An Introduction</u> by physicist turned theologian, John Polkinghorne (Polkinghorne, 1998) provides an excellent and easy introduction to this difficult subject.

2.2 Acquisition of Data

If the foundation of the scientific method is observation of nature, then the starting place for those observations must lie in an understanding of the tools with which we control and measure nature. In electrical and computer engineering, the phenomena we wish to observe involve electricity, magnetism, and electromagnetic fields that span a wide range of frequencies from fractions of a Hertz to GHz. In introductory courses, we confine ourselves primarily to the measurement of electrical phenomena—time independent and low-frequency, time-varying voltages and currents. We need both apparatuses that will generate the necessary voltages and/or currents as well as measurement tools that will allow us to record the response of an electric circuit to such applied voltages and

11

currents. In addition to these tools, we need electrical devices that will respond to the applied voltages and currents in different, but known ways. Such devices include wires, resistors, capacitors, inductors, operational amplifiers, and LEDs. In electronics courses, we will add additional devices such as diodes and transistors and will examine increasingly complex combinations of all of these devices both as discrete components and as complex integrated circuits. We will operate them at increasingly higher frequencies, thus requiring increasingly sophisticated (and expensive!) sources for our input signals and instruments for measuring their responses.

Lab-in-a-Box provides a gentle, inexpensive, and yet sophisticated introduction to this exciting field. We will build circuits primarily with discrete components (see Sections 3.7 through 3.13) on a powered breadboard (Section 3.3). We will power them with on-board power supplies, drive them with both on-board and external programmable function generators, and measure them with a digital multimeter (Section 3.5) and an oscilloscope (Section 3.6). We will learn proper wiring techniques (Section 3.4) to assure that our circuits perform the same way, every time. We will concern ourselves with laboratory safety (Section 3.1) to assure that we damage neither ourselves nor our equipment. And, we will learn about keeping proper laboratory notebooks (Section 3.2), not only to record the results of our work in preparation for publication of the results in the form of reports, papers, or public oral presentation, but also to meet the legal requirements for protecting our intellectual property in preparation for a patent application. In some of the early experiments we shall spend time measuring the reproducibility of our tools and/or our discrete components (Experiments 1 and 2) or in verifying well-established laws (Experiments 3 through 9). The objective of these seemingly trivial efforts, often derided by students eager to get on to "doing real engineering," is to assure that you begin to understand the intricacies of such critical, but mundane tasks as wiring a circuit or measuring voltages and currents.

When one makes a measurement, it is hoped that the measured value is as close to the true value as possible. Such a measurement is an *accurate* measurement. On the other hand, when we repeat a measurement, we hope that the repeated values are a close to each other as possible. Such measurements are *precise*. It is entirely possible, for example when an instrument is out of calibration, for the measurements to be precise but not accurate. The reproducibility or precision of a set of measurements depends both on the experimental techniques used in making the measurements and on the design and construction of the measuring instrument. In general, the more precise an instrument, the more costly it is. One may test the precision of a set of measurements by making the same measurement multiple times under controlled conditions. This concept will be tested in Experiment 2. One would hope that the measurement precision of an experiment would be as good as the precision of the instrument quoted in the specification sheet. It is always wise to read, and check, the precision of the data acquisition instrumentation.

How does one check the accuracy of a set of measurements? The American Society for Testing Materials (ASTM) is a national organization for developing standard test procedures for testing a wide variety of materials and components. And, the National Institute of Standards and Technology (NIST) is the branch of the Federal Government whose mission is "to promote U.S. innovation and industrial competitiveness by advancing measurement science, standards, and technology in ways that enhance economic security and improve our quality of life." For measurements where high accuracy is required, one may often be able to have an instrument calibrated traceable to NIST, or one may be able to purchase a calibrated sample, also traceable to NIST. The websites for both organizations should be consulted for further details (http://www.astm.org and http://www.nist.gov). In some cases, one may easily obtain a standard sample that is "accurate enough" for the work at hand without going to such lengths as certifying NIST traceability. For example, we could calibrate the accuracy and precision of the built-in ohmmeter of the MY-64 DMM recommended for use with Lab-in-a-Box by purchasing a set of HR175N 0.01% ultra-precision resistors from Precision Resistor Company for a few cents each. Similar precision capacitors and inductors can also be found. For the most part we will find that, for the experiments described in this text, it will be sufficient to accept the accuracy of the instrument specified in specification sheet. But, as we shall see in Section 3.5, the accuracy of the MY-64 is dependent on using fresh batteries in the unit. The careful experimentalist will always be on the lookout for experimental artifacts that degrade the accuracy and precision of her instruments.

Clearly, attention must be paid to a myriad of such details if one is to perform excellent science and/or engineering.

2.3 Analysis of Data

There are two considerations in the analysis of carefully gathered experimental data. First, we must determine the reproducibility (precision) and the accuracy of the data. Second, we must seek either an analytical or an empirical model or expression that describes the pattern of the observed data and from which we hope to interpolate or extrapolate to other experimental conditions. Of course, it is imperative, and tacitly assumed, that we are using our measurement tools (in our case, our breadboard, DMM, and oscilloscope) correctly. With the complexity of even such simple tools as used in the experiments presented in this text, it is surprising how often this assumption will not be valid. It is an objective of this text is to teach you how to identify and avoid such experimental problems.

Assuming that one can rely on the quality of the measured data, we must determine whether or not certain observations are correct or are possibly erroneous or spurious. In order to manipulate the possibly large amount of data that may be acquired during the experiment, we will use some form of scientific data processing program, possibly embedded in a hand-held programmable scientific calculator or more likely installed on a laptop or tablet personal computer. There is a wide variety of computer software that could be used for such tasks. We have selected MATLAB[†] to meet the needs of the experiments that will be described in Chapter 4. MATLAB is appropriate for complex tasks such as solving symbolic equations that will arise in many of the analytical steps of the experiments. Your preferred scientific graphing application may also suffice. Although there is much on-line free help for learning these programs, it has been our experience that it is useful to have a hard copy of a reference manual for each. Of the dozens of available books, we especially recommend both Hanselman and Littlefield (2005) and Hunt et al. (2006) for MATLAB. Unfortunately, Hanselman and Littlefield cover only the core MATLAB program and provide no coverage for any of the many toolboxes that can be added to increase the power of this program. Of these toolboxes, the Symbolic Toolbox, which comes with the Student Edition of MATLAB, which is essential for solving many problems in AC circuit analysis. Hunt et al. (2006) have a brief introduction to using this toolbox while Gilat (2008) provides considerably more on this important topic. You will find MATLAB essential for analyzing data, fitting models, and preparing graphs (see the next section). It is well worth the effort to become proficient in this program; it will be a good friend throughout your engineering career.

Despite the enormous capability of the many scientific data analysis and graphing programs available, we have found that there is no substitute for scientific handbooks such as Fischbeck and Fischbeck's (1987) "Formulas, Facts and Constants."

As an important part of our analysis of experimental data, we will need to perform a wide variety of statistical analyses. It is not our goal here to teach you everything you will ever need to know about statistical analysis of data. You will learn much more in formal statistics courses taken later in the curriculum. However, even in introductory courses that are taken prior to a formal course in statistical analysis, it is necessary to perform some simple analyses if we are to correctly interpret our experimental data. Therefore, in this section, we briefly outline several techniques that will be employed in this text. These, and many other techniques, are covered in detail in any number of texts on statistics. Several which we have found to be excellent are those by Miller and Freund (1977), Mandel (1964), Glantz (2005), and Montgomery and Runger (2006). We recommend the little paperback by Glantz as a text that should be on every scientist's and engineer's bookshelf. We also note that MATLAB has a wide range of built-in statistical functions which will allow very easy implementation of many of the calculations described in the following paragraphs. In addition, MATLAB has a powerful Statistical Analysis Toolbox which, unfortunately, is available only as an extra-cost add-in to the program. The built-in functions for

---

[†] As an alternative to MATLAB, we mention the open source program SciLab. (See **http://www.scilab.org/**) Although not 100% compatible with MATLAB, it includes Simulink and many of the toolboxes. This is an excellent choice for those students who do not have access to MATLAB as part of their academic program.

MATLAB are described in Hanselman and Littlefield (2005) and Hunt et al. (2006).

It is not appropriate to delve into too many of the details in an introductory text such as this. However, it is important that you have an understanding of several statistical ideas—the basic concepts of the mean, variance, and standard error of a set of measurements; how to determine confidence limits for measured data; the rudiments of how to perform a simple hypothesis test; and the method of least squares for fitting equations to observed data. You will meet all of these concepts later in your statistics courses. For the present purposes, a cursory overview of these ideas is presented in Appendix C. many of the experiments presented in Chapter 4 will make use of these concepts.

2.4 Presentation of Data

Data may be presented in a report, paper, or talk in several forms. They may be described and/or listed in the text in an in-line list or as a text- table.[†] They may be presented in tables of varying complexity. Or, they may be presented in a wide variety of graphical forms. How does one select the best and most appropriate design for a given purpose? Edward Tufte and Howard Wainer address these questions in an elegant series of books (Tufte, 1983; Tufte, 1990; Tufte, 1997; Wainer, 1997; Wainer, 2005). We have identified Tufte (1983) and Wainer (1997) as books that should be on every scientist's and engineer's bookshelf (see Appendix B).

Where do we begin? Tufte (1983) points out that no more than two numbers should be presented in-line within the text. With only a few data, they may be presented in a text-table, a design that increases the ability of the reader to discern comparisons. A formal table is appropriate for presenting data when exact values need to be preserved. If there is a large number of data, it is important to organize the data into logically related groups so that comparisons among the data are readily made. Often, especially when trends among data are to be examined, graphical (pictorial) representation of the data may be most effective.

There is a wide range of formats for plotting scientific data which may be classified into categories that are designed to convey different information. According to Kosslyn (1994), these include:

- *Graphs for Representing Percentages and Proportions*
  - *Pie charts*[‡]
  - *Divided bar graph*

[†] A text-table is a short table, without caption, that is inserted between lines of text and displays a few lines of data. It is a superior way to present a few numerical items instead of putting them as in-line text. (See page 178 of Tufte, 1983).

[‡] Both Tufte (1983) and Wainer (1997) argue convincingly that pie charts, especially grouped pie charts, are worthless for conveying information and should never be used.

- *Graphs for Representing Quantitative and Rank–Order Data*
  - *Visual tables*
  - *Line graphs*
  - *Bar graphs*
  - *Side-by-side bar graphs*
  - *Step graphs*
  - *Scatter graphs*
- *Graphs for Representing Cumulative Totals*
  - *Stacked bar graphs*
  - *Layer graphs*

Of course, one may place multiple graphs from any of the formats above into a single panel.

The goal of any of the above formats is the clear and concise visual representation of the data. Tufte (1983) notes, and we quote, that "*graphical displays should:*

- *Show the data*
- *Induce the viewer to think about the substance rather than about the methodology, graphic design, the technology of graphic production, or something else*
- *Avoid distorting what the data have to say*
- *Present many numbers in a small space*
- *Make large data sets coherent*
- *Encourage the eye to compare different pieces of data*
- *Reveal the data at several levels of detail, from a broad overview to the fine structure*
- *Serve a reasonably clear purpose: description, exploration, tabulation, or decoration*
- *Be closely integrated with the statistical and verbal description of the data*"

In his first book, Tufte (1983) develops the concept of data density in which he computed the number of data points per square inch. An examination of a variety of venues of publication showed that highly regarded journals had a data density in the range of 10–20; Nature, one of the most highly regarded science publications, had a density of 50 while Pravda, a Russian newspaper published in the former Soviet Union, had a density of zero! An effective scientific graph should have a high data density, an admonition consistent with several of the points listed above.

It has been our experience that students tend to have several common problems associated with graphical representation of data. Among these are:

- an inability to select the best format for the graph or plot. Sometimes the problem is simply the decision of when to use a linear versus a semi-log or a log-log graph, and sometimes it is the decision of what type of graph best displays the data clearly;
- failure to clearly label the axes and/or the datasets;

- failure to include units on the axis labels;
- failure to set the proper significant figures on axis labels;
- failure to use appropriate colors for the datasets and other features of the graph;
- failure to use appropriate curve-fitting routines to represent curves and/or functions that fit the data; and/or
- failure to show data points and their associated error bars.

Reexamination of Tufte's recommendations above clearly shows that each of these problems violates one or more of his maxims. On the other hand, the subtitle of Howard Wainer's fascinating book is "Graphical Tales of Fate and Deception from Napoleon Bonaparte to Ross Perot" (Wainer, 1997). In this book, he embarks on a tongue-in-cheek journey to show how data can be presented badly to obfuscate the data and confuse the reader by deliberately violating Tufte's suggestions. The impact is stunning. Another delightful book along the same vein is Huff's How to Lie with Statistics (1993). Learning to present data to your audience well is as important as writing well.

Of the weaknesses noted above, one that warrants further attention is the use of color as it is seldom discussed in the traditional technical writing literature. There are, of course, many instances where color serves as an indispensible variable in representing complex multidimensional data. However, one must be cautious. Approximately 7% of US males (but only 0.4% of US females) cannot distinguish red from green, or see these colors differently. There are also several other forms of color blindness, but their occurrence is a significantly smaller proportion of the population (HHMI, 2008). These data imply that good graphic design either takes colorblindness into consideration, or avoids colors altogether.[†] Apart from issues of colorblindness, your report is likely to be duplicated for wider dissemination, often by others. Most times, these copies will be made in black and white and not in color. Thus, in the copied report, your lines and colors become gray-scale and become illegible. Finally, because most people do not color-calibrate either their computer printers or their display screens, very often colors close to each other on a color wheel will merge and become illegible. Thus, two colors that may be clearly distinguishable to you on your screen and/or printer may not be distinguishable to others when your report is viewed on their screen or printed on their printer. Although Pantone (2010) offers a variety of inexpensive and easy-to-use color control and calibration tools that assure the consistency of color in your applications, few other than professionals use such tools. For all of these reasons, we recommend that when preparing reports, students are well-advised to use as little color as possible. Instead, use a variety of dashed lines or use other forms of labeling to distinguish various datasets on your graph. If color is essential, then you should consult the literature and try to

---

[†] For those who do not have a color deficiency, Waggoner (2008) provides an excellent tool at **http://colorvisiontesting.com** where one can test their own color acuity and can also see what those who do have color deficiencies might see.

select color pallets that make the data as accessible as possible to those with color deficiencies.

Beginning scientists and engineers face a formidable problem. Unlike years ago when corporations and even universities had professional graphic arts groups who prepared scientific graphics for their engineers, such facilities have long since disappeared. It is now the engineer's responsibility to prepare her own graphics. An entire industry has built up around creating software packages to aid in the process. For example, Microsoft Office (Microsoft, 2010) and Open Office (Open Office, 2010) have a wide range of graphic capabilities built in, while there are a large number of stand-alone graphics packages such as AutoCAD (Autodesk, 2010) or SketchUp (Google, 2010) for making 2- and 3-D drawings, and KaleidaGraph (Synergy Software, 2010) and SigmaPlot (Systat Software, 2010) for making scientific plots and graphics. In addition, mathematical manipulation programs such as MATLAB (MathWorks, 2010) and Mathematica (Wolfram Research, 2010) also have powerful built-in scientific graphic capabilities. Graphics produced by both can be exceptionally elegant. MATLAB is the lingua franca of the electrical engineering community and is a program that all electrical and computer engineering students should learn well. There are numerous on-line tutorials and many soft-back books that will teach you how to use MATLAB. Of these, we distinguish between the books and on-line resources that are once-through "how to" tutorials versus books that will serve you well as long-term references. Among the latter, we are especially fond of both Hanselman and Littlefield (2005) and Hunt et al. (2006). Both are worth space on your bookshelf.

One of the great difficulties with many of these packages is the ease with which one may, either by design or ignorance, plot data using an inappropriate format, use inappropriate axes, mislabel the axes, and/or fill the graph with chartjunk. Learning to avoid these problems and to make judicious choices of format and data representation takes years of training and study. There is no substitute for experience. It is our recommendation that Tufte (1983) and Wainer (1997) are well-worth careful study.

2.5 Preparation of Reports and Papers

Scientific and engineering results, no matter how good or novel, if not reported clearly and carefully such that others can reproduce the results, is, for all practical purposes, research not performed. The last step in an excellent scientific or engineering project is thus the decision of how and where to publish these results. The choices are many and are usually determined by the audience. Most large corporations and government laboratories have style guides for preparing reports and technical notes. Publishers have style guides for authors of books. As a good example, see the guidelines prepared by our publisher (Wiley, 2008). Although you will not likely be a published book author until later in your career, the tips given on the Wiley site for preparing camera-ready copy and PDF files could be helpful in assuring that even the lab reports you prepare for Lab-in-a-

Box can be read by your instructor without problem. Of course, each technical journal has its own style guide. For an excellent example of the latter, see the website of the IEEE (2008).

As with the preparation of graphics, dedicated technical editing offices that help the scientist and engineer prepare excellent documents are almost a thing of the past. With the advent of powerful word and text processing software such as Microsoft Office, OpenOffice, and LaTeX, engineers and scientists are now expected to prepare their own documents with little corporate support.

Where does a student begin? In many cases, you are on your own. You must find appropriate books and/or literature and read and study. In a University environment, English departments or possibly University Honors programs or similar entities offer writing centers that can help you. You are encouraged to seek out such centers if they exist on your campus. In some cases, even departments in colleges of engineering across the country are beginning to recognize these problems and are implementing writing and communication within their engineering professionalism programs. Hendricks and Pappas (1996) describe one early such program that has proven to be highly successful. Regardless these efforts, it is the experience of the authors that learning to write well requires extensive study and effort. You can help yourself immeasurably by acquiring a good library of supporting materials. In the following paragraph we present a few of the references that we have found to be most helpful.

First and foremost, it is essential to have a good dictionary and a thesaurus. Both are built-in in Microsoft Word, but we find they have many limitations and have learned that there is no substitute for hard copies such as Webster's New Collegiate Dictionary and Roget's Thesaurus. Tarutz (1992) has prepared an excellent introduction to preparing and editing technical documents. For assistance with writing organization, Kane (1988), van Leunen (1992), Gibaldi (2003) and Turabian (2007) are all helpful. Turabian is the classic in this field. For help with grammar, Fowler and Burchfield (2000), Strunk and White (2000), Merriam-Webster (2001), the Chicago Manual of Style (2003), and Strumpf and Douglass (2004) are good. The Chicago Manual of Style, Fowler and Burchfield, and Strunk and White are the classics in this genre. A visit to the reference section of your local university bookstore or to a superstore (e.g., Barnes and Noble or Borders) or to an on-line store such as Amazon will reveal an enormous number of books. Most are paperback and many are available on-line from used book vendors at very reasonable prices.

2.6 References

Section 2.1: The Scientific Method

*Booth, W.C., G.G. Colomb, and J.M. Williams, (2008). <u>The Craft of Research</u> (3/E). Chicago: Univ. Chicago Press.

Feyerabend, P., (1993). <u>Against Method</u>. London: Verso Press.

Grant, J., (2006). <u>Discarded Science: Ideas that seemed good at the time...</u> Surrey, UK: AAPPL Press.

*Grant, J., (2007). <u>Corrupted Science: Fraud, ideology and politics in science.</u> Surrey, UK: AAPPL Press.

Hall, A.R., (1954). <u>The Scientific Revolution: 1500–1800 The Formation of the Modern Scientific Attitude.</u> Boston: Beacon Press.

Kuhn, T.S., (1996). <u>The Structure of Scientific Revolutions</u> (3/E). Chicago: Univ. Chicago Press.

Latour, B., (1988). <u>Science in Action: How To Follow Scientists and Engineers Through Society.</u> Cambridge, MA: Harvard Univ. Press.

Merton, K., (1979). <u>Sociology and Science: Theoretical and Empirical Investigations.</u> Chicago: Univ. of Chicago Press.

*Newton, R.G., (1997). <u>The Truth of Science.</u> Cambridge, MA: Harvard Univ. Press.

Pierce, C.S., (1998). <u>Chance, Love, and Logic: Philosophical Essays.</u> Lincoln, NB: Univ. of Nebraska Press.

*Polkinghorne, J., (1998). <u>Science and Theology: An Introduction.</u> Minneapolis: SPCK/Fortress Press.

*Sagan, C., (1996). <u>The Demon-Haunted World.</u> New York: Ballantine.

*Valiela, I., (2001). <u>Doing Science.</u> New York: Oxford Univ. Press.

*Wilson, E.B., (1952). <u>An Introduction to Scientific Research.</u> New York: McGraw-Hill. (reprinted in 1990 by Dover Publications.)

Wolfs, F., (2008). "Introduction to the Scientific Method," 5 June 2010 <http://teacher.pas.rochester.edu/phy_labs/AppendixE/AppendixE.html>.

Godfrey-Smith, Peter (2003). <u>Theory and Reality: An Introduction to the philosophy of science.</u> Chicago: Univ. Chicago Press.

Section 2.2: Acquisition of Data

*Valiela, I., (2001). <u>Doing Science.</u> New York: Oxford Univ. Press.

*Wilson, E.B., (1952). <u>An Introduction to Scientific Research.</u> New York: McGraw-Hill. (reprinted in 1990 by Dover Publications.)

Section 2.3: Analysis of Data

*Fischbech, H.J., and K.H. Fischbeck, (1987). <u>Formulas, Facts and Constants for Students and Professionals in Engineering, Chemistry, and Physics</u> (2/E). Berlin: Springer-Verlag.

Gilat, A., (2008). <u>MATLAB: An Introduction with Applications</u> (3/E). Hoboken, NJ: John Wiley & Sons.

*Glantz, S.A., (2005). <u>Primer of Biostatistics</u> (6/E), New York: McGraw-Hill.

*Hanselman, D., and B. Littlefield (2005). <u>Mastering MATLAB 7</u>, Upper Saddle River, NJ: Prentice-Hall.

*Hunt, B.R., R.L. Lipsman, J.M. Rosenberg, K.R. Coombes, J.E. Osborn, and G.J. Stuck, (2006). <u>A Guide to MATLAB for Beginners and Experienced Users</u> (2/E). Cambridge: Cambridge University Press.

Mandel, J., (1964). <u>The Statistical Analysis of Experimental Data</u>. New York: John Wiley & Sons. (Reprinted in 1984 by Dover Publications.)

Miller, I., and J.E. Freund, (1977). <u>Probability and Statistics for Engineers</u> (2/E). Englewood Cliffs, NJ: Prentice –Hall.

Montgomery, D.C. and G.C. Runger, (2006). <u>Applied Statistics and Probability for Engineers</u> (4E). New York: Wiley.

Section 2.4: Presentation of Data

Autodesk, (2010). 5 June 2010 <http://usa.autodesk.com>.

Google, (2010). "Google SketchUp." 5 June 2010 <http://sketchup.google.com>.

*Hanselman, D., and B. Littlefield (2005). <u>Mastering MATLAB 7</u>, Upper Saddle River, NJ: Prentice-Hall.

*Huff, D., (1993). <u>How to Lie with Statistics</u>. New York: W.W. Norton Company.

*Hunt, B.R., R.L. Lipsman, J.M. Rosenberg, K.R. Coombes, J.E. Osborn, and G.J. Stuck, (2006). <u>A Guide to MATLAB for Beginners and Experienced Users</u> (2/E). Cambridge: Cambridge University Press.

Kosslyn, S.M., (1994). <u>Elements of Graph Design</u>. San Francisco: W.H. Freeman.

MathWorks, (2010). 5 June 2010 <http://www.matlab.com>.

Microsoft, (2010). 5 June 2010 < http://office.microsoft.com/en-us/FX102855291033.aspx>.

Open Office, (2010). 5 June 2010 < http://openoffice-software.com >.

Pantone, (2010). 5 June 2010 <http://www.pantone.com/pages/pantone/index.aspx>.

Systat Software, (2008). 5 June 2010 <http://www.systat.com>.

Synergy Software, (2010). 5 June 2010 <http://www.synergy.com>.

*Tufte, E.R., (1983). <u>The Visual Display of Quantitative Information</u>. Cheshire, CT: Graphics Press.

Tufte, E.R., (1990). <u>Envisioning Information</u>. Cheshire, CT: Graphics Press.

Tufte, E.R., (1997). <u>Visual Explanations</u>. Cheshire, CT: Graphics Press.

Waggoner, T.L., (2008). "Colorblind Homepage." 5 June 2010 <http://colorvisiontesting.com>.

*Wainer, H., (1997). <u>Visual Revelations</u>. New York: Copernicus (Springer-Verlag).

Wainer, H., (2005). <u>Graphic Discovery</u>. Princeton, NJ: Princeton.

HHMI, (2008). "Color Blindness: More Prevalent Among Males." 5 June 2010 <http://www.hhmi.org/senses/b130.html>

Wolfram Research, (2010). 5 June 2010 <http://www.wolfram.com>.

Section 2.5: Preparation of Reports and Papers

*<u>The Chicago Manual of Style</u> (15/E), (2003). Chicago: Univ. Chicago Press.

*Gibaldi, J., (2003). <u>MLA Handbook for Writers of Research Papers</u> (6/E). New York: Modern Language Association of America.

Fowler, H.W. and R.W. Burchfield, (2000). <u>Fowler's Modern English Usage</u> (3/E). Oxford: Oxford Univ. Press.

Hendricks, R.W., and E.C. Pappas, (1996). "Advanced Engineering Communication: An Integrated Writing and Communication Program for Materials Engineers," J. Eng. Ed. **85**(4), 346–352.

IEEE, (2006). "Information for Authors." 5 June 2010 <http://www.ieee.org/portal/cms_docs/pubs/transactions/auinfo03.pdf>.

*Kane, T.S., (1988). <u>The New Oxford Guide to Writing</u>. Oxford: Oxford Univ. Press.

Merriam-Webster, (2001). <u>Guide to Punctuation and Style</u> (2/E). Springfield, MA: Merriam-Webster.

*Strumpf, M. and A. Douglas, (2004). <u>The Grammar Bible</u>. New York: H. Holt.

*Strunk, W. and E.B. White, (2000). <u>The Elements of Style</u> (4/E). Needham, MA: Allyn & Bacon.

*Tarutz, J.A., (1992). <u>Technical Editing: The Practical Guide for Editors and Writers</u>. Reading, MA: Addison-Wesley.

*Turabian, K.L., (2007). <u>A Manual for Writers of Term Papers, Theses and Dissertations</u> (7/E). Chicago: Univ. Chicago Press.

Van Leunen, M.-C., (1992). <u>A Handbook for Scholars</u> (2/E). Wiley, (2008). "Resources for Authors" 27 November 2008 < http://he-cda.wiley.com/WileyCDA/Section/id-100214.html >.

Chapter 3: Experimental Methods

The material presented in this chapter provides information about the basic tools and components to be used in introductory electric circuits courses. In the first two sections, we introduce various safety considerations designed to protect the student from personal injury and to protect the breadboard and other equipment from damage (Section 3.1), while also introducing policies and procedures for creating and maintaining good laboratory notebooks (Section 3.2). In the next two sections, we discuss the powered breadboard, or 'lab kit,' on which you will build all of your experiments (Section 3.3) and offer some suggestions for developing good wiring techniques (Section 3.4). We then describe the use of the MY-64 digital multimeter (DMM) (Section 3.5) and the oscilloscope (Section 3.6). Following these wiring and equipment descriptions, we describe the properties of and nomenclature for identifying wires (Section 3.7); resistors (Section 3.8); capacitors (Section 3.9); inductors (Section 3.10); trimmer potentiometers or 'trim pots' (Section 3.11); op amps (Section 3.12); and LEDs (Section 3.13). You need to understand and be intimately familiar with each of these sections in order to correctly identify and use these components. None of this material is taught in your lecture course, but is learned by hands-on experience with Lab-in-a-Box. Refer to this material as necessary when doing the various experiments.

3.1 Laboratory Safety

Your personal safety is of utmost concern to your instructors, to your department, and to your college or university. Although you are dealing with seemingly innocuous low-voltage equipment, there are still a number of dangerous situations which can arise. Furthermore, in following laboratories, or in project courses in which you may develop circuits on your own, more dangerous situations than those which arise in this introductory circuits course may be encountered. The prudent student will learn good laboratory practice from the beginning and will be properly prepared to deal with such occasions.

There are two important aspects of safety of which all beginning students of electrical and computer engineering must be aware. First, and most importantly, is personal safety. Although the voltages developed in powered breadboards such as the RSR/VT Analog and Digital Trainer (ANDY board) are low (usually less than 12 VDC or ±12 VAC), it is still possible to be injured by electrical shock if you are careless with the equipment. In this case, the old adage of 'no pain, no gain' is certainly incorrect. There is no point of suffering needless painful situations, especially if they could be life-threatening. Second, it is also possible to damage your breadboard, your DMM, and/or your personal computer if certain errors are made. Such can be both time-consuming and/or expensive to repair and also can lead to delays that may cause significant grade penalty for your work. The following paragraphs describe some of these issues. They should be read with care and thoughtful consideration.

Personal Safety

The human body reacts physiologically to an applied electric current in three ways. First, there can be damage to the nervous system and the heart. Second, there can be heating and/or burning of body organs. And third, electric currents can cause muscle contraction which can, for example, prevent a person from letting go of an inadvertently grabbed 'hot' wire. This latter is known as *tetanus*, an involuntary contraction of muscles, and can be particularly dangerous when a wire is grasped by the hands because the muscles involved in bending the fingers are much better developed than those involved in extending them as discussed by Casini in the report published by the National Institute for Occupational Safety and Health (1998). Another excellent discussion is the online reference "All About Circuits" by Kuphaldt (2008).

The severity of these effects depends on how current passes through the body. The most dangerous situation is when the current passes through the trunk, in the vicinity of the heart. Such situations occur when the human body completes an electrical circuit and current passes from one limb through the trunk to a second limb such as from a hand to a grounded foot, or from one hand to the other. Although electrical effects in most devices are controlled by the flow of electrons, in the human body the current is carried by charged ions in the body fluids—primarily Na^+, K^+, and Cl^-. The electrical conductivity of human blood is thus quite high. Note that it is the current that controls the effects, and the role of voltage is simply as the driving force. Thus, the current that flows depends on the resistance of the human body between the two points of contact with the electrical source. It is the skin that forms the high resistivity barrier between the highly conductive blood plasma and the external source of current. Thus, the electrical resistivity of the human body between various extremities depends strongly on the environment surrounding the skin. The resistance between a grounded human and an electrical potential may be as high as 20 MΩ through a rubber glove, but is reduced to 100 kΩ to 500 kΩ through a dry leather shoe sole, and is only 5 kΩ to 20 kΩ through a wet leather shoe sole (Kuphaldt, 2008). More significantly, the resistance of the body between the left and right hand is of the order of 1 MΩ if the skin is dry. For damp or wet skin, this value may be as low as 1 kΩ. In the event of contact between cut skin or flesh where the skin has been burned off may be as low as 500 Ω. Since the resistance varies inversely with the area of contact, A, between the body and the voltage source via the relationship $R = \rho L / A$, electrical contact with a ring is particularly dangerous. Thus, it is recommended that wedding bands and other jewelry be removed when working near electrical sources.

From this discussion, it is seen that, depending on the voltage applied to the limbs and the condition of the skin, currents as small as microamperes to as large as several amperes can be expected to flow through the body. Furthermore, the severity of these effects is different for AC and DC currents, and is different for males and females. DC currents more readily cause tetanus, while AC currents are more apt to disrupt the rhythm of the heart and thus lead to fibrillation. Although there appears to be no conclusive information in the literature, one

Table 8: Estimated Effects of DC and AC Currents (in mA)[†]

Bodily Effect	DC	60 Hz AC	10 kHz AC
Slight sensation	Men = 1.0 Women = 0.6	Men = 1.0 Women = 0.6	Men = 1.0 Women = 0.6
Threshold of Perception	Men = 5.2 Women = 3.5	Men = 5.2 Women = 3.5	Men = 5.2 Women = 3.5
Painful, voluntary muscle control maintained	Men = 62 Women = 41	Men = 62 Women = 41	Men = 62 Women = 41
Painful, unable to let go	Men = 76 Women = 51	Men = 76 Women = 51	Men = 76 Women = 51
Severe pain, difficulty in breathing	Men = 90 Women = 60	Men = 90 Women = 60	Men = 90 Women = 60
Possible heart fibrillation after 3 seconds	Men = 500 Women = 500	Men = 500 Women = 500	Men = 500 Women = 500

[†]Data taken from Kuphaldt (2008).

might suspect that a possible explanation for the reduced effect on females compared to males is because females are, on average, smaller than males, thus reducing R by reducing L. The effects vary from imperceptible to lethal, as shown in Table 8. Note that the common household fuse or circuit breaker (typically 15 or 20 A) is designed to protect electrical equipment, not humans!

Safety Glasses Because of the possibility, no matter how remote, that components could inadvertently explode and thus produce small projectiles, it is strongly recommended that eye protection be worn while working on Lab-in-a-Box experiments. Normal eyeglasses are sufficient for those who wear them; for others, an inexpensive set of safety goggles such as those used in chemistry laboratories are recommended. Such goggles are included in the Lab-in-a-Box parts, as listed in Appendix A.

Powered Breadboards It is important that you never wire a circuit or make connections while power is applied to your ANDY board. Many components, such as integrated circuits (ICs) and LEDs are extremely sensitive to voltage spikes and are easily damaged if they are inserted while power is applied to a circuit. You should always double-check your circuit before you turn on the power to ensure that it is wired correctly.

Shorted Power Supplies Note that if one of the power supplies of your ANDY board is connected directly to ground (i.e., shorted out), depending on its design, the power supply may overheat and could be ruined. Even though the ANDY board has been designed to survive such a direct short on any one of the three power supplies, it is important to ensure that your circuit does not inadvertently make such a shorting connection. It is not good practice to test this feature experimentally!

Reusing Wires

You should never reuse wires. Because of the fine wire gauge used in breadboarding a circuit, the wire may break within the insulation, thus causing an open circuit, or worse, an intermittent circuit, that is nearly impossible to diagnose. Furthermore, a stripped end of a wire that has been bent several times may break inside one of the sockets of your breadboard, thus making that hole unusable. If such a break occurs, the broken piece of wire left in the hole can often be removed with a needle after first unplugging the power.

DMM Measurements

When making measurements with your digital multimeter (DMM), never attempt to insert the pointed probe tips of the multimeter leads into the sockets of the breadboard. As noted in Section 3.4, the probe tips are too large and could stretch the springs of the socket connector such that the hole will no longer make good contact with wires when they are inserted into the hole. Such 'sprung' sockets cannot be repaired—the entire breadboard must be replaced. There are several techniques for making the necessary contact between the DMM probe and the component or wire on the board. First, components such as resistors, capacitors, inductors, and ICs all have bare leads that rise above the socket. Just touch the DMM probe tip to such an exposed wire at the desired node. Or, if every connection to a node is a wire with no exposed lead, one may insert, in the same column of the breadboard, a short wire with a bare end to which the probe tip can be touched. A stiff piece of wire, such as the cut lead from a resistor, makes a very good probe connection.

Resistors

It is very important that the power tolerance of a resistor not be exceeded. All resistors used in the experiments described in this book (see Appendix A) are ½ W resistors. This means that they should never be connected in a circuit such that they will attempt to dissipate more than this amount of power, or they could be severely overheated and could cause burns if touched. For example, a 1 Ω resistor connected directly across a +5 VDC power supply will attempt to dissipate $P = V^2 / R = 5^2 / 1 = 25$ W , which is 50 times its power rating. Under these conditions, the resistor will most likely burn up, and in so doing, could damage (melt) the underlying plastic breadboard, ruining it. Depending on the failure mode, the resistor could explode and thus cause eye or other injury to you or to others near your breadboard.

You should always calculate the minimum resistor size that can be used without exceeding its maximum power rating, using the above relationship with P set to 0.5 W (or the appropriate power rating if you are using other than ½ W resistors (See Section 3.8). Always be extra cautious in wiring any circuit in which any resistor smaller than this value is required. In the case of lab kits with bipolar power supplies, the worst possible case would involve a resistor that is connected from the negative to the positive power supply terminal. For example, in a powered breadboard with +5 V and ± 9 V power supplies, the worst case scenario would exceed the ½W limit with resistors smaller than $R = V^2 / 0.5 = (9+9)^2 / 0.5 = 648\ \Omega$. Thus, one must be particularly careful using resistors smaller than about 700 Ω with such lab kits.

Capacitors Another component that can cause a problem is the electrolytic capacitor (see Section 3.9). These devices have polarities and, if connected incorrectly, may explode even in circuits with small applied voltages. It is imperative that the negative polarity lead be connected to a lower potential than the positive polarity lead. Never use an electrolytic capacitor where an AC voltage can be applied without an appropriate DC bias to assure that the positive electrode always remains at a higher potential than the negative electrode.

3.2 Laboratory Notebooks

Laboratory notebooks are an essential component of all research and development projects. Well-kept notebooks serve several functions:

- they allow the researcher to keep track of all work performed, so that effort is not needlessly repeated;
- they provide immediate access to all results when reporting work to colleagues and superiors;
- they provide a historical record of the R&D intellectual property of an organization; and
- if properly prepared, dated, and witnessed, they provide the critical supporting material for the patent process.

University Environments In an academic environment, undergraduate students may be under the impression that work performed in laboratory experiments such as those described here do not require such record keeping. Nothing could be further from the truth! Consider the case in which you are unable to obtain results that appear to be reasonable for the project at hand. If you have carefully documented both your analytical calculations as well as your experimental work, you will be able to communicate your results clearly and efficiently to your teaching assistant or instructor. Given the time press on these individuals, such efficiency can make the difference between receiving the assistance you need or not. But, perhaps most importantly, employers place great value on students who have learned good laboratory habits, including note-keeping, as an employee's long-term success depends on his ability to protect and exploit the company's intellectual property.

In the university environment, intellectual property (IP) created by a student who uses no university resources is owned by the student. However, if any university resources (e.g., laboratory equipment, computers, etc.) are used, or if the student is employed by the university on a contract under which the IP is created, then the university usually will own that IP. The university thus expects students in its employ to keep laboratory notebooks that meet the conditions

27

described in the following paragraph. Every student is encouraged to read her institution's IP policy (e.g., see Virginia Tech, 2008).

Industrial Environments

It is very important to note that, as a condition of employment in almost every organization, an employee must sign an employment contract that will assign to the employer the rights to all IP developed by the employee that is related in even the remotest manner to the employee's work assignment. Laboratory notebooks that are dated and have numbered pages are often furnished by the employee's organization. Such notebooks are the property of the employer and must be returned when the employee leaves the firm.

Traditional Notebooks

Traditionally, laboratory notebooks are hard-covered, bound notebooks with numbered pages. They may have quadrille or lined pages. In recording the results of experiments, the following guidelines are followed:

1. Information is recorded in ink.
2. Each entry is dated with the full date, including the year.
3. No page is ever torn out of a notebook.
4. No page is ever left blank. If a page is inadvertently skipped, then a diagonal line is drawn through that page.
5. A record is kept of all calculations, sketches of instruments or instrumental set-ups, and all raw experimental data and all interpretations thereof.
6. Each page is signed in the experimenter's own handwriting.
7. Periodically, a colleague who is qualified to understand the data should sign the notebook with the entry 'I have read and understand the information recorded on pages xx—yy' or some similar phrase. This witness is critical to protect intellectual property for patent purposes.

Suggestions for keeping a notebook have been presented by the Office of Technology Licensing at Stanford University (2008), while an excellent outline of the 'do's and don'ts' of keeping a notebook has been prepared by Peter Fasse (2000).

It is perhaps overkill to require students to keep laboratory notebooks with the degree of formality described above, but the astute student will learn and practice the spirit of these guidelines in preparation for her research or engineering development career. Regardless, what is clearly unacceptable is to record notes on loose-leaf or other random sheets of paper, and/or pages torn from a spiral notebook.

Electronic Notebooks

An important variation of the process involves procedures for recording notes electronically. At this time, electronic laboratory notebooks have not been approved by the courts. However, facilities such as Oak Ridge National Laboratory have been working to develop a secure computer system that meets the requirements set forth above (Geist et al., 2008). This system involves secure servers that assure that data, once entered, cannot be changed. It is designed to allow multiple researchers to share data for various projects, and to do it in such a way as to assure proper IP protection. Clearly, such a system is not appropriate for students participating in courses that use Lab-in-a-Box.

Diane Gardner (2000) has developed a set of 'Do's and Don'ts for e-Lab Notebooks.' Some of these guidelines include procedures for backing up data, retaining permanent copies, preventing modification of electronic records, etc. Although one could develop suitable procedures that meet her guidelines using word processing software (e.g., MS Word) or even computational programs such as MATLAB or MathCAD, the difficulties of assembling the wide range of data, such as graphs, drawings, circuit diagrams, equations, raw data, notes and thoughts, make all but the word processor less than ideal for such purposes.

Experiment Templates

To assist in the submission of all-electronic laboratory notebooks and laboratory reports, we have developed a folder with MS Word templates for reporting the results of each experiment. These templates are available on the book's website at **http://www.lab-in-a-box.net**.

3.3 The RSR/VT Analog & Digital Trainer

The objective of the RSR/VT Analog & Digital Trainer (ANDY board) is to provide the student with an easy-to-use, mobile, multipurpose learning tool that can be used to develop many aspects of circuit design and analysis. The ANDY board, designed by Virginia Tech especially for use in introductory courses in electric circuits and computer engineering and shown in Figure 1 (found in Chapter 1), supports a rich, hands-on experience in digital logic and AC and DC circuit analysis through the use of take-home labs and design projects. The board provides plenty of breadboard space for students who may need to do more than one lab concurrently for different courses. Because of its small size and external power supply, the board is mobile, providing the student with the opportunity to work on experiments wherever she or he feels comfortable. The ANDY board provides a more relaxed environment to learn material, which leads to better comprehension.

Detailed specifications for the ANDY board are given in the User Manual and Test Procedure (Lineberry et al., 2006). In this section, we describe only those features of the board necessary to get started with your experimental work. The silk-screen of the ANDY board is shown in Figure 4. The six different sections of the board that are used to connect to the breadboard are labeled and outlined: the power sources; the digital logic probes; the digital switches; the digital pulsers; a digital clock; and a function generator. Each section has labeled socket headers associated with it. Socket headers are the black boxes surrounding the breadboards into which wires can be inserted. For digital electronics courses, you will use the +5 V power supply, the digital switches and digital I/O ports, the

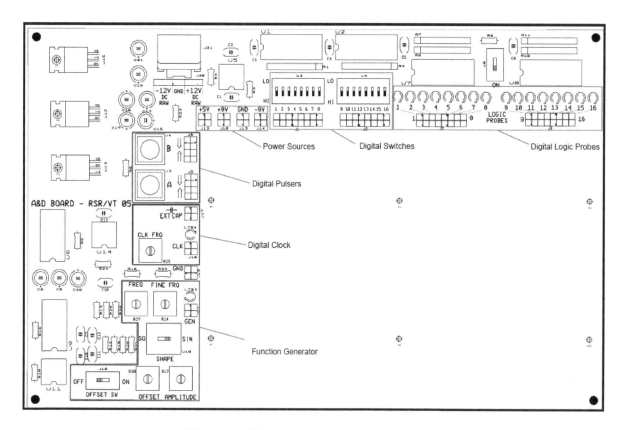

Figure 4: Silk screen layout of the RSR/VT A&D (ANDY) board.

digital clock, and the digital pulsers. For courses in analog circuits, you will use all of the power supplies, the function generator, and the digital pulsers. You should familiarize yourself fully with each of these sections, as it is here that you will make connections between your circuits and the functions provided by the board. The function and operation of each section of the board is discussed in detail in the User Manual and Test Procedure (Lineberry et al., 2006).

The test procedure for the ANDY board should be followed when the board is first received to verify that it is functioning according to specifications (Lineberry et al., 2006). Of course, by performing the full test procedure, you will not only verify the correct operation of the board, but you will also learn the details of operation of each function of the board. When a problem arises, the test procedure can be used to narrow the scope of the problem.

3.4 Circuit Breadboarding and Wiring

This section, written by Robert Lineberry, is based on 20 years of experience teaching undergraduates and describes good laboratory practice for wiring circuits with any general-purpose prototype board.

Overview

Before wiring any circuit, generate a neat, complete circuit or logic diagram and simulate it either analytically or with PSpice so you know the circuit functions properly. Once you have a working circuit diagram, the following general instructions should be followed.

1. An inexpensive tool kit for wiring your project boards is sold through Electronix Express (2008). The kit contains a wire cutter/stripper, a small screwdriver, and forceps. If you are not sure how to cut wires and strip insulation from them safely, see your instructor for assistance.

2. Every time you add a wire or component to the physical circuit, mark off the corresponding part of the wiring diagram with a colored pencil or marker. This makes it easy to see what parts of the circuit have been built so far. If you make any circuit changes, draw these on your wiring diagram. (For lab reports, hand in a final logic diagram that is clean and unmarked.)

3. Insert components and IC packages into the appropriate breadboard area before inserting any wires. You will usually need to bend the IC leads (pins) slightly inward so that the spacing closely matches the spacing of sockets on the breadboard. Be careful to check that all IC leads are actually inserted into the correct sockets. Also make sure that pin 1 of the IC is in the correct position. Note that the ICs should straddle the central channel of the breadboard (see Figures 9 and 10.)

4. To remove an IC, use an extraction tool, screwdriver, pliers or tweezers to avoid bending or breaking IC leads.

5. Use only solid-conductor wire in the size range of AWG 20 to AWG 26 (see the table of AW sizes in Section 3.7). Wire with a larger diameter may damage the socket spring clips of the breadboard. Wire strippers should be used to cut wires to appropriate lengths and to check wires that are suspected of having a larger diameter than permitted. Note that some wire strippers have measuring devices for determining the wire gauge or diameter. Trim and re-strip the end of any jumper wire that appears badly nicked or overly flexed.

6. It is possible to insert most wires by hand. In tight places, using the forceps or needle-nose pliers from the tool kit can make the job much easier. In either case, wires are easier to insert if they have been cut at an angle of approximately 45 degrees with respect to the axis of the wire.

7. When removing wires, be sure to pull perpendicular to the plane of the breadboard to avoid damage to the socket.

8. Route wires around components and IC packages, not over them. Occasionally, a component or an IC turns out to be defective. If wires have been placed over a component, you will have to remove them so that the component can be replaced.

9. It is best to wire a circuit in stages, beginning with power and ground connections. Add wires with the power switch OFF. Before turning the power ON, remove all hand jewelry and make sure that no foreign metal objects are near the circuit. Check every IC to make sure it is not overheating. If any IC is too hot to touch, immediately shut the power off and check all leads. (Be careful, because shorted ICs can become very hot and could leave a 'brand' on your finger!) Also, make sure that no IC has been inserted backwards. (See, e.g., Section 3.12.)

10. Logic devices can be damaged if the absolute maximum ratings are exceeded. For 74HC series of devices, the supply voltage must be between -0.5 V and +7.0 V, with respect to ground. Damage may also occur if the supply voltage connection is removed from the IC pin while power is still being applied to the circuit. Note that some op amps require higher input voltages and will not work correctly on 5 V sources. Be sure to check the component datasheet for proper voltages. Many IC and op amp specifications may be found, for example, at the National Semiconductor (2008) or Texas Instruments (2008) websites.[†] If you cannot find your component at either of these sites, try Google.

11. To debug a circuit, use a logic probe that is calibrated for the appropriate logic family. For 74HC devices with a supply voltage of 5.0V, a low logic level is below 1.5V and a high logic level is above 3.5V. Between 1.5V and 3.5V, the logic level is undefined. Use the multimeter to check node voltages and branch currents. Start at a position in the circuit where the logic level or node voltage is known to be correct, and work outward from there. If a component or IC does not appear to produce the correct signal or voltage, check that power and ground are correctly connected to the IC; also check all inputs to the component. Finally, check that the output of the IC is not incorrectly connected to some other signal.

If you cannot get your circuit to work, bring it and a current circuit diagram or schematic to your instructor for help.

Wiring Guidelines

Wire is as critical an electrical component of your circuit as are devices such as resistors, capacitors, inductors, op amps, ICs, etc. (see Section 3.7). The following guidelines will help assure that your wire is unflawed.

1. Use new wire.

   a. Spools of wire are provided in your parts kit. Additional spools may be ordered from Electronix Express.

   b. Old wire can break inside the insulation, causing incorrect circuit behavior that is difficult to troubleshoot.

[†] Hint: At the TI website home page, enter the part name of interest (e.g., LM324) in the key word search.

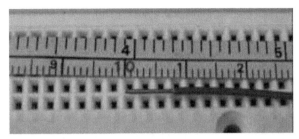

Figure 5: Correct length to strip wire's insulation.

Figure 6: Proper insertion of wire into bread-board contacts.

2. Strip approximately 5/16 inch, or 8 mm, of insulation off the ends of a wire, as shown in Figure 5. This is about the length of four breadboard holes.

   a. If you strip off too much insulation, the wires in adjacent breadboard columns can touch, causing a short circuit and most likely incorrect behavior of the circuit.

   b. If you don't strip enough, the insulation can prevent the spring clips in the breadboard holes from closing properly around the uninsulated part of the wire that is inserted into the hole, creating an open circuit.

   c. The proper insertion of the wire into the clip beneath the breadboard is shown in Figure 6.

3. Create power and ground busses at the top and bottom of your breadboard.

   a. The connection pattern of a typical breadboard is shown schematically in Figure 7, and a photo of a breadboard back plane is shown in Figure 8. The top and bottom rows can be used to distribute +5 VDC, +9 VDC, -9 VDC, and ground to the circuits (see Figure 9). This makes your wiring less crowded and makes it easy to see

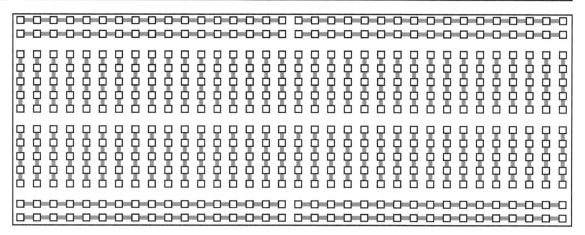

Figure 7: Connection pattern of a typical breadboard.

power and ground connections. This feature makes it possible to build two independent projects on the breadboards at once and have them operate independently. Note that the top and bottom 'bus' rows may have a break in the very middle! If you want a power or ground bus to run the length of the breadboard, you may need to insert a jumper in the middle of the row to join the two half rows together. (See Figure 9.) Also note carefully the difference between the busses on this breadboard and those on the ANDY board shown in Figure 1, where there are breaks between every fifth hole in the horizontal busses.

4. Run all power signals in red wire and all ground signals in black wire.

   a. Do not use red or black wire for any other signals. This makes it easy to tell which wires are power and ground wires, and which are actual signal wires.

   b. Use a single power or ground wire from the bus to the chip. Do not daisy-chain power or ground connections. Think parallel, not serial. (See Figure 9.)

   c. You may wire from the bus to the breadboard hole at the end of the same column as the chip. This makes it easy to see that the power and ground wires are connected to the correct pin. This also allows more room for signal wires, without covering the power and ground wires. (See Figure 10.)

5. Color code your wiring using the additional colors provided in your parts kit. Here are some suggestions to make it easier to trace your wiring:

   a. Use the same color for all the wires of a signal that runs to multiple gates. Use different colors for different inputs of a gate.

   b. If you have a bus, make all the wires of the bus the same color. However, if you have long runs of parallel wires that are the same

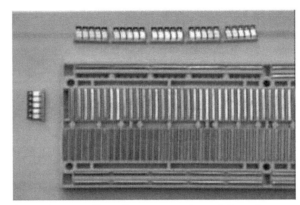

Figure 8: Breadboard contacts viewed from bottom.

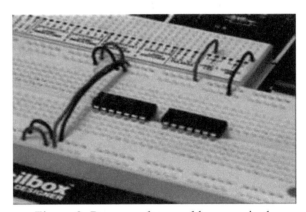

Figure 9: Power and ground busses wired.

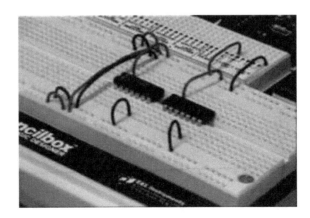

Figure 10: Power and ground wired from bus to chip.

color, it will be more difficult to trace individual bits of the bus.

6. Wires should be routed less than ½ in. (12 mm), above the breadboard.

   a. If the wires are too high, it will be difficult to trace signals through your circuit and easy to pull a wire out of the breadboard.

   b. If the wires are low, be sure the stripped wire ends are seated firmly in the breadboard. Careful routing is essential for efficient troubleshooting.

   c. Avoid sharp bends in the wires. Sharp bends in the wire can cause the wire to break inside the insulation.

7. Run wires around or between chips and components rather than over them.

   a. Your chip or component may become defective or damaged while in use, and it is much easier to remove it for testing/replacement if you do not have to remove your wiring in order to remove the device.

   b. When possible, leave two or three rows of the breadboard between chips to allow room for signal wires to pass from one side of the IC to the other.

8. Make wire lengths from source to destination short.

   a. Route wires point to point, rather than squaring corners.

   b. Do not daisy-chain power and ground wires. Think parallel, not serial.

9. Wire from a complete schematic diagram. Be sure that the wiring to each chip's pin number and that all of the component values match the component values shown in the circuit schematic and/or logic diagram.

Good and Poor Wiring

Finally, we can compare 'good wiring' shown in Figure 11 to 'poor wiring' as shown in Figure 12.

Figure 11: Good wiring.

Figure 12: Poor wiring.

3.5 Digital Multimeter

The MY-64 digital multimeter (DMM) shown in Figure 13 is used for a variety of functions. It can measure AC and DC voltages and currents, resistance, capacitance, frequency, temperature, and some transistor properties. You should read the specification sheet for your multimeter. A key point is that a digital multimeter often becomes a circuit element, similar to other circuit elements, and can inadvertently affect the circuit if care is not taken. Learning to use your digital multimeter correctly and safely is a critical aspect of becoming an excellent electrical or computer engineer. The following paragraphs provide an introduction to this topic. More detail is given in the excellent article by Kuphaldt (2008) which we highly recommend.

Leads

The test leads of the multimeter connect to the jacks at the bottom of the multimeter. The color-coded black test lead goes into the black jack labeled 'COM,' which stands for 'common.' When measuring voltage, frequency, or resistance the red test lead goes into the red jack labeled 'V,' 'Hz,' and 'Ω,' respectively. When measuring small currents, the red test lead goes into the red jack labeled 'mA.' For measuring large currents, the test lead goes into the red jack labeled '10A.' Note that the 'mA' jack is fused at 200 to 250 mA.

Voltage

To measure DC voltage, plug the red test lead into the appropriate red jack, as described above. Turn the multimeter dial to the DC voltage setting, which is denoted by the letter 'V' and a symbol consisting of a straight line with a dotted line beneath it. Then measure with the multimeter in *parallel* to the component for which you are measuring voltages (refer to Figure 14 below). The input resistance of the meter in this mode is very high and, thus, should not affect the circuit unless the device being measured has a resistance of the same order of magnitude as the input resistance of the meter. The numbers under the DC voltage setting indicate the upper limit of measurable voltage. If a letter is next to the number, it indicates a prefix for an order of magnitude. For example, a lower-case 'm' indicates milli- (for 10^{-3}) and a 'k' indicates kilo (for 10^{3}). The list provided in Appendix E contains the commonly used prefixes in electrical engineering If the measured voltage is larger than the upper limit of the instrument, then a '1' will be displayed in the left most digit, indicating overflow.

> **Important Note:** When measuring voltage, connect the red probe to the appropriate voltage jack on the multimeter, and always measure voltage by placing the test leads in parallel with the circuit component that you are testing.

To measure AC voltage, plug the red test lead into the appropriate red jack as described above. Turn the multimeter dial to the AC voltage setting, which is denoted by 'V~'. Then measure with the multimeter in parallel to the component for which you are measuring voltages as above. The AC voltage measured is the RMS value. The peak-to-peak voltage is $V_{pp} = 2\sqrt{2}V_{rms} = 2.83V_{rms}$, assuming the signal is a single frequency sine wave.

Figure 13: MY-64 Digital multimeter.

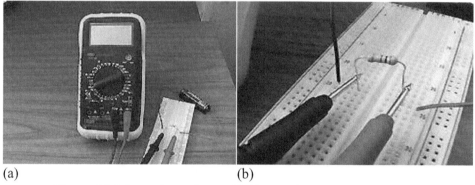

(a)   (b)

Figure 14: Measuring voltage. (a) Connection to DMM, and
(b) connection to component.

Important Notes:
1. Never measure an AC voltage on a DC voltage setting. While the result should be 0 V, the peak voltages applied to the circuitry in the DMM may be sufficient to damage the meter.
2. Never measure a DC voltage on an AC voltage setting. This will result in an incorrect answer as the display result is the RMS value of the peak voltage and your result will be off by $\sqrt{2}$.

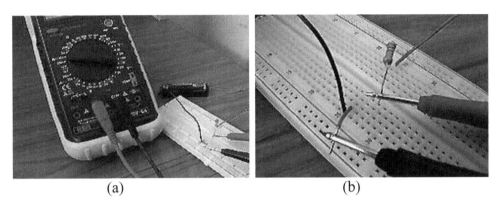

(a) (b)

Figure 15: Measuring current. (a) Connection to DMM and
(b) connection to component.

Current

To measure current, plug the red test lead into the red jack labeled '10A' and turn the dial to the DC current setting, which is denoted by the letter 'A' and a symbol consisting of a straight line with a dotted line beneath it. Then measure current with the multimeter in *series* with the component through which you are trying to measure current. This requires that you disconnect a circuit component in the branch of interest so that you create an open circuit. You will then have to place the multimeter in series in the open circuit in order to close the open circuit and complete the circuit. *This process is critical.* The input resistance of the meter in the current mode is very low and can cause a significant current to flow through the meter if it is placed in parallel with a high-resistance component. If the meter indicates a small current on the 10A scale, change the red current probe to the 'mA' jack (see Figure 15) and measure the current again. Note that the meter is fused at 200 mA on the 2, 20, and 200 mA scales and that you will blow the fuse if a current above this limit passes through the device. Again, the numbers indicate the upper limit of measurable current. Prefixes for the order of magnitude will often be provided as well. If the current is greater than the upper limit, a '1' will be shown on the left-most side of the display, indicating overflow.

If you blow the fuse, your meter will always read '0' on the 'mA' scales. A simple test to determine if you have blown a fuse is to use the multimeter to measure the resistance of its own fuse as follows (see also Kuphald, 2008): Set the meter to measure resistance (use the 200 Ω scale). Insert the red lead into the V-Ω-Hz (red) socket, and insert the black lead into the mA (red) socket. Then touch the probe tips together. A good fuse will indicate a small resistance (perhaps 0.5 Ω) while a blown fuse will indicate an overflow, or an open circuit. You may change a blown fuse be removing the back cover of the meter. The process is easy but tedious. If you are unsure of how to do this, detailed instructions may be found at **http://www.lab-in-a-box.net**.

Resistance   To measure resistance, put the red test lead into the red jack with the 'Ω' symbol (see Figure 16(a)). Turn the dial to the resistance setting, also marked by the 'Ω' symbol. Measure a resistor by touching the red and black probe leads to each side of the resistor. To obtain an accurate measurement of resistance, it is critical that the resistor be disconnected from the circuit. The easiest way is to measure it free-standing. If the resistor in question is already installed in a circuit, first, be sure to first turn off the power to the circuit. Then, remove the resistor from the circuit and measure its value. Alternatively, you may measure the resistor in place by removing one end of the resistor from the socket and leaving it free-standing.

Capacitance   To measure a capacitor, turn the dial to the capacitance setting, indicated by the letter 'F.' Remove the capacitor from the circuit and insert it into the slots on the lower left of the meter marked with a 'Cx' (see Figure 16(b)). Be sure that the capacitor has been fully discharged (by momentarily connecting its leads together) before connecting it to the meter. When you have finished your measurement, return the capacitor to the circuit.

Frequency   To measure frequency, connect the black lead to the COM jack and the red test lead to the V-Ω-Hz jack, set the switch to kHz, and touch the test leads across the load under test.

Temperature   The MY-64 also includes a Type J thermocouple for temperature measurement. Note: the welded tip on the fine wire of the thermocouple is very delicate. Treat it with care. Plug the thermocouple jack into the green female plug on the DMM, and set the knob to read either degrees Celsius or degrees Fahrenheit. Then carefully place the welded tip of the thermocouple in direct contact with the material or component whose temperature is to be measured.

Trouble Shooting   Some common difficulties encountered with the MY-64 DMM include:

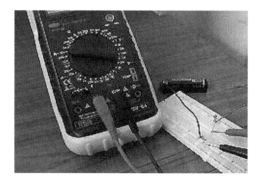 

(a)   (b)

Figure 16: Measuring (a) resistance and (b) capacitance.

- the current measured on the 200 mA scale is always zero
- the measured voltage does not match measurements with a calibrated meter
- the resistance of a resistor measures significantly below the tolerance specifications of that resistor

The 200 mA current input is fused with a 200 to 250 mA fuse. If the current reads zero and you are sure there should be a current flowing in the branch, the most likely problem is a blown fuse. The instructions for changing a fuse in the MY-64 Operator's manual are correct, but cryptic. There are also step-by-step instructions on our website at **http://www.lab-in-a-box.net**.

The MY-64 DMM is provided with a low-cost, short-life battery at the factory. When the battery voltage drops below a certain level, the DMM voltmeter does not measure accurately. It is not cost-effective to replace this battery either at the factory or at the distributor. Thus, a high-performance alkaline battery is included with the parts kit (see Appendix A). It is recommended that you change the battery in the DMM before starting any measurements and that the battery be replaced with an equivalent long-life alkaline battery at least once every year.

If you measure a population of resistors, as is done in Experiment 2, the likelihood that the entire population is out of specification is essentially nil. Thus, if you determine that the mean of a population of resistors is out of specification, it is most likely that there is a calibration error associated with the resistance measurements of the DMM. We have observed that when an old battery is used, the DMM resistance readings will be low. Replacing the battery eliminates this effect.

3.6 Oscilloscope

The experiments in the previous editions of this laboratory manual were designed so that a software oscilloscope provided by Christian Zeitnitz (Zeitnitz, 2008a, 2008b) with a sound card interface could be used to perform all of the time-varying voltage measurements. To perform many of the experiments described in this edition of the laboratory manual, you will use a USB-powered oscilloscope with arbitrary function generator, Model PCSGU250, manufactured by Velleman Incorporated. This is the major change in laboratory equipment that was adopted for the revised 3th edition of the textbook. As a result of this change, several experiments have been modified and additional experiments have been developed to take advantage of the measurement capabilities of the oscilloscope.

The features of this oscilloscope include:

Oscilloscope:
- Dual trace with DC to 12 MHz +/- 3dB bandwidth
- Maximum of 30 V (AC plus DC) input voltage
- 250 Hz – 25 MHz sampling frequency

- Several trigger modes
- Signals on the two channels can be added, subtracted and multiplied
- x-y plots
- Record length of 4 ksamples/channel
- 1 MΩ/30pF input impedance
- Single 1x/10x probe

Function Generator:
- Generates sine, square, and triangle output signals
- 100 mVpp to 10 Vpp amplitude range (1 kHz/600 Ω/0 V offset)
- -5V to +5V DC offsets (0.4% of full scale resolution)
- Arbitrary functions can be uploaded into the signal library
- 50 mHz to 500 kHz frequency range
- 50 Ω output impedance

Spectrum Analyzer:
- Displays frequency spectrum and phase plot of input signal
- Frequency ranges for measurement of DC, 120 Hz to 12 MHz
- Fast Fourier transform resolution of 2048 lines.
- Selectable windows for discrete Fourier transforms
- Cursors for measuring frequencies and phase
- Bode plot option displays frequency spectrum and phase plot of input signal
- Frequency ranges for Bode plot of 1 kHz, 10 kHz, 100 kHz, and 500 kHz

Other Oscilloscopes

Rack-mounted or benchtop hardware oscilloscopes have specifications that exceed those listed for the Velleman PCSGU250 oscilloscope. However the list price for these oscilloscopes can easily exceed $1,000, well above the price range for the typical student. Furthermore, these systems do not usually have an integrated function generator. Thus, to perform Experiments 11-30, a separate function generator as well as the one on the ANDY board is necessary.

In addition to the rack-mounted or benchtop hardware oscilloscopes, there are a growing number of USB-based oscilloscopes that are now commercially available. Many, though not all, meet or exceed the specifications listed above for the Velleman PCSGU250 oscilloscope. The USB-based PC oscilloscopes that we have tested in addition to the Velleman oscilloscope included those from Parallax (2008), Pico Technology (2008), Syscomp Design (2006), and USB Instruments (2008). The selection of the Velleman PCSGU250 was made based upon several criteria including dual trace capability, maximum operating frequency of the oscilloscope and function generator, ease of use, and cost. Given the speed at which new inexpensive USB-power oscilloscopes are entering the market, we suggest that you review the specifications listed above to determine whether another vendor's oscilloscope can be substituted.

Figure 17 shows the main display screen of the Velleman oscilloscope. There are four sections to the display. First, there is the display area where the signal is observed. Second, a toolbar immediately above the display selects the function to be displayed (oscilloscope, spectrum analyzer, transient recorder, and circuit analyzer). Calibration of the oscilloscope is performed by selecting "Calibrate" under the "Options" tool when "Oscilloscope" is selected. It is highly recommended that calibration of the oscilloscope be done immediately after launching the Velleman Pclab2000LT program, the software package that allows you to control the oscilloscope from your computer. Cursors, or markers, to measure time, frequency, or amplitude can be selected from the "View" tool. Automatic calculations of several quantities from the measurements display in the window are available under "View/Waveform Parameters". The addition, subtraction, multiplication, and division of two traces as well as the option to plot one trace with respect to the other (x-y plot) can be selected from the "Math" tool.

On the lower left below the window in which the measured signals are display are the settings that the user can select. These include the volt/division for Channel 1 (blue trace) and Channel 2 (red trace), whether the voltage is being measured using a 1x or 10x probe, and the type of coupling used between the oscilloscope and the probe. DC coupling will allow both DC and AC signals to be displayed on the screen. AC coupling filters all DC components from the measured signal before the signal is displayed. And, GND sets the voltage displayed for the channel selected to 0 V.

The trigger options are displayed to the right. Triggering on a signal helps stabilize the image displayed on the screen. Options include the selection of which signal (Ch1 or Ch2) will be used as the trigger and whether the display of the measured voltages will begin as the voltage of the selected signal increases or decrease – the trigger is on the rising edge or falling edge of the signal. To the right of the displayed measurements is a box where the time/division can be selected based upon the choices of the "Freq. Range" and "Zoom". Clicking "Run" starts the data collection.

To the far right is a window entitled "Function Generator", which allows the user to select between a sine wave, square wave, triangular wave, and waveforms that have been stored under the "More Func". It is possible to upload waveforms that you have designed and instructions on how to do this are posted on **www.lab-in-a-box.net**. The frequency of the waveform selected from this window. The amplitude of the peak-to-peak time-varying signal and DC offset are entered using the buttons and/or boxes located at the bottom right. The function generator operates independently of the oscilloscope; the output is immediately available at the BNC jack of the Velleman instrument. So you may generate signals with the function generator simultaneously while using the scope to observe their effect on a circuit.

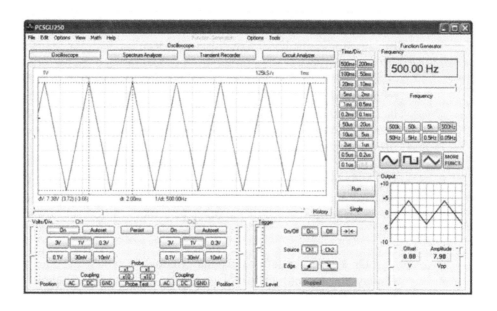

Figure 17: Velleman PCSGU250 oscilloscope main screen.

Complete instructions and details for using all of these features are provided in the instruction posted on the **www.lab-in-a-box.net** website.

3.7 Working with Wires and AWG Wire Sizes

Wires for electrical and electronic work are manufactured from annealed, high-purity, oxygen-free (HPOF) copper because of its high electrical conductivity, good ductility, and reasonable corrosion resistance and cost. The electrical resistivity of this material is given by $\rho = \rho_o[1 + \alpha(T - 20)]$, where $\rho_o = 1.7241 \times 10^{-8}$ $\Omega \cdot$m is the resistivity at 20°C, T is the temperature ($^{\circ}$C), and $\alpha = \dfrac{1}{\rho_o} \dfrac{\Delta \rho}{\Delta T}$ is the temperature coefficient (Fischbeck and Fischbeck, 1982). A mean value of $\alpha = 3.9 \times 10^{-3}$ per $^{\circ}$C is sufficiently accurate for most electronics work. The resistivity is a property of the material and is independent of the shape of the wire. The resistance of a given copper wire is $R = \rho L / A$, where L is the length of the wire and A is its cross-sectional area. Wires are drawn to a series of standard diameters or cross-sectional areas. There are two standards—the American Wire Gauge (AWG) and the Metric Wire Gauge (MWG). Each is described below.

American

In the AWG system, diameters can be calculated by applying the formula

44

Wire Gauge

$D(AWG) = 0.005 \cdot 92^{((36-AWG)/39)}$ inch (Powerstream, 2007). For the 00, 000, 0000, etc., gauges, use -1, -2, -3, respectively, which makes more sense than 'double nought.' This means that in the AWG system, every six gauge decrease gives a doubling of the wire diameter, while every three gauge decrease doubles the wire cross-sectional area. Note the similarity to dB in signal levels. Table 9 shows the sizes of wires in the AWG system as well as other information described in the following paragraphs. Also note that, in this table, the wire resistances are calculated for 20°C. If the operating temperature is different from this value, the correct resistance can be computed from the equations above.

Metric Wire Gauge

In the MWG system, the gauge is ten times the diameter in millimeters, so a 50 gauge metric wire would be 5 mm in diameter. Note that in AWG system the diameter goes up as the gauge goes down while in the metric system the diameter does the opposite. Probably because of this confusion, most of the time metric-sized wire is specified in millimeters rather than metric gauges.

Load-Carrying Capacities

Table 9 also provides a guideline of *ampacity* for copper wire current-carrying capacity, following the *Handbook of Electronics Tables and Formulas* (Sams, 1986). As you might guess, the rated ampacities are just a rule of thumb. In careful engineering, the insulation temperature limit, thickness, thermal conductivity, and air convection and temperature should all be taken into account. The Maximum Amps for Power Transmission column uses the 700 circular mils per amp rule, which is very conservative. The Maximum Amps for Chassis Wiring column is also a conservative rating but is meant for wiring in air and not in a bundle. For short lengths of wire, such as are used in battery packs, you must trade off the resistance and load with size, weight, and flexibility.

Frequency Effects

As the frequency of the current flowing in a wire increases, the current is confined to a layer near the surface of the wire. The thickness of this layer is called the skin depth (Jackson, 1962; Wikipedia, 2008). The skin depth is given by

$$d = \sqrt{\frac{2\rho}{\omega\mu}} \tag{1}$$

where ρ is the bulk resistivity of the metal, μ is its absolute magnetic permeability, and ω is the angular frequency of the current (see, e.g., Mohan et al., 2003). Substituting for the variables, it is found that for pure copper,

$$d = \frac{66.3}{\sqrt{f}} \text{ mm} \tag{2}$$

where f is the AC frequency in Hz and d is in mm. If it is assumed that all of the current is carried uniformly in a layer of thickness d, then it is easily shown that the resistance R of a wire of diameter D and length L is

$$R = \frac{\rho}{d} \left(\frac{L}{\pi(D-d)} \right) \; \Omega \qquad (3)$$

In Eq (3) it is assumed that $d \leq D/2$. In the special case where $d = D/2$, then Eq (3) reduces to the DC result, for which $R = \rho L / A$ and A is the cross-sectional area of the wire. This implies that for wire diameters $D \geq 2d$, the wire will show an increased resistance for current frequencies above those given by Eq (2). Conversely, for wires of diameter $D \leq 2d$, the AC skin effect can be neglected. Note that Eq (3) is not valid when $D \leq d$.

For copper, the frequency at which there will be an increased resistance over the DC value is related to the AWG wire diameter by

$$f = 257 e^{0.232 \cdot (AWG)} \; \text{Hz} \qquad (4)$$

where AWG is the American Wire Gauge size (see Table 9). Terman (1943) showed that the diameter of a wire D_W for which there is a 10 percent increase in the resistance at a given frequency is

$$D_W = \frac{200}{\sqrt{f}} \; \text{mm} \qquad (5)$$

These results show that the increase in resistance of a wire can be significant in large wires at low frequencies and in small wires at high frequencies. For the experiments in this book, the frequencies are low enough that these effects can be neglected except possibly for the equivalent series resistance (ESR) of inductors that are wound with very fine wires (see Section 3.10).

Inductance of Wires

One must also consider the inductance of a wire. The DC and AC inductances of straight wires are (Rosa, 1908), respectively

$$L_{DC} = 2L \left[\ln \left(\frac{L}{D} \right) - 0.75 \right] \; \text{nH} \qquad (6)$$

and

$$L_{AC} = 2L \left[\ln \left(\frac{L}{D} \right) - 1.00 \right] \; \text{nH} \qquad (7)$$

where L is the length of the wire (in cm) and D its diameter (in cm). Eq (7) is valid for frequencies for which the skin depth does not become a limitation (see discussion above regarding skin depth). Using Eq (6) and data from Table 9, the inductance of 5 cm of 22 AWG wire is 36 nH. This is a small value and the inductance of wires can be neglected in most of the experiments described in this text. However, at high frequencies and the very small wire diameters encountered in integrated circuits and/or computer electronics, such effects are no longer negligible.

Table 9: AWG Wire Sizes and Maximum Currents

AWG gauge	Diameter Inches	Diameter mm	Ohms per 1000 ft	Ohms per km	Maximum amps for chassis wiring	Maximum amps for power transmission
OOOO	0.460	11.7	0.049	0.161	380	302
OOO	0.410	10.4	0.062	0.201	328	239
OO	0.365	9.27	0.078	0.256	283	190
0	0.325	8.25	0.098	0.322	245	150
1	0.289	7.35	0.124	0.406	211	119
2	0.258	6.54	0.156	0.513	181	94
3	0.229	5.83	0.197	0.646	158	75
4	0.204	5.19	0.249	0.815	135	60
5	0.182	4.62	0.313	1.03	118	47
6	0.162	4.11	0.395	1.30	101	37
7	0.144	3.67	0.498	1.63	89	30
8	0.129	3.26	0.628	2.06	73	24
9	0.114	2.91	0.792	2.60	64	19
10	0.102	2.59	0.999	3.28	55	15
11	0.0907	2.30	1.26	4.13	47	12
12	0.0808	2.05	1.59	5.21	41	9.3
13	0.0720	1.83	2.00	6.57	35	7.4
14	0.0641	1.63	2.53	8.28	32	5.9
15	0.0571	1.45	3.18	10.4	28	4.7
16	0.0508	1.29	4.02	13.2	22	3.7
17	0.0453	1.15	5.06	16.6	19	2.9
18	0.0403	1.02	6.39	20.9	16	2.3
19	0.0359	0.912	8.05	26.4	14	1.8
20	0.0320	0.812	10.2	33.3	11	1.5
21	0.0285	0.724	12.8	42.0	9.0	1.2
22	0.0254	0.645	16.1	52.9	7.0	0.92
23	0.0226	0.574	20.4	66.8	4.7	0.73
24	0.0201	0.511	25.7	84.2	3.5	0.58
25	0.0179	0.455	32.4	106	2.7	0.46
26	0.0159	0.404	40.8	134	2.2	0.36
27	0.0142	0.361	51.5	169	1.7	0.29
28	0.0126	0.320	64.9	213	1.4	0.23
29	0.0113	0.287	81.8	268	1.2	0.18
30	0.0100	0.254	103	338	0.86	0.14
31	0.0089	0.226	130	427	0.70	0.11
32	0.0080	0.203	164	538	0.53	0.091

Data courtesy of Powerstream Corp (http://www.powerstream.com).

3.8 Resistors

Resistors are produced using a variety of technologies, each of which meets certain requirements of value, precision, power rating, stability, temperature coefficient, and cost. The most common resistors include wire-wound, thin film metal, thin film metal oxide, and thin film carbon. Configurations include cylindrical 2-wire devices, as well as single in-line packages (SIP), dual in-line packages (DIP), and surface mount devices. Typical resistances range from about 1 Ω to around 20 MΩ. Resistor power ratings vary from 1/16 W surface mount devices to 25 W fixed power resistors. The tolerance of a resistor defines the range around the nominal value within which its resistance is guaranteed to lie. Tolerances vary from 0.1 percent to 50 percent of nominal. And, the value of a resistor can be anything the manufacturer desires. The internal construction of a typical thin-film resistor is shown in Figure 18(a). Metal end-caps crimped onto the surface resistance coating produce the telltale bulges on the ends of a thin-film resistor. Figure 18(b) shows another type of resistor with a uniform cylindrical body and no bulges on its ends. These are carbon-composition resistors, which were last mass-produced in the 1990s; they were the most popular resistors during the previous 60 years. Because of the greater volume of resistance material in carbon-composition resistors, they can tolerate much greater momentary power overloads for longer periods of time without permanent damage than thin-film resistors. A Google search of the Internet for resistors manufactured by various technologies returns a wealth of information.

EIA Standards

In the experiments described in this book, you will only use cylindrical, carbon film resistors with axial electrodes. They are typically available as ¼, ½, 1, and 2W devices with tolerances of 5 percent or 10 percent. Resistors with tighter tolerances (0.1 percent to 1 percent) are typically made of thin metal films and are more expensive than the carbon film devices. Even within this small subset of resistors, a wide range of resistance values could still be manufactured. To eliminate the chaos that would result without national and international standards, the Electronic Industries Association (EIA) and other bodies have agreed on standard values for resistors. In addition, they have devised a coding methodology for identifying a resistor of any given value. It is critical that you learn these standards to build, test, and analyze real electric circuits.

EIA Resistor Values

Consider a resistor manufacturing technology that can produce a resistor of any given nominal value with a tolerance of 10 percent. What values of resistors should be manufactured? Clearly, if we start by manufacturing resistors with a nominal value of 100 Ω, it makes little sense to offer 105 Ω resistors because they fall within the tolerance band of the 100 Ω resistor. In fact, the next value that should be made would be 120 Ω. In this case, all 100 Ω resistors fall between 90 Ω and 110 Ω while all 120 Ω resistors fall between 108 Ω and 132 Ω. The next nominal value is then 150 Ω with a tolerance band of 135 Ω to 165 Ω. Following this logic, the series 100, 120, 150, 180, 220, 270, 330, 390, 470, 560, 680, and 820 Ω of nominal values is developed for 10 percent resistors. This is known as the EIA 'E' series of preferred values; it is specifically called the E12 series because there are 12 values in the decade. The series is extended to values in other decades by multiplying or dividing by powers of ten. Using a similar logic, the preferred values for resistors of different precisions can be developed. Those with larger (lower) tolerances have fewer values, while resistors with smaller (higher or tighter) tolerances have more. The EIA standard preferred series are given in Table 10, while the preferred resistor values for the E6, E12, E24 and E48 series are given in Table 11. The values for the E96 and E192 series may be found on the AnaLog Services website (AnaLog Services, 2008). The resistors in the resistor kit used in this course are ½ W, 5 percent carbon film resistors but are taken from the E12 rather than the E24 preferred series (see Appendix A, Table A.2.)

EIA Resistor Color Codes

Resistors have color codes to convey their values because they are too small to put numbers on. Also, by putting a color band around the resistor, its value may be read regardless of the orientation of the resistor—an important consideration when placing a small, cylindrical object on a printed circuit board.

The color bands are usually offset closer to one end. Start by reading the band closest to the end. This first color band signifies the first digit of the resistor value, the second color band signifies the second digit, and the third color band signifies the multiplier factor. In order to figure out a resistor's value, look up the first and second digits based upon the color code shown in Table 12. Because this book is printed in grayscale rather than color, a resistor color code chart is included in the parts kit (see Appendix A). Next, multiply the number by 10^X, where X is the value of the third color band. The third color band follows the same color code as the first and second color bands. The scaled value is labeled relative to ohms. The color band on the side opposite to the resistor value color bands signifies the tolerance of the resistor. The tolerance is the maximum percentage difference between the measured resistance value and the marked nominal resistance value. The resistors used in the experiments in this text are all

Table 10: Tolerances of EIA Preferred Resistor Series

EIA Series	Tolerance
E3	50% (no longer used)
E6	20% (seldom used)
E12	10%
E24	5% (and usually 2%)
E48	2%
E96	1%
E192	0.5, 0.25, 0.1% and higher

Data courtesy of AnaLog Services Inc. (http://www.logwell.com)

Table 11: Standard EIA Decade Values Table

E6	E12	E24	E48	E6	E12	E24	E48	E6	E12	E24	E48
100	100	100	100	220	220	220	215	470	470	470	464
			105				226				487
		110	110			240	237			511	511
			115				249				536
	120	120	121		270	270	261		560	560	562
			127				274				590
		130	133			300	287			620	619
			140				301				649
150	150	150	147	330	330	330	316	680	680	680	681
			154				332				715
		160	162			360	348			750	750
			169				365				787
	180	180	178		390	390	383		820	820	825
			187				402				866
		200	196			430	422			910	909
			205				442				953

Data courtesy of AnaLog Services Inc. (http://www.logwell.com)

5 percent tolerance resistors; in other words, the measured resistance will have a maximum deviation from the marked value of plus or minus 5 percent of the marked value. This 5 percent tolerance is identified with a gold band.

An example of a 2 MΩ resistor is shown in Figure 18(b). Notice the color bands. The colors are red (2), black (0), and green (10^5). These colors translate to: 20×10^5 Ω or 2 MΩ. The silver band on the right signifies a 10% tolerance.

High Frequency Effects

As noted above, the cylinder is one of the most common resistor structures. Thus, in addition to the designed resistance of the device, it has an associated capacitance and inductance. A circuit model of such effects would be similar to that for an inductor as is shown in Figure 23 (see Section 3.10 on inductors). Typically, the capacitances are measured in femto-Faradays while the inductances are measured in nano-Henry's. Thus, the self-resonant frequencies for such devices are in the range of hundreds of megahertz or gigahertz and are thus of no significance for the low frequencies encountered in the experiments encountered in this text. However, the student is cautioned to be cognizant of the possibility of such effects when working with increasingly common high-frequency digital circuits.

Table 12: Standard EIA Resistor Color Code Table
(Courtesy of Action electronics, Inc.)

Standard EIA Color Code Table 4 Band: ±2%, ±5%, and ±10%

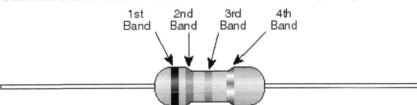

Color	1st Band (1st figure)	2nd Band (2nd figure)	3rd Band (multiplier)	4th Band (tolerance)
Black	0	0	10^0	
Brown	1	1	10^1	
Red	2	2	10^2	±2%
Orange	3	3	10^3	
Yellow	4	4	10^4	
Green	5	5	10^5	
Blue	6	6	10^6	
Violet	7	7	10^7	
Gray	8	8	10^8	
White	9	9	10^9	
Gold			10^{-1}	±5%
Silver			10^{-2}	±10%

Action-Electronics.com

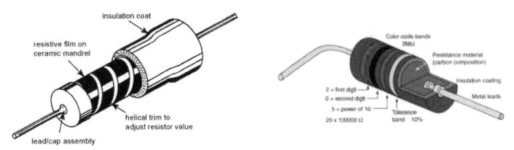

(a) thin film   (b) carbon composition

Figure 18: internal structure of resistors.
(Internet source: unknown)

3.9 Capacitors

Capacitors are passive devices that store energy in their electric fields. They come in a wide variety of sizes, shapes, construction, and electrical properties. When using capacitors, as with all devices, it is important to read the specification or datasheet for the devices at hand.

Geometry and Manufacture

Capacitors are manufactured using a variety of technologies, the choice of which depends on the capacitor's size, performance specifications, cost, and application. Common devices are classified in four groups: film, ceramic, electrolytic, and miscellaneous. They are manufactured as both two-wire, through-hole devices, and as surface mount devices. Only the former will be used in the experiments described in this book. Some examples are shown in Figure 19. Good reviews of the properties, classification, construction, reliability, and markings of capacitors are given by Horn (1992) and are on the CapSite 2008 website (Endl, 2008). Characteristics that need to be considered for each application include: the aging rate; the capacitance versus size, frequency, and voltage; drift versus temperature; cost and availability; current carrying capacity; dielectric absorption; the dissipation factor and its voltage, frequency, and temperature dependence; equivalent series resistance (ESR), which is made up of lead and end-termination resistances, electrode resistance, and dielectric loss; frequency range; insulation resistance; noise; packaging and construction;

Figure 19: Various capacitors: (a) electrolytic (left); (b) Mylar (middle); and (c) ceramic disk (right).

reliability; temperature limits; and voltage limits. Capsite 2008 has an excellent discussion of all of these considerations. The capacitors used for this course are ceramic disk, Mylar film, or electrolytic devices that have been selected for acceptable performance and low cost.

Capacitor Marking

There is little consistency among manufacturers as to the identification markings on capacitors; they range all the way from full details of capacitance, working voltage, and temperature ratings, to nothing at all, depending on the physical size of the capacitor. On smaller devices, there may be a code which depends on the type of capacitor. Thus, the availability of a digital capacitance meter, such as is provided in the MY-64 DMM recommended for use here, is a great asset.

Of particular importance is the working voltage, commonly labeled as 'WV,' or perhaps just as 'V.' This is the maximum voltage that can be safely applied to the device. For AC voltages, this is the peak voltage and not the root mean square (*rms*) voltage. You should always be sure to compute the peak voltage as $\sqrt{2}V_{rms}$ for sinusoidal voltages.

A color code system reminiscent of the resistor color coding described in Section 3.8 was used many years ago and only shows up on very old (obsolete) paper and mica devices. This system is described in Horn (1992) and will be required only if you are working on older equipment.

Electrolytic Capacitors

Most currently used capacitors are marked with numbers instead of a color code. Several examples are shown in Figure 19. Electrolytic capacitors (Figure 19 left) are usually labeled in microfarads. The capacitance value is written with the corresponding units directly on the capacitor. The device shown is a 50 V, 100 µF electrolytic capacitor. Electrolytic capacitors have a polarity, so the lead with the negative sign must be connected to a lower potential node in your circuit than the positive lead. Note the negative polarity mark.

> **Note:** It is important to bear in mind that if an electrolytic capacitor is connected with the wrong polarity, it is possible that the device could explode.

Mylar and Ceramic Disk Capacitors

For Mylar (plastic film) and ceramic disk capacitors shown in Figure 19 (middle and right, respectively), the numbers are labeled relative to picofarads (10^{-12} F). The first number is the first digit, the second number is the second digit, and the third number is the multiplier factor. Multiply the value shown by the first two digits by 10^X, where X is the value of the multiplier factor (see Table 13). Examples are the two ceramic disk capacitors in Figure 19 marked 470 and 102. These numbers translate to 47 pF and 1000 pF, or 1 nF, respectively. If the third number is missing, then it is to be treated as an implied zero. Thus, a capacitor with the coding 33 would be read as a 33 pF (33 'puffs') capacitor. Note especially from Table 13 that the third digit multiplier is used differently for the last several digits (digits 6–9). Additional information may be provided in this nomenclature, as shown by the Mylar capacitors in Figure 19. There may be a tolerance code which is given as a single letter, as shown in Table 14.

Sometimes there is a letter-number-letter code at the end, instead of a simple letter. An example would be a 104Z6V. Here, the 104 is read as in Table 13 while the Z6V would be read as a +10 to +105 deg C, +22 percent, -82 percent specification as shown in Table 15. Finally, there are two additional numbering systems seen on capacitors. The first is an EIA code, which is recognized by its starting with an 'R,' and the second is a 'Mil Spec.' Details of these codes are given at the Transtronics (2008) website.

Electrical Model

As with all devices, real capacitors show a wide variety of non-ideal properties, many of which are frequency dependent. A common model for a capacitor (Endl, 2008) is shown in Figure 20. In this model, C is the capacitance as marked on the device, ESR is the equivalent series resistance and includes such effects as lead, end termination, and electrode resistance, ESL is the series equivalent inductance, R_L is the insulation resistance, and R_{DA} and C_{DA} are the resistance and capacitance associated with the dielectric absorption. Some manufacturers offer more complex PSpice models. Capsite 2008 (Endl, 2008) is a good place to begin gathering information on these effects. For the frequencies and devices used in the experiments described here, all of these effects are small and can be neglected. Thus, we may assume that $ESR = ESL = 0$, $RL = \infty$, $C_{DA} = 0$, and $R_{DA} = \infty$. Also, the impedance due to the dielectric absorption may become very large when compared to the capacitor impedance. However, these effects need to be taken into account when accurate modeling of a circuit is required, especially at high frequencies where they become non-negligible.

Table 13: Capacitor Digit Multipliers

Third Digit	Multiplier
0	1
1	10
2	100
3	1,000
4	10,000
5	100,000
6	Not used
7	Not used
8	0.01
9	0.10

Table 14: Capacitor Letter Tolerance Codes.

Letter Symbol	Tolerance (%)
B	± 0.10%
C	± 0.25%
D	± 0.5%
E	± 0.5%
F	± 1%
G	± 2%
H	± 3%
J	± 5%
K	± 10%
M	± 20%
N	± 0.05%
P	+100%, -0%
Z	+80%. -20%

3.10 Inductors

Inductors are passive devices that store energy in their magnetic fields. They are usually coils of wire wound on a wide variety of magnetic cores and come in many shapes and sizes, some of which are shown in Figure 21.

Geometry and Manufacture

The design and testing of an inductor to meet the specific needs of an application is a complex process. Of the various designs, bobbin-wound inductors are a common type of structure for inductors and chokes. All of the devices shown in Figure 21 are bobbin wound. As shown, they can be wound as toroids, pot cores, and a variety of 'E-I' shapes (Butler Winding 2008). A variety of core materials are used, including ferromagnetic alloys (silicon steel, Ni-Fe alloys, Co alloys), powdered ferromagnetic alloys (Fe and Ni), or various ferrites. Some have air cores. Details of various core types are given by Clapper (2004). Crane (2008) discusses the differences between using powdered alloys and ferrites in the design of power inductors. Of critical importance is the saturation of the core at high currents; ferrite cores retain constant inductance to higher currents, but then drop off more rapidly than powdered metals. Ferrites also do not show the eddy current core losses of metals. A standard figure of merit that includes the core losses is the equivalent series resistance (ESR), which will be discussed shortly.

Table 15: Capacitor Temperature Range/Stability Codes

First Symbol (letter)	Low Temperature Requirement	Second Symbol (number)	High Temperature Requirement	Third Symbol (letter)	Max Cap Change Over Temperature
Z	+10 deg. C	2	+45 deg. C	A	±1.0%
Y	-30 deg. C	4	+65 deg. C	B	±1.5%
X	-55 deg. C	5	+85 deg. C	C	±2.2%
		6	+105 deg. C	D	±3.3%
		7	+125 deg. C	E	±4.7%
				F	±7.5%
				P	±10.0%
				R	±15.0%
				S	±22.0%
				T	+22%, -33%
				U	+22%, -56%
				V	+22%, -82%

Data provided courtesy of R. Endl (2008) (http://my.execpc.com/~endlr/)

Crane shows that ferrites and powdered metal cores are almost indistinguishable at low frequencies, but at 500 kHz and above, the ESR of ferrite cores is much less than that of powdered metals.

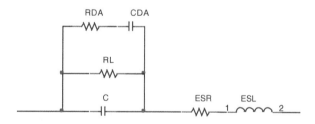

Figure 20: An electrical model of a capacitor.

3.10 Inductors

Inductors are passive devices that store energy in their magnetic fields. They are usually coils of wire wound on a wide variety of magnetic cores and come in many shapes and sizes, some of which are shown in Figure 21.

Geometry and Manufacture

The design and testing of an inductor to meet the specific needs of an application is a complex process. Of the various designs, bobbin-wound inductors are a common type of structure for inductors and chokes. All of the devices shown in Figure 21 are bobbin wound. As shown, they can be wound as toroids, pot cores, and a variety of 'E-I' shapes (Butler Winding 2008). A variety of core materials are used, including ferromagnetic alloys (silicon steel, Ni-Fe alloys, Co alloys), powdered ferromagnetic alloys (Fe and Ni), or various ferrites. Some have air cores. Details of various core types are given by Clapper (2004). Crane (2008) discusses the differences between using powdered alloys and ferrites in the design of power inductors. Of critical importance is the saturation of the core at high currents; ferrite cores retain constant inductance to higher currents, but then drop off more rapidly than powdered metals. Ferrites also do not show the eddy current core losses of metals. A standard figure of merit that includes the core losses is the equivalent series resistance (ESR), which will be discussed shortly. Crane shows that ferrites and powdered metal cores are almost indistinguishable at low frequencies, but at 500 kHz and above, the ESR of ferrite cores is much less than that of powdered metals.

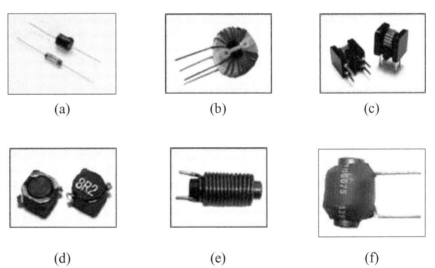

(a) (b) (c)

(d) (e) (f)

Figure 21: Various inductors. (a) rod-type low-current axial-leaded differential mode choke. (b) toroidal low-current common mode line choke. (c) low-power line filters for video signals. (d) low-current surface mount EMI filter inductor. (e) rod-type high- current vertical and horizontal differential mode chokes. (f) High-current RF choke. (Images courtesy of Coil Winding Specialists <http://www.coilws.com>).

Of particular importance is the designed operating temperature of the device. This is based on its self-heating due to the resistive losses within the coil, the eddy current losses within the core, and the thermal paths by which heat may dissipate from the core and windings to the exterior of the device. Core losses are determined by the electrical and magnetic properties of the core material.

Generally, materials with high electrical resistivity, such as ferrites, have very low core losses (Crane, 2006). Depending on the wire diameter and the frequency of operation, the thermal losses may increase due to an increased AC resistance of the wire (see Section 3.8). Garcia (2005) discusses the basic formulas for

determining the power loss in an inductor for sine wave signals. More complex analysis is required for other signal shapes as is discussed in a Coilcraft application note (Coilcraft, 2006). It is important to know if the maximum rms current of the device is greater or less than its saturation current; if it is greater, then the inductance of the device will be less than the specified value. The Coilcraft application note gives details of how to interpret the current and temperature ratings of the device. The company also provides a variety of computer simulation models for estimating these effects. For simple electronic applications such as those described in this text, the most important parameter is the maximum coil current, which is usually specified as I_{rms}.

Finally, there will be a distributed capacitance that depends on the structure of the winding and is determined primarily by the winding-to-winding geometry. Simple functional electrical models of the inductor will treat this as a single parallel capacitor. This capacitance results in a self-resonance in the device, as will be discussed shortly.

Testing

There are few standards for characterizing inductors. Important parameters include measuring the inductance and the self-resonant frequency. It is also important to test inductors at their application frequencies. Coilcraft has prepared several useful application notes to assist designers with these tasks. These include a note on testing inductors at application frequencies (Coilcraft, 2002), a note on measuring self- resonant frequencies (Coilcraft, 2003a), and a note on the calibration, compensation, and correlation of inductors (Coilcraft, 2003b).

Markings

As with capacitors, there is no industry standard for marking inductors. Often inductors will have their value clearly written on them. A pot core device similar to the devices used in the experiments described in this text is shown in Figure 22. The value is written along with its corresponding unit. The capital letter 'M' in 'MH' shown in Figure 22 indicates millihenry, not megahenry, so the device is a 100 mH inductor.

Electrical Model

Based on the concepts discussed above, one electrical model of an inductor (of many possible) is shown in Figure 23. A more complex model is given in the application note by Coilcraft (2003a). The inductance, L, is the value marked on the device. The capacitance, C, is the distributed capacitance of the windings and is usually not specified directly, but is given indirectly in either the self-resonant frequency (SRF) or by the Q-value. The resistance, R, is the equivalent series resistance (ESR) and includes the DC resistance of the windings and the core losses. If an AC resistance, which is frequency dependent, must be included, it is added as a frequency-dependent resistor in series with L and inside the parallel capacitor, C (see Coilcraft, 2003a).

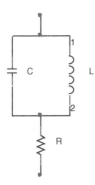

Figure 22: A 100 mH inductor.

Figure 23: Simplified inductor model.

The self-resonant frequency for the electrical model given in Figure 23 is given by $\omega_o = 1/\sqrt{LC}$ and the effective inductance can be shown to be

$$
L_{\text{eff}} = \frac{L}{1 - \dfrac{\omega^2}{\omega_o^2}}
$$
(8)

Thus, if the operating frequency $\omega < 0.1\omega_o$, the discrepancy between the effective and the nominal inductance will be less than 1%. However, as the frequency increases, the effective inductance increases over the nominal or stated value. This is shown in Coilcraft (2003a). Note that as the frequency approaches the SRF, the approximation of Eq (8) breaks down and additional terms must be taken into consideration, otherwise the effective inductance would become infinite. Typical properties of non-magnetically shielded pot core inductors such as those shown in Figure 22 are given in Table 16.

3.11 Trimmer Potentiometers (Trim pots)

Variable Resistors

The resistors described thus far are fixed resistors. A fixed resistor has a resistance that is relatively independent of environmental conditions such as temperature or pressure and the applied voltage and current. However, they to change the value of a resistor after it has been wired into a circuit a ions the circuit operation has many uses. One can tune the operation of th well as adjusting the value of one or more resistors, compensating for ared to the from nominal resistances of the other resistors in the cir discrepancies in the actual magnitude of the applied voltage r is a trimmer values used during the circuit design. One such variable ments throughout potentiometer or trim pot, which are used in a number of e

Table 16: Typical properties of pot core inductors.

L (mH)	Test Frequency (kHz)	DCR (ohms)	IMAX (Arms)	SRF (kHz)	Q
1.0	252	4	250	1400	80
2.2	252	7	150	1000	80
4.7	252	14	100	630	80
6.8	79.6	17	100	600	80
10	79.6	34	80	350	80
22	79.6	40	100	180	60
33	79.6	55	50	160	60
47	79.6	72	80	130	35
68	79.6	120	50	110	35
100	25.2	150	30	80	30
150	25.2	250	30	60	30
220	25.2	300	20	40	30
470	–	600	30	20	16
1000	–	1000	30	12	12

Notes: (1) All L values are those stated on the devices. (2) No test data are available for the 470 and 1000 mH devices. The SRF and Q values are extrapolated from the values above and assume a test frequency of 0 Hz.

(Data courtesy of Sol Kaye at Electronix Express.)

this text. Or, a resistor whose resistance is strongly dependent on a parameter can be used as a sensor. A thermistor is used to measure the temperature of the surface on which the thermistor is bonded. One class of piezoelectric sensors have resistances that change with the magnitude of mechanical or atmospheric pressure applied to the sensor. A resistance of a photoresistor (also known as a photoconductor) is dependent on the intensity of light that is on the active surface of the resistor. In Experiment 30: Design a Night Light, a voltage divider consisting of a photoresistor and a fixed resistor is used as the input to a circuit that regulates whether an LED is off – when the active surface of photoresistor is illuminated and the resistance of the photoresistor is small – or the LED is on – when the photoresistor is in the dark and its resistance is large.

re₃ trimmer potentiometer (pot, potentiometer, or trim pot) is a variable
ᵥith three leads and a simple mechanism that allows you to easily change

its resistance value. A typical device is shown in Figure 24. Note the white circle where a small screwdriver may be inserted. Other devices have a shaft protruding from the device.

Wiring A trim pot is wired as shown in Figure 25. The outermost leads are the ends of the resistor, and the middle lead is connected to the twisting dial of the trim pot. If only the two outer leads are used (e.g., pins 1 and 3 in Figure 25), the trim pot behaves as a normal, non-variable resistor. If a circuit is connected to either of the outer leads (e.g., pin 1) and the middle lead (pin 2), then the trim pot will behave as a variable resistor. When the dial is turned all the way to one side,

Figure 24: A 1 kΩ potentiometer.

Figure 25: PSpice symbol for a potentiometer

there will be no resistance and when the dial is turned all the way to the other side, there will be the full resistance of the trim pot.

The trim pot may be used in two modes. If only pin 1 and pin 2 are used, the device is a variable resistor. If pin 1 is connected to a voltage source, pin 3 is connected to ground, and pin 2 to the circuit, then the device becomes a voltage divider. One must be careful with this wiring; sometimes it is required that the device behave as a variable resistor and sometimes as a voltage divider. These are different devices and will perform differently in the circuit. When using the trim pot as variable resistor, it is good practice to always short the unused pin to the wiper pin (pin 2 in Figure 25 above.)

Nomenclature The value of the trim pot is signified by the three-digit number on the top row of lettering shown on one side (Figure 24). The first number is the first digit of the resistance value, the second number is the second digit, and the third number is the multiplier factor. The value of the first and second digits is multiplied by 10^X, where X is the value of the multiplier factor. The scaled value is labeled relative to ohms. For example, the trim pot shown in Figure 24 reads 102 and is a 1kΩ (10×10^2) device.

3.12 Operational Amplifiers

An operational amplifier (op amp) is a device that behaves like a voltage-controlled voltage source (VCVS). In the earliest days, these were vacuum tube devices. Later, they were built from discrete semiconductors and other passive devices. Currently, most op amps are integrated circuits like the LM324 shown in Figure 26.

Figure 26: The LM324 Op amp

Op Amp Properties

For the most part, the op amps discussed in introductory texts such as those listed in Table 2 are treated as ideal devices. They have infinite open loop gain, zero output resistance, infinite input resistance, operate with any voltage supply the user wishes to provide, are capable of providing all output power required by the circuit they are driving, and will respond instantaneously to any change in the input signal.

Real op amps approximate some of these properties but have significant limitations. They have a high, but finite input open loop gain; a high, but finite,

Table 17: Properties of the LM324 Op Amp

Property	Specification
DC gain	112 dB
Bandwidth (unity gain)	1 MHz
Power supply range	±1.5 V to ±16 V
Output voltage swing	-9 V to +8 V for $V^\pm = 9$ V
Output current/device (source)	40 mA (typical)
Output current/device (sink)	20 mA (typical)
Power dissipation (LM324N)	1134 mW
Offset voltage	2 mV
Offset current	5 nA

Data compiled from the National Semiconductor LM324 Datasheet.

input resistance; and a low, but finite, output resistance. They operate only within certain bounds on their power supply voltages, can produce only limited output power, and can change their output only at a certain maximum rate (the slew rate) for an infinitely fast change of input voltage. It is, therefore, very important for the user to learn how to read the datasheet for the device in use. Datasheets may be obtained on the internet, which is also known as the World Wide Web (WWW). The Texas Instruments (Texas Instruments, 2008) and National Semiconductor (National Semiconductor, 2008) sites are particularly valuable. In addition to containing important data information, these sites also include PSpice models for most real devices. These are invaluable for accurate work using Spice. However, those using the free demo version of PSpice from OrCAD must be careful because that program is limited to circuits with 64 nodes, and most op amp models contain 30 or more nodes per device.

An examination of the datasheet for the LM324, for example, provides the data given in Table 17. From this table, we deduce several important properties.

a) The open loop gain is $A = 400,000$ as determined from the stated gain of 112 dB. ($112 = 20\log_{10} A; A = 398,107$)

b) The gain as a function of input signal frequency is given by $G_{dB} = 120 - \log_{10} f$, as determined from the stated gain-bandwidth product. Combining this with the result from (a) shows that the open loop gain is constant up to $f \approx 2.5$ Hz, at which point it decreases by 20 dB/decade.

c) The devices will operate in either of two modes. They may be used with a unipolar power supply with a minimum of 3 V to a maximum of 32 V on pin 4 and with pin 11 grounded (see next paragraph and Figure 27 for device pin-outs). Or, they may be used with a bipolar power supply within the range of ±1.5 V to ±16 V with the positive supply provided to pin 4 and the negative supply provided to pin 11.

d) The output voltage is confined to a range that is less that the input voltage range. There is a graph on the datasheet that shows the output range as a function of V^+ and V^-. (Note that the power supplies are denoted as V^+ and V^- on the datasheet while they are denoted as V_{CC+} and V_{CC-} in Figure 27. These are synonymous.) The LM324 is interesting because its minimum output voltage is equal to V^-, while its maximum output is approximately $V^+ - 1.5$ V. This asymmetry can be important in circuit design and the designer should examine this graph carefully to assure that the power supplies will produce sufficient range for the desired output. Note that for experiments built on the ANDY board (Section 3.3), the power supplies are normally ±9 V, thus confining the output signal of the LM324 to the range -9 V $\leq V_o \leq +7.5$ V.

e) Each op amp can supply (typically) 40 mA when V_o is positive but may sink[†] only 20 mA (typically) when V_o is negative. The designer should design the op amp loads not to exceed these ratings, although the datasheet also shows that the LM324 is very robust. It will not exceed its maximum temperature ratings if the output is inadvertently shorted to ground. Of course, it is not recommended that this property be tested experimentally!

f) The IC package may dissipate up to 1134 mW, total, for all four devices.

These points only highlight the operating conditions and specifications for this op amp. The designer should be cognizant of all of the device specifications as learned from a careful reading of the full datasheet.

Op Amp Pin-outs

The op amp chips provided in the parts kit include the LM324, the LF356, and the μ741. The LM324 contains four op amps per chip with pin-outs as shown in Figure 27. The LF356 and the μ741 have a single device per chip. The pin-outs for the LF356 are shown in Figure 28.

Notice the semicircular shaped figure on the left of Figure 26 and on the top of both drawings in Figures 27 and 28. This is used to identify the location of pin 1, which is always to the left of this mark when looking at the device from the top. Note also that the pin numbers are counted sequentially starting at pin 1 and proceeding counter-clockwise around the device.

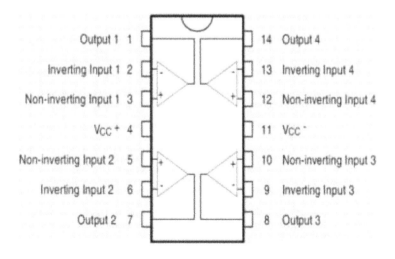

Figure 27: LM324 Op amp pin-outs.
Image courtesy of STMicrosystems
(http://www.stonline.com)

[†] Sinking a current implies that current will flow into the device through its output pin.

Dual-In-Line Package (M and N)

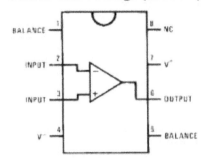

Figure 28: LF356 Op amp pin-outs.

Image courtesy of National Semiconductor
(http://www.national.com).

In the case of the LM324, each op amp has its own input and output pins. One input is the inverting input to the op amp which is labeled with a minus ('-'). The other input is the non-inverting input into the op amp which is labeled with a plus ('+'). All four op amps use the same power supply voltages. On some manufacturer's datasheets, the positive power supply, or V_{CC+}, is labeled V^+ but is still found on pin 4. The negative power supply is V_{CC-}. Note that V_{CC-} is, somewhat confusingly, labeled GND or V^- on some datasheets. You should connect this pin as V_{CC-}. Recall that the output will lie within the range $-V_{cc-} \leq V_o \leq V_{cc+}$.

Further information for these and a wide range of other devices can be found on the internet at several sites. The Texas Instruments (Texas Instruments, 2008) and the National Semiconductor (National Semiconductor, 2008) websites are particularly valuable and have a wealth of information on most of the common IC chips you will use. If you cannot find the device of interest on these sites, try Google.

3.13 Light-Emitting Diodes (LEDs)

A diode is a non-linear circuit element that only allows current to flow through it in one direction. Its I–V relationship is given by the diode equation

$$I = I_0(e^{qV/nkT} - 1) \qquad (9)$$

where q is the charge on an electron, V is the applied voltage, n is the ideality factor ($1 \leq n \leq 2$), k is Boltzmann's constant, T is the absolute temperature (K), and I_o is the reverse saturation current, which is related to the composition of the semiconductor junction. A diode is forward biased when current flows from the anode (+) side to the cathode (-) side. This is defined so that a positive voltage is a forward bias voltage. When an LED is forward biased, it also emits light. Typically, an LED will glow at the desired luminosity if it has a current of about

65

10 mA passing through it. For most common LEDs, this current may be achieved with an applied voltage of about 1.4 V, which is about the band gap of GaAs.

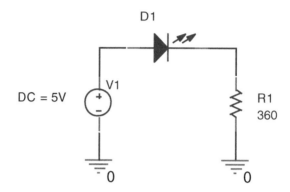

Figure 29: An LED with a current-limiting resistor.[†]

The resistance of the LED depends on the current passing through it and may be estimated from the inverse of the derivative of Eq (9) with respect to voltage. This value is very sensitive to the parameters in Eq (9) and is best determined experimentally for each LED. Typically, it will be about 150 Ω at a device current of 10 mA and will increase as the current decreases. Clearly, from Eq (9), as the bias increases, the current increases exponentially and can become so large that I^2R heating will damage or destroy the device. Many LEDs will be irreversibly destroyed with a 5 V bias, a common digital board voltage. To avoid this problem, a current-limiting resistor, R1, is placed in series with the LED, as shown in Figure 29.

The value of the bias resistor R1 is computed from the value of the bias applied to the device and the desired maximum current. If the bias voltage is 5V and the desired maximum current is 10 mA, then by Ohm's law, R1 = (5.0-1.4)/0.010 = 360 Ω. On the other hand, if the bias voltage is 9 V, a voltage also provided by the ANDY board and used for the experiments described in this text, then the current-limiting resistor should be 760 Ω. The designer should read the device specifications carefully as many newer devices require higher voltages (some require as much as 4.5 V) to operate correctly and/or may operate properly at higher currents. The current-limiting resistor should be adjusted accordingly. For the experiments described in this text, the 1.4 V bias is appropriate and the current-limiting resistor should be either the 330 Ω or 390 Ω resistor (available in

---

[†] Note that the Demo version of PSpice, which is used for most academic work, does not have an LED in its parts libraries. To create circuits that are to be simulated, one must enter properties for an LED into the diode part in the Breakout library. For purposes of illustration, various LEDs (including the 10 LED bar graph included in the Lab-in-a-Box kit) may be found in the DISCRETE library which is found in the path immediately above the standard PSpice parts libraries. However, these components have been disabled for simulation use in the Demo version of PSpice.

the resistor kit listed in Appendix A) if the 5 V supply is used or the 820 Ω resistor (also available in the resistor kit) if the 9 V supply is used.

Three types of LEDs are used in the experiments described in this text. The first, and the most common, is a plastic dome with two pigtail leads, as shown in Figures 30 and 31. For these devices, the anode side is indicated with a long lead and the cathode side is indicated with a short lead (see left side of Figure 30).

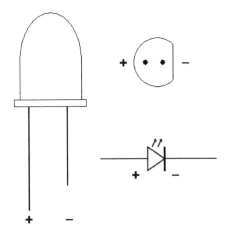

Figure 30: LED configuration and notation.

Figure 31: A red LED (left) and a LED bar graph (right).

Also, the cathode side is indicated with a flat section on the plastic casing of the diode (see top right side of Figure 30 and the left side of Figure 31). On the circuit diagram, an LED is indicated by an isosceles triangle (see bottom right side of Figure 30). At the apex of the triangle is a line that is parallel to the base of the triangle. The anode side is at the base of the triangle and the cathode side is

67

at the line at the apex of the triangle. When current tries to flow in the reverse direction (from the cathode to the anode) a diode will block the current flow. This is called reverse biasing. When an LED is reverse biased, current does not flow, and no light is emitted. Note that an LED is easily damaged when reverse biased, so this biasing condition should be avoided.

Light-emitting diodes can be connected in an array to make objects such as an LED bar graph, as shown in Figure 31(right). This combination of several devices in a single package (ten devices in the package shown in Figure 31) is the second type of LED and falls into the class of multi-segment LEDs. Each LED bar segment of the bar graph contains an anode and a cathode, just like an individual LED. In fact, an LED bar graph is nothing more than several individual LEDs connected in parallel with each other, with all of their anodes and cathodes oriented the same way. The anode side of the LED bar graph is the side that has lettering on the bar graph casing. The cathode side is the side opposite to the anode side. As with the discrete devices, the proper current-limiting resistors should be used with each LED in the structure.

The third type of device, the bi-color LED, has two LEDs, one red and one green, built into the same package, usually a plastic dome, as shown in Figure 30. A typical circuit is shown in Figure 32. Such circuits have four possible states:—dark, red, green, and yellow. If no signal is applied to the input at R1, both LEDs are dark. If the input is a positive DC voltage greater than the LED turn-on voltage, D1 glows red and D2 is dark. If the input is negative and greater than the

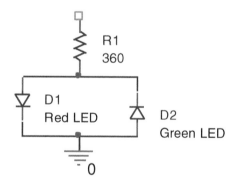

Figure 32: A bi-color LED.

turn-on voltage, D2 glows green. And, because the human eye cannot resolve light flashes faster than about 15 to 30 Hz, if the input is AC, both LEDs flash red and green alternately, but at a speed such that the eye 'sees' both as simultaneously on and the device appears yellow (the combination of red and green). The logic probes on the ANDY board light red for a high logic input, green for a low logic input, and oscillate between red and green for undefined logic states.

3.14 555 Timer

A 555 timer is a digital integrated circuit (IC) that will produce single voltage pulses when configured in a circuit known as a monostable multivibrator or will output a square wave when configured in a circuit known as an astable multivibrator. The pinout for the dual-inline package is shown in Figure 33.

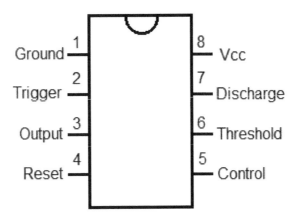

Fig. 33: Pin connection diagram for a 555 timer in a DIP package.

Operation of Timer

Internal to the 555 timer chip are two voltage comparators U1 and U2 (see Fig.34). **555** These two comparators are designed to keep the voltage across pins 2 and 6 of the 555 timer chip, between 1.67 V and 3.33 V. The reference voltage for the voltage comparators is equal to 1/3 and 2/3 of the voltage at pin 8 for U2 and U1, respectively; these voltages are the result of the voltage divider form by the three equal value resistors (R) fabricated on the timer IC. Note that a connection between wires that cross in a schematic is only made when a node, "●", is shown at the intersection of the wires.

First, the operation of the timer will be described assuming that pin 4 is tied to 5V which causes the preset on the RS flip-flop (U2A) to be disabled and pin 5 is floating, or not connected to a DC voltage. When $V_{pin\ 6} \geq 3.33\ V$, the output of comparator 1 resets the RS flip-flop (U2A) and causes a transistor is activated, which connects ground (pin 1) to pin 7 of the timer chip. When $V_{pin\ 2} \leq 1.67\ V$, the second comparator sets the RS flip-flop and causes the transistor to be turned off, opening a switch between ground and pin 7. The output of the 555 timer (pin 3) is the output Q of the RS flip-flop whose state is set and reset by the output of voltage comparator U2 and U1, respectively. Thus, the output from a 555 timer is a logical "1" when the voltage on pin 2 is less than or equal to 1.67V and is a logical "0" when the voltage on pin 6 is greater than or equal to 3.33V. The voltages that are outputted are dependent on V_{CC}, the voltage applied to pin 8. Should $V_{CC} = 5V$, $V_{pin\ 3} \cong 5V$ when $V_{pin\ 2} \leq 1.67\ V$ and $V_{pin\ 3} \cong 0V$ when $V_{pin\ 3} \cong 5V$ when $V_{pin\ 6} \geq 3.33\ V$. The output voltage for the case where $V_{pin\ 2} \geq 1.67\ V$ and $V_{pin\ 6} \leq 3.33\ V$ will depend on the last state of the flip-flop.

69

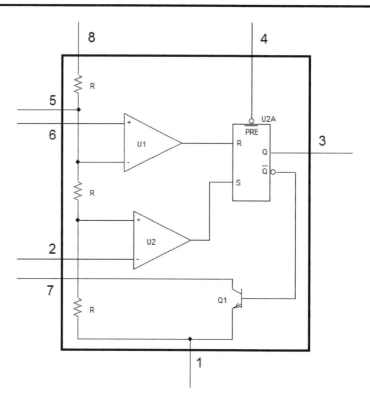

Fig. 34: Schematic of the 555 timer with pinouts labeled

The operation of the RD flip-flop is independent of voltages at the R and S input terminals on UA2 when the pin 4 is connected to a voltage that is recognized by the digital circuitry as a logical "0" and the output of the RS flip-flop Q will be equal to a logical "1". In this case, $V_{pin\,3}$ will not change no matter what the voltages are on pins 2, 5, and 6 of the 555 timer until the voltage at pin 4 is set to a logical "0". Again, the exact voltages that are treated as a logical "0" and "1" are dependent on the value of V_{CC}, the voltage applied to pin 8.

The reference voltage for voltage comparator U1 can be altered by applying a voltage to pin 5. This is used for certain pulse modulation circuits such as the pulse width modulation circuit used in Experiment 22.

3.15 References

Action Electronics, (2008). 16 November 2008
<http://www.action-electronics.com/resistor.htm>.

AnaLog Services, (2008). 16 November 2008
<http://www.logwell.com/tech/components/resistor_values.html>.

Bikson, M., (2008). 'A Review of Hazards Associated with Exposure to Low
Voltages.' 16 November 2008
<http://bme.ccny.cuny.edu/faculty/mbikson/BiksonMSafeVoltageReview.pdf>.

Butler Winding, (2008). 16 November 2008 <http://www.butlerwinding.com>.

Casini, V. and S. Kisner, (1998). Worker Deaths by Electrocution, DHHS
(NIOSH) Pub. 98-131. 16 November 2008
< http://www.cdc.gov/niosh/docs/98-131/pdfs/98-131.pdf>.

Computer Engineering Laboratory (CEL 2008), ECE Department, Virginia Tech.
16 November 2008 < http://www.ece.vt.edu/cel/Site-Map.html#2074_3074 >.

Clapper, T.C., (2004). 'Electronic Transformers and Inductor Core Types.' 16
November 2008 <http://www.butlerwinding.com/core-types/index.html>.

Coilcraft, (2002). 'Testing Inductors at Application Frequencies' Doc 119-1.
16 November 2008 < http://www.coilcraft.com/pdfs/doc119_TestAppFreq.pdf >.

Coilcraft, (2003a). 'Measuring Self Resonant Frequency.' Document 363-1. 16
November 2008 < http://www.coilcraft.com/pdfs/Doc363_MeasuringSRF.pdf >.

Coilcraft, (2003b). 'Calibration, Compensation and Correlation.'
Document 364-1. 16 November 2008
<http://www.coilcraft.com/pdfs/Doc364_CalCompCor.pdf>.

Coilcraft, (2008). 'Current and Temperature Ratings.' Document 361-1. 16
November 2008 <http://www.coilcraft.com/pdfs/Doc361_Current&Temp.pdf>.

Crane, L., (2006). 'Ferrite and Powder Core Materials for Power Inductors.'
Document 496-1. 16 November 2008 < http://www.coilcraft.com/pdfs/
Doc496_Ferrite&Powder_Core_Power_Inductors.pdf >.

Endl, R., (2008). 'CapSite 2008: Introduction to Capacitors, Release 4.1.' 16
November 2008 <http://my.execpc.com/~endlr/index.html>.

Electronix Express, (2008). 365 Blair Road, Avenel, New Jersey 07001 10
November 2008 <http://www.elexp.com>.

Fasse, P., (2000). 'Do's and Don'ts for Keeping Laboratory Notebooks.' 16
November 2008 <http://www.fr.com/news/articledetail.cfm?articleid=72>.

Fischbeck, H.J., and K.H. Fischbeck, (1982). Formulas, Facts and Constants for
Students and Professionals in Engineering, Chemistry, and Physics, Berlin:
Springer-Verlag, p208.

Garcia, N., (2005). 'Determining Inductor Power Loss.' Document 486. 16
November 2008 <http://www.coilcraft.com/pdfs/doc486_inductorlosses.pdf>.

Gardner, D., (2000). 'Do's and Don'ts for e-Lab Notebooks.' 16 November 2008 <http://www.fr.com/news/articledetail.cfm?articleid=73>.

Geist, A., J. Schwidder, D. Jung, and N. Nachtigal (2008). 'ORNL Electronic Notebook Project,' 16 November, 2008 <http://www.csm.ornl.gov/~geist/java/applets/enote/ >.

Horn, D.T., (1992). Electronic Components: A Complete Guide for Project Builders, New York: TAB Books. p68.

Jackson, J.D., (1962). Classical Electrodynamics, New York: John Wiley & Sons, p. 225.

Kuphaldt, T.R., (2008). All About Circuits, Vol. I, Ch. 3, Electrical Safety. 16 November 2008 <http://www.allaboutcircuits.com/vol_1/chpt_3/1.html>.

Lineberry, R.B., W.C. Headley, and R.W. Hendricks, (2006). 'RSR/VT A&D ANDY Board User Manual and Test Procedure.' The Bradley Department of Electrical and Computer Engineering, Virginia Polytechnic Institute and State University, Blacksburg, VA 24061. (**http://www.lab-in-a-box.net**).

Mohan, N., T.M. Undeland, and W.P. Robbins, (2003). Power Electronics, Hoboken, NJ: Wiley. pp 748–754

National Semiconductor, (2008). "LM324 - Low Power Quad Operational Amplifier." 16 November 2008 <(http://www.national.com/pf/LM/LM324.html>.

Parallax Inc., (2006). 599 Menlo Drive, Suite 100, Rocklin, California 95765. (http://www.parallax.com) See, e.g., the Parallax USB Oscilloscope.

Pico Technology Ltd., (2006). The Mill House, Cambridge St., St. Neots, Cambridgeshire, PE19 1QB, UK. Distributed in the US by CRAG Technologies, 2820 E. Schulman Ave., Suite C, Garden City, KS 67846. (http://www.picotech.com) See, e.g., the PicoScope Model 2202.

PowerStream Technology, (2007). 16 November 2008 <http://www.powerstream.com/Wire_Size.htm>.

Rosa, E.B., (1908). "The Self and Mutual Inductances of Linear Conductors." Bull. Bureau of Standards, **4**(2), p301.

Sams, H.W., (1986). Handbook of Electronics Tables and Formulas (6e), Upper Saddle River, NJ: Prentice Hall.

Stanford University, Office of Technology Licensing. (2008). 'Suggestions for Keeping Laboratory Notebooks.' 16 November 2008 <http://otl.stanford.edu/inventors/resources/labnotebooks.html>.

Syscomp Electronic Design Ltd., (2006). 55 Grandview Avenue, Toronto, Ontario, Canada M4K 1J1. 15 November 2008 <http://www.syscompdesign.com/oscilloscope.htm>

Terman, F.E., (1943). Radio Engineers' Handbook, New York: McGraw-Hill.

Texas Instruments, (2008). 25 November 2008
<http://focus.ti.com>.

Transtronics Inc., (2008). 16 November 2008
<http://www.transtronics.com/kits/ccode.htm>.

USB Instruments (2008). 373 Scotland St., Glasgow G58QB, UK. Distributed in
the US by EasySync Ltd., Hillsboro, OR 97124. 11 November 2008
<http://www.usb-instruments.com>. (See, e.g., the DS1M12 Stingray USB
Oscilloscope.)

Virginia Tech, (2008). 'Policy 13000 Rev.: 3. Policy on Intellectual Property'
16 November 2008 < http://www.policies.vt.edu/13000.pdf >.

Wikipedia, (2008). 16 November 2008
<http://en.wikipedia.org/wiki/Skin_effect>.

Zeitnitz, C., (2008a). 25 November 2008
<http://www.zeitnitz.de/Christian/Scope/Scope_en.html>.

Zeitnitz, C., (2008b). 25 November 2008
<http://www.zeitnitz.eu/scope/manual_scope_v130.pdf>.

Chapter 4: Experiments

This chapter presents thirty-eight experiments that have been developed for introducing the student to both DC and AC circuits. The experiments follow the presentation of several standard introductory electric circuit texts such as those listed in Table 18 and can be divided into two groups. The first group is a series of experiments associated with DC circuits, while the second group is associated with AC circuits. In the first group, following two experiments in which the student is introduced to the breadboard, its wiring diagram, and its internal resistances (Experiment 1), and to the tolerances of real components (Experiment 2), there are two experiments on basic circuit laws (Experiment 3—Ohm's law and Experiment 4—Kirchhoff's laws). The student then performs experiments on series and parallel resistors (Experiment 5) and voltage and current dividers (Experiment 6), on delta-to-wye transformations (Experiment 7), and on mesh currents and node voltages (Experiment 8), and superposition and the Thévenin equivalent (Experiment 9). In Experiements 1-9, all measurements are made with a DMM.

The first measurements using the USB oscilloscope is in Experiment 10. Students determine the Thévenin equivalent resistance of the Velleman oscilloscope and the function generator, which provides them with the information to determine loading effects when the voltage sources are driving low resistance loads and voltage measurements are made across high resistance components (Experiment 10). Following these introductory circuit experiments, the student may build two op amp circuits, one with an inverting amplifier (Experiment 11) and one with a non-inverting amplifier (Experiment 12). These experiments are followed by one in which the student builds a constant current source (Experiment 13) and explores the condition under which it is stable. Then, the natural response of an RC circuit is illustrated by turning off an LED (Experiment 14). Students then construct an electronic metronome using a speaker and an aa 555 timer configured as an astable multivibrator where adjusting the frequency of the beat by varying a RC time constant using a trim potentiometer and capacitor (Experiment 15). First order circuits are illustrated in the following three experiments. An ideal and then practical differentiator circuit is designed and characterized (Experiment 16). The frequency dependence of the gain of a differentiator circuit and the impact of high frequency noise is demonstrated (Experiment 17). Then, the design and operation of an integrator circuit is explored (Experiment 18).

Three introductory design projects are introduced, any of which can be used to conclude a course in DC circuits. The first (Experiment 19) is a project in which the student uses a number of resistors, op amps, and an LED bar graph to design a simple graphical voltmeter. The second project (Experiment 20) uses most of the information from Experiment 19 and takes it one step further to construct a logic probe. The third project (Experiment 21) uses LEDs, op amps, resistors, and capacitors to design a simple blinking arrow similar to those often used for safety warning at highway construction sites. Unlike the first eighteen homework experiments in which a predefined circuit is analyzed, built, and measured, these three experiments are introductory engineering design projects where only a component list and some hints are given for creating a circuit that must meet the project specifications.

Table 18: Related Electric Circuits Texts

1. C.K. Alexander and M.N.O. Sadiku
   Fundamentals of Electric Circuits (4/E)
   New York: McGraw-Hill (2009)

2. R.C. Dorf and J.A. Svoboda
   Introduction to Electric Circuits (7/E)
   New York: John Wiley (2006)

3. W.H. Hayt and J. Kemmerly
   Engineering Circuit Analysis (7/E)
   New York: McGraw Hill (2007)

4. J.D. Irwin and R.M. Nelms
   Basic Engineering Circuit Analysis (9/E)
   New York: John Wiley (2008)

5. J.W. Nilsson and S. Riedel
   Electric Circuits with PSpice (8/E)
   Englewood Cliffs: Prentice Hall (2008)

In the second group of experiments, which are designed for a second course in AC circuits, there are two experiments that introduce phasors (Experiment 22) and phasor analysis and Kirchhoff's current law (Experiment 23). Following these, there is an experiment on AC nodal analysis (Experiment 24) and on the gyrator (Experiment 25), a circuit that simulates an inductor. The student then builds a Wien bridge oscillator (Experiment 26) and studies the properties of power including power factor measurement and correction (Experiment 27). Next, a circuit is built which provides the capabilities of a three-phase power supply (Experiment 28) and then uses this power supply to investigate some issues associated with three-phase power distribution (Experiment 29). Next, the student learns the basic properties of an ideal transformer (Experiment 30) and then studies the properties of a real transformer (Experiment 31). The results of these experiments are then used to examine hybrid couplers that may be used to isolate signals (Experiment 32). There are then three experiments on filters. The first examines simple first-order passive filters (Experiment 33) while the second is a second order active filter (Experiment 34). Then, the sweep capabilities of the oscilloscope are used to examine the frequency response of a passive band-pass and a passive band-reject filter (Experiment 35). Next, an experiment is introduced which examines the properties of two-port networks (Experiment 36).

Finally, two experiments on electromagnetic interference (EMI) are performed. The first is a simple experiment in which the student creates and examines EMI (Experiment 37), while the second is an experiment in which the student superimposes a desired signal on top of a noise source and examines the common mode rejection ratio (CMRR) of an instrumentation amplifier.

Each experiment follows a similar format and has nine sections. First, the developers of the experiment are identified. Then, the objectives of the experiment are given. A bar graph showing the distribution of times required to perform the experiment by previous classes of students is useful to determine how much time might be required to perform the experiment.[†] Then, recommended student preparation is presented. This includes reading assignments in both the lecture course circuits textbook and in this text, as well as reading of instruction manuals for various equipment and/or product data sheets for various components to be used in the experiment. Next comes a background section that either concisely reviews material from the textbook or provides more detailed description of materials not found in the textbook. This section also describes the experiment to be performed. This is followed by references to special literature and readings. A list of all equipment and components required to perform the experiment is given. The experimental procedure has either two or three sub-parts. First, the student is asked to analyze the circuit and/or to model the circuit in PSpice, as appropriate. The objective is to assure that the student fully understands the experiment to be performed and has a good feel for the expected experimental results. Only after analyzing and/or modeling the circuit does the student perform the experiment following detailed experimental procedures designed to assure that she may safely perform the experiment on her own. In some cases, as section on error analysis requires the student to estimate the accuracy and/or precision of his measurements and to estimate the reliability with which conclusions about the performance of the circuit may be drawn. Finally, each experiment carries a revision date so that as modifications and/or corrections are posted to the text website (**http://www.lab-in-a-box.net**) students and instructors will always be able to keep track of the most current version of each experiment.

[†] For some experiments there are, at this time, insufficient data to create a meaningful histogram. In these cases we show a single bar based on our personal experience in building and testing the experiment.

Experiment 1: Breadboard Basics

Developers   KM Lai, JB Webb, and RW Hendricks

Objectives   The objective of this experiment is to measure and to draw the electrical connections within the ANDY board breadboard.

Estimated Time for Completion

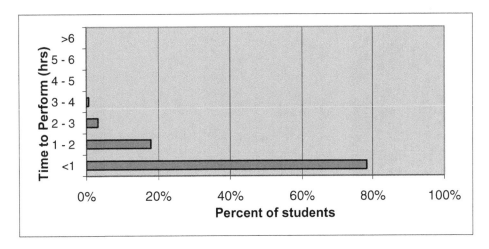

Preparation   Read the general descriptions of the ANDY board and the digital multimeter given in Sections 3.3 and 3.5 of this text, respectively. Also read the ANDY Board User Manual and Test Procedure and be sure that you have performed the entire acceptance test procedure as described therein. Finally, read the hand-held DMM operator's manual that came with the MY-64 DMM. If you are using some other DMM, read the users' manual that accompanied it.

Background   With the exception of Experiment 2, all of the experiments described in this book will be built on a platform called a breadboard. The breadboard consists of a series of holes behind which are spring contacts that make electrical connection with wires that are inserted into the holes. These springs are connected together in various combinations to create electrical nodes. All the wires connected to springs that are connected together will be at the same potential. In this experiment, you will experimentally determine which holes are connected together to create electrical nodes for the breadboard associated with your lab kit. Although breadboards are manufactured by many firms, there is some consistency between them. However, there are also some very important differences. Thus, it is imperative that you verify for yourself how your particular breadboard is wired. Depending on the lab kit provided for your experiments, this breadboard may be stand-alone (unpowered) in which you will use batteries to provide a source of DC power, all the way to fully powered lab "trainer kits" such as the ANDY board in which various voltage sources, clocks, and/or function generators may be provided. Regardless of these additional features, the breadboard remains essentially independent of them.

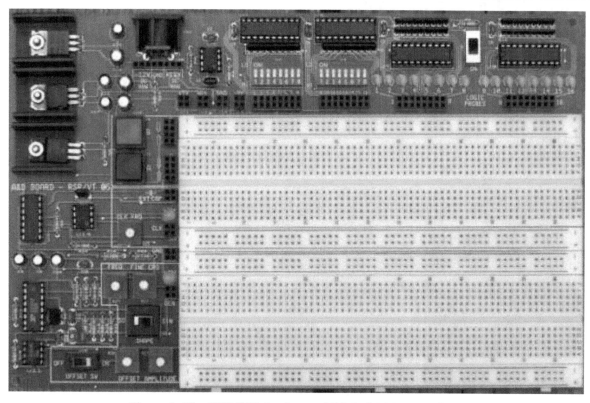

Figure 1: The RSR/VT Analog and Digital ANDY Trainer

Breadboard
Construction

There is a great variety of breadboards, each having a different number of columns and with different numbers of vertically connected holes (usually five or six.). Some have single troughs in the middle of the board and some have two troughs. Some boards have all of the holes in the outer two rows connected and some have a break in the connection in the middle. The student needs to be aware of these many variations and needs to be able to quickly determine how the board she is using is connected internally. A typical breadboard will look similar to the picture shown in Figure 1. Note that the RSR/VT ANDY trainer shown in Figure 1 has two identical breadboards—an upper board and a lower board.

Figure 2(a) shows the layout of a segment of a typical breadboard while Figure 2(b) shows the wiring diagram of its backplane. In both figures, the top two horizontal rows and the bottom two horizontal rows of the breadboard are typically used for power busses and ground busses. A bus is simply a node with multiple connection points all of which are at the same electrical potential or voltage. These busses are clearly marked in Figure 1 with a red "+" and a blue "-" on each end of the row and with long horizontal red and blue lines. The rows on the breadboards in Figure 1 are labeled with letters (A, B, C, ⋯) while the columns are numbered (1, 5, 10, ⋯) thus allowing specific identification of each node. Other boards may be marked differently or may be unmarked.

Notice that the breaks in the busses in Figures 1 and 2 differ. In Figure 1 there is a break every five holes while in Figure 2 there is a break only in the middle of the board. Figure 2(b) indicates that there is a break in the wiring between the two sides of the board, while the blue and red horizontal lines might imply that there is no such break in the wiring in Figure 1. Thus, you must determine experimentally if there is or is not a connection between the breaks on the ANDY board. If there is no electrical connection between the two sides you must remember to use a jumper wire to connect them if you desire to have a bus that runs the entire width of the board. (See, e.g., Figures 9 and 10.)

The vertical columns of holes are also busses and are typically used for inserting devices and wires. Notice the horizontal break or trough in the vertical columns in the middle of the breadboard. In Figure 2 there is no electrical connection between the upper and lower halves. The break in the vertical columns has a special purpose. It provides a convenient place for inserting integrated circuit chips into the breadboard. The hole spacing between the upper and lower rows on each side of the trough is exactly the pin spacing of the dual inline pins (DIP) of the chips used in the experiments. By placing a chip so that it straddles the trough between the upper and lower halves, the pins on the opposite sides of the chip are isolated from each other. In placing chips and other components on the breadboard, it is imperative to be sure that each pin on the device is in a separate column, otherwise they will be shorted together. Connections between columns must be made by the designer using wires on the component side of the board.

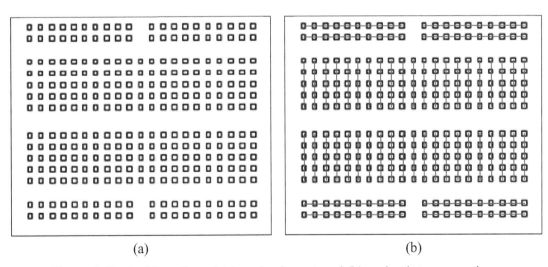

| (a) | (b) |

Figure 2: Typical breadboard (a) socket layout, and (b) socket interconnections.

Experiment 1

References   Lineberry, R.B., W.C. Headley, and R.W. Hendricks, (2006). "RSR/VT ANDY Board User Manual and Test Procedure." The Bradley Department of Electrical and Computer Engineering, Virginia Polytechnic Institute and State University, Blacksburg, VA 24061 (Available at **http://www.lab-in-a-box.net**)

Materials   The equipment and components required to perform this experiment are:
- ANDY board
- Digital multimeter
- Wire
- Wire strippers

Procedure   Following the concepts of Figure 3, verify the electrical connections in the breadboard. Be sure to orient your breadboard in the same way as the picture. To measure resistance, insert the red DMM test lead into the red jack on the DMM labeled with 'V', 'Ω', and 'Hz'. Turn the DMM knob to the setting marked with the 'Ω' symbol. Put the resistance setting on the lowest scale. If the multimeter

---

Notes:

1. The pointed tips on the DMM test leads are too large for the holes in the breadboard. If you try to force the tip into the hole, you may stretch the contact spring beyond its elastic limit and thus ruin the spring. To avoid this, cut and strip two short pieces of wire from your wire spool. Insert the wires into the breadboard at the desired locations (see below) and then touch your DMM test leads to the wire ends.

2. **Do not plug in the power supply for your breadboard** while performing this experiment.

---

registers an overflow, write overflow (see Section 3.5 for a discussion of the DMM overflow). You are trying to verify the connections in the breadboard as shown (typically) in the diagram. It is not critical which holes you measure so long as you measure holes as typically shown in Figure 3. For busses, you will get a low resistance (typically about an ohm). For non-connected input points, points not in a bus or on the same node, you will get an overflow.

1. Measure the resistance within one row in the power bus. This is (typically) from points 1 to 2 in Figure 3.

2. Measure the resistance between vertically separated rows of power busses. This is (typically) from points 1 to 3 in Figure 3.

3. Measure the resistance between horizontally separated rows in the power busses. This is (typically) from points 2 to 4 in Figure 3. How are the power busses in the ANDY board wired?

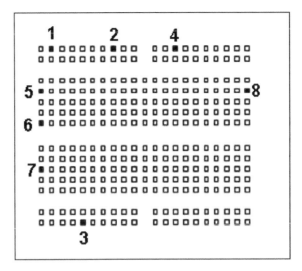

Figure 3: Breadboard measurement locations.

4. Measure the resistance within one column of the device working area. This is (typically) from points 5 to 6 in Figure 3.

5. Measure the resistance between nodes in the same column, but which are separated by the horizontal channel. This is (typically) from points 6 to 7 in Figure 3.

6. Measure the resistance between horizontally separated columns in the working area. This is (typically) from points 5 to 8 in Figure 3.

7. Measure the resistance between rows and columns (i.e., between the power busses and the columns in the working area.) This is (typically) from points 1 to 5 in Figure 3.

8. Prepare a drawing of your breadboard and mark the back plane connections as is illustrated in Figure 2(b). Your drawing need not be to scale. However, it should show all of the rows of the board but only a sufficient number of columns to be representative.

9. For future reference, save a copy of your drawing with your lab kit.

Last Revision   12/31/2008

Experiment 2: Component Tolerances

Developer   RW Hendricks

Objectives   The objective of this experiment is to investigate the variability of nominally equivalent resistors and capacitors.

Estimated Time For Completion

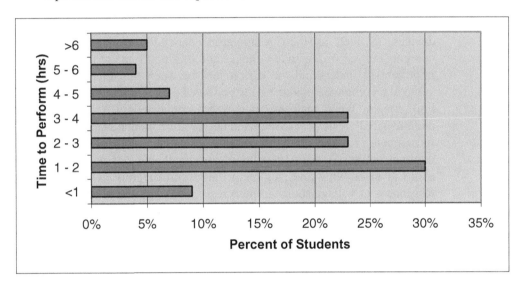

Preparation   Read Sections 2.3, Appendix C, 3.5, 3.8, and 3.9 of this text which describe the analysis of data, using the MY-64 DMM, and the properties and color coding of resistors and capacitors, respectively. You may also wish to consult a text on statistics. Three that we find to be of value include those by Mandel (1964), Glantz (2005), and Montgomery and Runger (2006).

Background   When analyses or computer simulations of a circuit are performed, the nominal values of various components are used as specified on the circuit diagrams. Nominal values are the exact, intended values of the components. However, the true values of real components are almost never the same as the nominal values. One example of value discrepancy between a measured value and the nominal value is the voltage of a source. The differences may be caused by various factors. If the source is a battery, its output voltage will decrease with time and use due to changes in the internal resistance of the battery. If the source is an electrical power supply such as a wall outlet, the output voltage will also vary. For example, a wall outlet wired with 12 gauge (AWG) wire and located 100 feet from a 20 A circuit breaker will see a 6.5 V drop in the line voltage (113.5 V at the outlet versus a nominal 120 V supply). In addition, brownouts due to heavy use of the electric power grid during exceptionally hot or cold weather will usually cause substantial variations in the nominal supply voltage. Even laboratory power supplies designed to compensate for such effects can never be made perfectly, so their output will never be exactly the same as their nominal output value.

Similarly, there will always be manufacturing tolerances on all components such as resistors, capacitors, and inductors. The tighter the tolerance specification (or, the less variation from the nominal value) you are willing to accept, the more you should expect to pay for the component. When one analyzes a circuit with a program such as PSpice it is often possible to specify the tolerances of the devices, as well as their temperature dependences, and have the program compute ranges for the node voltages and mesh currents of the circuit.[†] Thus, it is important to understand the differences between the tolerance of the nominal value of a component and the distribution of the manufactured component values. Furthermore, when real components are connected in a real circuit, there are unanticipated resistances, capacitances, and inductances. For example, in Experiment 1, you determined that the internal resistances of the node interconnections in your breadboard are small, but not negligible as is usually assumed in drawing and analyzing the circuit diagram. There are also internal resistances in voltage sources; these resistances also cause voltage drops. Finally, there is resistance in the wires that you use to connect components in a circuit (see Section 3.7). These wire resistances will also contribute to voltage discrepancies between your analysis and the real circuit.

In this experiment, you will examine the variability of two components: resistors and capacitors. We will also introduce some basic statistical considerations. You will explore these concepts in much more detail in a statistics course that will likely come later in your curriculum. For purposes of this experiment, the discussion in Appendix C of this text should be adequate. You will determine the mean and standard error of the mean of representative resistors and capacitors provided in your lab kit and will compare these results with their nominal values and the stated tolerances of the devices. The objective of the experiment is to give you a physical feel for the magnitude of the variances and an understanding of the tolerances of the components used to build real circuits.

It is important to note that the manufacturing tolerance is not related to the variance of the sample distribution. Rather, it is an absolute value outside of which you will never find a device. Thus, it is entirely possible, and indeed likely, that you will find a distribution of devices that are statistically different from the nominal value but are still within tolerance.

Given that manufacturing tolerances for resistors are very tight, there is almost zero probability that you will find resistors that are "out of tolerance." Thus, if you find that the mean of your resistors deviates by more than ±5% (for gold band resistors) from the nominal value, it is likely that there is an error in your measurements (e.g., your DMM is not properly calibrated or you did not perform the measurements properly.) The source of such error should be

---

[†]This is known as a Monte Carlo calculation and is introduced in Experiment 8.

determined and fully understood before continuing with the remaining experiments in this book.

References *Glantz, S.A., (2005). <u>Primer of Biostatistics</u> (6E), New York: McGraw-Hill.

Mandel, J., (1964). <u>The Statistical Analysis of Experimental Data</u>, New York: John Wiley & Sons. (Reprinted in 1984 by Dover Publications.)

Montgomery, D.C. and G.C. Runger, (2006). <u>Applied Statistics and Probability for Engineers</u> (4/E), New York: Wiley.

Materials The equipment and components required to perform this experiment are:
- Digital multimeter
- 15 ea 10 kΩ resistors
- 14 ea 0.1 μF Mylar capacitors

Procedure (Resistors) The first part of this experiment is designed to determine the reproducibly and thus the precision of your resistance measurements.

1. Gather fifteen 10 kΩ resistors. What is the color pattern of the bands? Five of these resistors are in the resistor kit and ten more are found in the plastic bag of course-dependent parts. If possible, keep the resistors from the two sources identifiably separate.

2. Read the instruction manual for your multimeter and record the specified accuracy for resistance measurements on the scale that includes 10 kΩ.

3. Select one of the resistors obtained in step 1. Following the procedures outlined in Section 3.5, measure its resistance at least 10 times. Be sure to use the same resistor for each measurement. Be sure to disconnect the resistor from the DMM and remount it between each measurement. (This step is to assure that errors that may arise due to mounting the resistor are included in the measurements.) Be sure to take notes on your measurement procedure.

4. Calculate the mean and standard deviation of the measurements made in step 3 using Eqs (1) through (3) of Appendix C. If you do the calculations manually, show your intermediate results. If you use a spread sheet, a calculator with statistical functions, or some other scientific program such as MATLAB, provide data to verify that you are calculating the unbiased variance.[†]

5. Is the sample mean found in step 4 within the specified 5% tolerance of the resistor? If not, re-read Section 3.5 carefully for reasons that may

---

[†] You may easily verify which calculation your calculator or program performs (Excel can do both, depending on the function you select!) by calculating the variance of the three numbers 1, 2 and 3. If the variance is 1.000 you are calculating the (correct) unbiased variance; if it is 0.667, you are calculating the (incorrect) biased variance.

explain this observation. If you find a reason, record it here and repeat the experiment starting at step 3. If you cannot find a reason, see your instructor for assistance.

6. Compare the results of step 4 with the accuracy of the meter as found in step 2. What is the precision of your measurements? What conclusions can you draw from these measurements? Comment on your ability to reproduce your measurement.

In the next part of the experiment, you will determine the variability of the resistors, being careful to keep track of the source of supply of the devices.

7. Following the procedures outlined in Section 3.5 and using the same techniques that you used in step 3, measure the resistance of each of the 15 resistors. If possible, record the data for the resistors from each source of supply separately.

8. Are any of the measured values outside the specified 5% tolerance of the resistors $(9,500 \le R \le 10,500)$? If so, re-read Section 3.5 and if you are unable to find a logical explanation, see your instructor.

9. Calculate the mean, the variance (s^2), and the standard deviation (s) of the measured values for the combined sample of all 15 resistors using equations provided in Appendix C. Is the variance different from the variance of your measurement technique as determined in step 4? [†]

10. Using Eq (9) from Appendix C calculate the 95% confidence interval for your measurement technique. Does this interval include the nominal value of 10 kΩ?

11. Calculate the value of t for the combined sample using Eq (10). Find the value of t for a sample size of 15 and 95% probability $(t_{0.025,14})$ from the table in Appendix C. Are the measured values of your resistors statistically significantly different from the nominal value of 10 kΩ? Explain. Take into consideration you observations in step 8.

12. If you have data for the resistors from each source separately, perform the following steps. Otherwise, proceed to step 16.

13. Using Eqs (1) through (3) of Appendix C, calculate the mean, the variance (s^2), and the standard deviation (s) of the measured values for each group of samples.

14. Calculate the value of t for each sample using Eq (10). Find the value of t for the correct degrees of freedom for each sample and 95% confidence

---

[†] For normal (Gaussian) distributions, the variances of the measurement technique and of the sample distribution add. Thus, if the standard error of the measurement technique is less than about 30% of the standard error of the measurement of the distribution of components then, for all practical purposes, one may ignore the contribution of the measurement technique to the observed distribution of the sample measurements.

from the table in Appendix C. Are the measured values of your resistors statistically significantly different from the nominal value of 10 kΩ? Explain.

15. Compare the two sources of supply of resistors using Eqs (12) and (13). Are the two samples (sources of supply) statistically significantly different? Explain.

Procedure (Capacitors)

In this part of the experiment, we repeat the experiments performed with resistors only this time using a sample of capacitors. Here, the measurements are much harder to make with precision and the tolerances are much larger.

16. Gather fourteen 0.1 μF Mylar capacitors. Determine the tolerance of these devices from their markings. Is the tolerance symmetric?

17. Read the instruction manual for your multimeter and record the specified accuracy for capacitance measurements on the scale that includes 0.1 μF.

18. Select one of the capacitors obtained in step 16. Following the procedure outlined in Section 3.5, measure its capacitance at least 10 times. Be sure to remove the capacitor from the DMM and remount it between each measurement. (This step is to assure that errors that may arise due to mounting the capacitor are included in the measurements.)

19. Calculate the mean, the variance, and the standard deviation of the data acquired in step 18. Pay attention to the cautions in step 4 and assure that you calculate unbiased values.

20. Compare the results of step 19 with the accuracy of your DMM as found in step 17. What conclusions can you draw from these measurements?

21. Following the procedure outlined in Section 3.5, measure the capacitance of each of the fourteen capacitors with the multimeter.

22. Calculate the mean, the variance (s^2), and the standard deviation(s) of the measured values. Be sure you are calculating unbiased values of the variance and standard error.

23. Calculate the value of t for these data at the 95% confidence level ($t_{0.025,v}$) from the table in Appendix C. Are the measured values of your capacitors statistically significantly different from the nominal value of 0.1 μF? Explain.

24. Using Eq (9), calculate the 95% confidence limits for your measurements of the capacitors. Does this confidence band include the nominal value of 0.1 μF?

25. What do you conclude about the sample of capacitors in your lab kit?

Last Revision   12/31/2008

Experiment 3: Ohm's Law

Developers   JB Webb, KM Lai and RW Hendricks

Objectives   The objective of this experiment is to verify Ohm's law.

Estimated Time for Completion

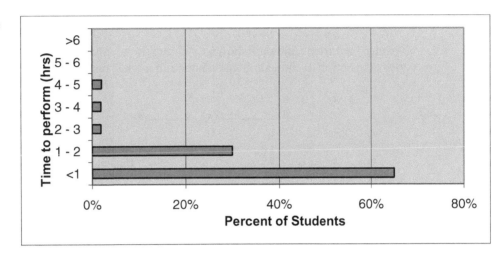

Preparation   Read the section on Ohm's law in your textbook. Also read Sections 2.3 (Analysis of Data), Appendix C, 3.3 (RSR/VT ANDY Board), 3.4 (Breadboarding and Wiring), 3.5 (Multimeter), and 3.8 (Resistors) of this book.

Background   Ohm's law states the relationship between the voltage (V, in volts) across a resistor and the current (I, in amperes) through that resistor is:

$$V = IR \qquad (1)$$

where R is the resistance (in ohms). This linear relationship is an approximation that has proven to be adequate for most work in electric circuit analysis. You will learn in more advanced courses that the relationship is not truly linear, but that depending on how and from what the resistor is made, the resistance may vary with applied voltage and magnetic field. There is also a significant change in resistance with temperature. These effects are discussed in most solid state physics texts such as Hook and Hall (1995). PSpice allows for corrections for the temperature dependence and other effects.

In this experiment you will verify Ohm's law by measuring the current through a resistor as a function of the applied voltage and will verify that the measured value of the resistor is within its specified tolerance. Note that all resistors provided with Lab-in-a-Box have a 5% tolerance, meaning that each resistor is within 5% of its nominal, or color-coded value.

References   Hook, J.R., and H.E. Hall, (1995). <u>Introduction to Solid State Physics</u> (8/E). New York: John Wiley & Sons.

Materials   The equipment and components required to perform this experiment are:

91

- ANDY Board
- Digital multimeter
- 1 ea 1000 Ω resistor (Brown Black Red Gold)
- 1 ea mystery resistor (Red Black Brown Gold). This resistor will be found in the bag of course-specific parts.

Procedure

Consider the circuit diagram shown in Figure 1. A voltage of 9V is applied to a series connection of the unknown resistor and a 1 kΩ resistor.

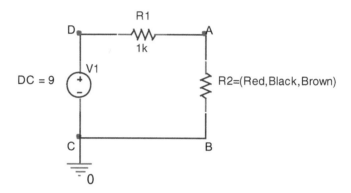

Figure 1: Circuit for verifying Ohm's law.

Analysis:

1. Identify the unknown resistor R_2 shown in Figure 1. What value does the color scheme "Red Black Brown" stand for?

2. Calculate the current I_{AB} flowing through the unknown resistor and the voltage V_{AB} across it.

3. What is the purpose of the 1 kΩ resistor?

Measurements:

4. Construct the circuit shown in Figure 1 on your breadboard. Note that the 9 V source is provided by the ANDY board.

5. Plug the black DMM probe into COM and the red probe into V. Set the switch to the lowest volts scale that will not overflow for the expected voltage.

6. Measure the voltage V_{AB} across the unknown resistor. (See Section 3.5 for good technique.) Make sure your polarities are correct. Be sure to include your units!

7. Disconnect the wire from the unknown resistor to ground (wire BC).

8. Move the red DMM probe from the "V" jack to the "mA" jack and set the DMM switch to the minimum full-scale current value that will not overflow for the expected current calculated in step 2.

9. Measure the current I_{BC} passing **through** the resistor by completing the circuit with the two DMM probes. To do this, place the red probe on node B and the black probe on node C. Review Section 3.5 for the proper technique for measuring current. Again, make sure your polarities are correct.

10. Using Ohm's law, find the resistance value of the unknown resistor.

$$R_{expt} = \frac{V_{meas}}{I_{meas}} \tag{2}$$

11. Remove the resistor from your circuit.

12. Move the red DMM probe to the "R" jack and measure the resistance of the unknown resistor.

13. What is the percent difference between your experimentally determined resistance in step 10 and the measured resistance value found in step 12?

$$\Delta = \frac{\left| R_{meas} - R_{expt} \right|}{R_{expt}} \times 100\% \tag{3}$$

14. What is the percent difference between the experimentally determined resistance found in step 10 and the nominal resistance value found in step 1?

$$\Delta = \frac{\left| R_{nom} - R_{expt} \right|}{R_{nom}} \times 100\% \tag{4}$$

15. Is the difference of the experimentally determined value in step 10 within 5% of the nominal value? Is the difference acceptable? Why or why not?

Error Analysis:

16. Following the methodology of the propagation of errors described in Appendix C, estimate the standard error of R_{expt} computed from Eq (2) above. Assume $\sigma_{V_{meas}}$ and $\sigma_{I_{meas}}$ are ±1 digit in the least significant digit of the scales used to measure the voltage and the current, respectively.

17. Using your estimate of $\sigma_{R_{expt}}$ from step 16 and an estimate of $\sigma_{R_{meas}}$ based on ±1 digit in the least significant digit of the scales used to measure the resistance, perform a t-test as described in Appendix C to determine if your experimental and measured values of the resistance are statistically significantly different from each other at the 95% confidence level. Explain any discrepancies.

18. Following the methodology of Appendix C, perform t-tests to determine if your measured and experimental values of the resistance are statistically

significantly different from the nominal value. Are they within the tolerance of the color band on the resistor? Explain.

Last Revision   12/31/2008

Experiment 4: Kirchhoff's Laws

Developers JB Webb, KM Lai and RW Hendricks

Objectives The objective of this experiment is to experimentally verify Kirchhoff's voltage and current laws and to perform a power check of a simple circuit.

Estimated Time for Completion

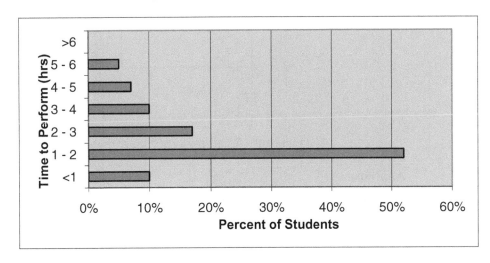

Preparation Read the section on Kirchhoff's laws in your textbook. Also read Sections 2.3 (Analysis of Data), Appendix C, 3.3 (RSR/VT ANDY Board), 3.4 (Breadboarding and Wiring), 3.5 (Digital Multimeter), and 3.8 (Resistors) of this book.

Background Kirchhoff's current law (KCL) states that the sum of all currents entering a node is zero. Kirchhoff's voltage law (KVL) states that the sum of the voltages around a closed loop is zero. In a power check, we verify that the sum of the power consumed is equal to the sum of the power generated.

In this experiment you will verify both of Kirchhoff's laws and will verify the power check by measuring the currents entering a node, the voltages around a loop, and the power consumed and delivered by the simple circuit shown in Figure 1. You will also be introduced to the powerful PSpice circuit modeling software to confirm your analytical and experimental results.

Materials The equipment and components required to perform this experiment are:
- ANDY board
- Digital multimeter
- PSpice software
- 1 ea 4.7 kΩ resistor
- 1 ea 8.2 kΩ resistor
- 1 ea 10 kΩ resistor

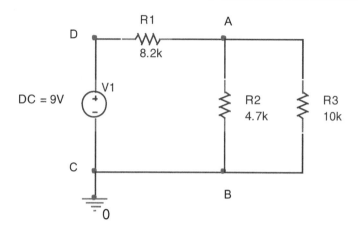

Figure 1: Circuit for verifying Kirchhoff's laws.

Procedure   **Analysis:**

1. Calculate V_{AB}, V_{DA}, I_{DA}, I_2 and I_3 where I_2 and I_3 are the currents in R_2 and R_3, respectively, as identified in Figure 1. Use the passive sign convention to determine the direction of positive current flow for I_2 and I_3.

2. Verify that $\Sigma_I = -I_{DA} + I_2 + I_3 = 0$.

3. Verify that $\Sigma_V = V_{CD} + V_{DA} + V_{AB} = 0$. (Note that $V_{CD} = V_s = V1$.)

4. Calculate the power dissipated in each resistor and the total power dissipated (P_{dis}) in the circuit. Be sure to follow the passive sign convention.

5. Calculate the power generated (P_{gen}) by the source, V_s.

6. Does the total power generated equal the total power dissipated? Does $\Sigma_P = -P_{gen} + P_{dis} = 0$?

Modeling:

7. Draw the circuit shown in Figure 1 in PSpice.

8. Calculate V_{AB}, V_{DA}, I_{DA}, I_2 and I_3. Show these results on the circuit diagram. Insert a printout of your results in your lab notebook.

9. Verify that the results from step 8 agree with the results of your analysis in step 1.

Measurements:

10. Construct the circuit shown in Figure 1 on your breadboard. Note that V1 is provided by the ANDY board.

11. Using your multimeter, measure V_{CD} $V_{AB}, V_{DA}, I_{DA}, I_2$ and I_3. Use the information from your analysis to determine the correct range on the DMM for each measurement. Follow the techniques developed in Experiment 3 for measuring the current in a branch of the circuit. Use the color coding of the DMM leads to determine the sign of each voltage and current. Use the passive sign convention that a voltage rise is positive and that a current leaving a node is positive.

12. Use the measured values to calculate $\Sigma_V = V_{CD} + V_{DA} + V_{AB}$. Is the result zero (within experimental error)? Is KVL satisfied?

13. Use the measured values to compute the current leaving node "A," $\Sigma_I = -I_{DA} + I_2 + I_3$. Note that the minus sign results because I_{DA} is entering node "A" as defined in step 1 above. Is the result zero (within experimental error)? Is KCL satisfied?

14. Use the measured values of the node voltages and branch currents to calculate the power dissipated in R_1, R_2, and R_3. Are these values all positive? Find the total power dissipated in the three resistors.

15. Calculate the power generated by the voltage source. Is this value negative?

16. The power check requires that $\Sigma_P = P_{gen} + P_{dis} = 0$. Is the power check satisfied?

Error Analysis:

17. Following the discussion of the propagation of errors in Appendix C, show that the standard errors of Σ_V and Σ_I are

$$\sigma_{\Sigma_V} = \sqrt{\sigma_{V_{AB}}^2 + \sigma_{V_{CD}}^2 + \sigma_{V_{DA}}^2} \tag{1}$$

and

$$\sigma_{\Sigma_I} = \sqrt{\sigma_{\Sigma_{DA}}^2 + \sigma_{\Sigma_2}^2 + \sigma_{\Sigma_3}^2} \tag{2}$$

respectively.

18. Assume that $\sigma_{V_{AB}}$, $\sigma_{V_{CD}}$, $\sigma_{V_{DA}}$, $\sigma_{I_{DA}}$, σ_{I_2}, and σ_{I_3} are ±1 digit in the least significant digit of the scales used to measure each voltage or current. From the results of step 17 and these values, compute σ_{Σ_V} and σ_{Σ_I}.

19. Following the methodology of Appendix C and using the estimates for σ_{Σ_V} and σ_{Σ_I} from step 18, perform a t-test to quantify your answers to steps 12 and 13 above.

20. Using the method of propagation of errors described in Appendix C, derive and expression for σ_{Σ_P}. Quantitatively evaluate this expression.

21. Using your estimate for σ_{Σ_P}, perform a t-test to quantify your answer to step 16.

Last Revision   1/04/2009

Experiment 5: Series and Parallel Resistors

Developers   KM Lai, JB Webb and RW Hendricks

Objectives   The objective of this experiment is to experimentally verify the rules for finding the equivalent resistance of resistors connected both in series and in parallel.

Estimated Time for Completion

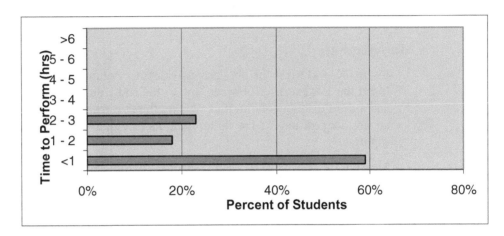

Preparation   Read the sections in your textbook involving networks of resistors connected in series and in parallel. Also read Sections 2.3 (Analysis of Data), Appendix C, 3.3 (ANDY Board), 3.4 (Breadboarding and Wiring), 3.5 (Multimeter), and 3.8 (Resistors) of this manual.

Background   The equivalent resistance of resistors connected in series is

$$R_{eq} = \sum_{i=1}^{n} R_i \tag{1}$$

while the equivalent resistance of resistors connected in parallel is

$$R_{eq} = \left(\sum_{i=1}^{N} \frac{1}{R_i} \right)^{-1} \tag{2}$$

In this experiment you will measure the resistance of two resistors connected in series and that of two resistors connected in parallel and will verify the two equivalence rules given above. You will also examine the standard error of the equivalent resistances.

Materials   The equipment and components required to perform this experiment are:
- ANDY board
- Digital multimeter
- 1 ea 1 kΩ, resistor (found in resistor kit)

99

- 1 ea 3 kΩ resistor (found in course-specific parts kit)

Procedure   **Analysis:**

1. Calculate the equivalent resistance of a 1 kΩ resistor connected in series with a 3 kΩ resistor.

2. Calculate the equivalent resistance of a 1 kΩ resistor connected in parallel with a 3 kΩ resistor.

Measurements:

3. Insert the 3 kΩ resistor between two distinct columns on your breadboard. Insert the 1 kΩ resistor between one of the end columns of the 3 kΩ resistor and a third distinct column thus placing the two resistors in series. **Caution:** do not connect any of the three columns to either ground or to any power supply.

4. Measure the resistance of each resistor with your multimeter by touching the probes to each end of the resistor (see Section 3.5). Be sure you make excellent contact between the probes and the resistors. Record each value.

5. Compute the percent difference between the nominal value of each resistor and the measured value. Are your resistors within the 5% tolerance?

6. Measure the resistance of the two resistors in series with your multimeter by touching the probes to each end of the resistor chain.

7. Compute the percent difference between the sum of the resistances determined in step 4 and the measured sum determined in step 6. Also compute the percent difference between the sum of the nominal values (step 1) and the experimental values (step 6). Is the rule for the series addition of resistances verified?

8. Remove the 1 kΩ resistor from the series chain created in step 3 and insert it between the same two columns as the 3 kΩ resistor, thus placing the two resistors in parallel. **Caution:** do not connect either of the columns to either ground or to any power supply.

9. Measure the resistance of the two resistors in parallel with your multimeter by touching the probes to each end of either resistor.

10. Compute the expected equivalent resistance for these resistors in parallel from the experimental values of the two resistors determined in step 4.

11. Compute the percent difference between the equivalent resistance computed in step 10 and the value determined experimentally in step 9.

12. Compute the percent difference between the experimental parallel resistance found in step 9 and the expected value computed in step 2.

13. Do your data confirm the rule for combining resistances in parallel? Why or why not?

Error Analysis:

14. Following the methodology of propagation of errors, calculate the standard error of two resistors connected in series based on the standard errors of each of the two individual resistors.

15. Assume σ_{R_1} and σ_{R_2} are ± 1 digit in the least significant digit of the scales used to measure the resistances of the two resistors in step 4. Estimate $\sigma_{R_{eq}}$ for the series connection described by Eq (1).

16. Following the methodology of Appendix C, calculate the 95% confidence limits for your measured value of R_{eq} as found in step 6.

17. Using the t-test described in Appendix C and the standard error of R_{eq} found in step 15, does your measured value of R_{eq} agree (95% confidence) with the computed values found in step 1?

18. Repeat steps 14 through 17 for the parallel combination of resistors.

19. What may you conclude from these analyses?

Last Revision   12/31/2008

Experiment 6: Voltage and Current Dividers

Developers
JB Webb, KM Lai and RW Hendricks

Objectives
The objective of this experiment is to build, measure, and analyze voltage and current dividers.

Estimated Time for Completion

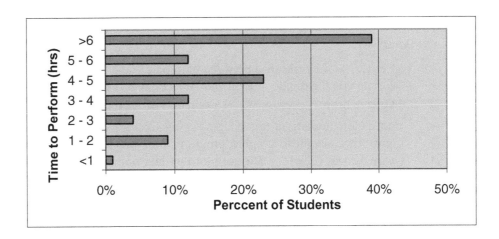

Preparation
Read the sections on networks involving voltage and current dividers in your textbook. Also read Section 3.3 (RSR/VT ANDY Board), 3.4 (Breadboarding and Wiring), 3.5 (Multimeter), 3.8 (Resistors), and 3.11 (Trim Pots) of this book.

Background
It is often necessary to provide voltage levels or current flows that are different from those available from the system power supplies. In such cases, it is sometimes possible to use either a voltage or a current divider to provide the desired voltage or current. A particular virtue of such circuits is that they are very inexpensive to implement. However, one must be very careful with the load that is driven by the divider. If the load has a very low impedance, then it may load a voltage divider in such a way as to significantly affect the voltage provided. Similarly, a high impedance load may significantly affect the current flow in a current divider. Such effects will be seen in several experiments where a voltage divider is used to provide a variable voltage signal to an operational amplifier.

In this experiment, you will build and study the properties of both a voltage and a current divider. You may show (for extra credit) that a trim pot, when used to create either a variable voltage divider or a variable current divider, behaves differently in the circuit depending on whether one end terminal of the device is left unconnected or if it is connected to ground.

References
*Hanselman, D., and B. Littlefield, (2005). <u>Mastering MATLAB 7</u>. Upper Saddle River, NJ: Pearson Prentice Hall.

Experiment 6

Materials

The equipment and components required to perform this experiment are:
- ANDY board
- Digital multimeter
- PSpice software
- 2 ea 1 kΩ, resistors
- 2 ea 3 kΩ resistors
- 2 ea 10 kΩ trim pots

Procedure

Analysis:

1. Let xR$_3$ be the resistance between terminals 2 and 3 of the (10 kΩ) trim pot R_3 for the voltage divider circuit shown in Figure 1. Derive an expression for the voltage drop V_{CD} across R_2 as a function of x. Note that terminal 1 of the trim pot is left floating in this circuit. Using Excel, MATLAB, or your choice of any other scientific graphic program, plot the resulting expression as x is varied from 0 to 1.[1, 2] Do not plot the data points, but only the lines joining them. Save this graph for use in steps 2 and 14.

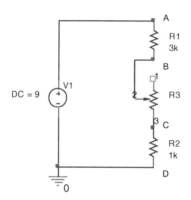

Figure 1: Voltage divider circuit.

2. **Extra Credit:** Ground terminal 1 of the trim pot and repeat the calculations of step 1. Plot the results of this calculation on the graph created in step 1. Explain the difference(s), if any, between the two curves. What is the effect of grounding terminal 1 of the trim pot?

---

[1] In Excel, create a column starting in A1 that increases from 0 to 1 in steps of 0.01. This is x. Compute the expected valued of V_{cd} in the adjacent column. Graph the data as a x-y scatter graph. Double click on a data point. Set the options to draw a line between the data points and not to plot the data points. Label the axes of the graph appropriately (with units!).

[2] It is very easy to plot multiple data sets on the same graph in MATLAB either with or without adjoining lines. See the code in Appendix D.2 for an example of how to do this. See also Hanselman and Littlefield (2005).

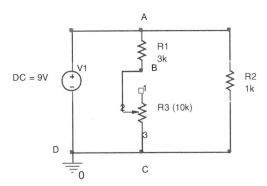

Figure 2: Current divider circuit.

3. Derive an expression for the current in the branch ABC and in the branch containing R_2 in the current divider circuit shown in Figure 2 as a function of x where x is defined in step 1. Note that terminal 1 of the trim pot is floating as in step 1. Plot the percentage of the total current generated by the source that flows through R_2 as a function of x. Save this graph for use in steps 4 and 24.

4. **Extra Credit:** Ground terminal 1 of the trim pot and repeat the calculations of step 3. Plot the results of this calculation on the graph created in step 3. Explain the difference(s), if any, between the two curves. What is the effect of grounding terminal 1 of the trim pot?

Modeling:

5. Model the circuits shown in Figures 1 and 2 in PSpice. Show the node voltages and the branch currents. Be sure the results agree with your analyses of steps 1 and 3. Insert a printed output for each circuit in your lab notebook. **Hints:** See step 7 for information on wiring pin 1 of the pot, and see the notes on how to sweep a trim pot in PSpice found on the course website at **http://www.lab-in-a-box.net**.

6. **Extra Credit:** Model the circuits shown in Figures 1 and 2 in PSpice with the trim pot grounded. Show the node voltages and the branch currents. Be sure the results agree with your analyses of steps 2 and 4. Insert a printed output for each circuit in your lab notebook

Measurements (Voltage Divider):

7. Construct the voltage divider circuit of Figure 1. Be sure to wire the trim pot so that you are using the middle pin and an outer pin. If you wire the trim pot using pins 1 and 3, it simply becomes a fixed 10 kΩ resistor. As noted in Section 3.11, it is good practice to short the unused pin of the trim pot (pin 1 in Figures 1 and 2) to the wiper (pin 2 in Figures 1 and 2.)

8. Turn the trim pot fully clockwise and measure the voltage drop V_{CD} across R_2 (the 1 kΩ resistor). Be sure the black probe is on the ground node.

9. Remove the trim pot from the circuit by disconnecting the appropriate wires and measure the resistance between the terminals used in step 8. Note that you cannot make this measurement with the trim pot wired into the circuit.

10. Measure the resistance between the two outer terminals (terminals 1 and 3) of the trim pot. Calculate the value of x for the setting of the trim pot used in step 8.

11. Return the trim pot to the circuit.

12. Turn the trim pot fully counter-clockwise and measure the voltage drop V_{CD} across R_2.

13. Measure the value of the trim pot resistance as was done in step 9. Calculate the value of x for this setting of the trim pot.

14. Repeat the measurements with the trim pot set at four additional positions between the fully clockwise and fully counter-clockwise positions. Calculate the value of x for each setting.

15. Enter the data acquired in steps 8 to 14 in the spreadsheet created in step 1 and plot the data points without any interconnecting lines.[3]

16. Do your data confirm the derivation of step 1?[4]

17. **Extra Credit:** If you are performing the extra credit parts of the experiment, repeat steps 7 through 16 with pin 1 of the Pot grounded.

Measurements (Current Divider):

18. Construct the current divider circuit of Figure 2. Be sure to wire the trim pot so that you are using the middle pin and an outer pin.

19. Turn the trim pot fully counter-clockwise.

20. Disconnect the trim pot and measure the resistance between the two active terminals (pins 2 and 3 as shown) as was done in step 9. Note: do not try to measure the resistance with the trim pot connected in the circuit.

---

[3] In Excel, select the graph. Select Chart→Source Data→Series and Add a new series. Enter the x-axis range for Column C and the y-axis data from column D. Your graph should now show a line for the anticipated results (done in footnote 1) and your experimental data points. The experimental data points should fall on or near the expected line.

[4] Note that "data" are plural. The singular is "datum." There is a point of disagreement among various technical writing and style manuals as to the correct way to present "data"—"…data is…" or "…data are… ." The authors prefer the plural (latter) usage.

21. Measure the resistance between the two outer terminals (terminals 1 and 3) of the trim pot. Calculate the value of x for the setting of the trim pot used in step 19.

22. Return the trim pot to the circuit.

23. Measure the current in branch CD and in the branch containing R_2. Be sure to follow the procedure described in Section 3.5.

24. Turn the trim pot a small increment clockwise and repeat steps 20 through 23.

25. Repeat step 24 until the trim pot is turned fully clockwise. Be sure you acquire data at least five different values of the trim pot.

26. Transfer the data gathered in steps 19 though 25 to the spreadsheet created in step 3.

27. Calculate the percent current that passes through R_2 for each value of the trim pot resistance. Using the same methodology as in step 15, plot the experimental data points on the graph.

28. Do your results confirm the derivation of step 3? If not, why not.

29. **Extra Credit:** If you are performing the extra credit parts of the experiment, repeat steps 18 through 28 with pin 1 of the Pot grounded.

30. **Extra Credit:** Comment on why you should not ground the unused pin of the trim pot.

Last Revision   1/01/2009

Experiment 7: Delta-Wye Configurations

Developers   JB Webb, RW Hendricks, and KM Lai

Objectives   The objective of this experiment is to verify the equivalence of the delta-wye transformation.

**Estimated
Time
for Completion**

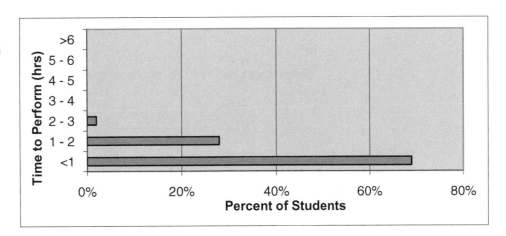

Preparation   Read the section on delta-wye transformations in your textbook.

Background   For many circuits, parallel and series simplification is possible; however, for some circuits such simplification does not work. In those cases, it might be possible to use a delta-to-wye transformation, or vice versa, to simplify the circuit to a point where series and/or parallel resistor simplifications are possible. Note that sometimes these transformations are also known as Δ–Y or Π–T transformations.

When the resistors are identified as shown in Figure 1, the delta-to-wye transformation is given by

$$R_1 = \frac{R_b R_c}{R_a + R_b + R_c}$$

$$R_2 = \frac{R_a R_c}{R_a + R_b + R_c} \tag{1}$$

$$R_3 = \frac{R_a R_b}{R_a + R_b + R_c}$$

while the wye-to-delta transformation is given by

109

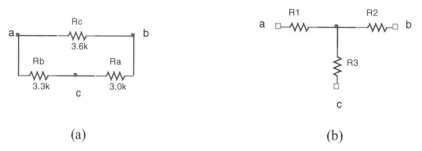

Figure 1: (a) Delta and (b) wye configurations.

$$R_a = \frac{R_1 R_2 + R_2 R_3 + R_3 R_1}{R_1}$$

$$R_b = \frac{R_1 R_2 + R_2 R_3 + R_3 R_1}{R_2} \qquad (2)$$

$$R_c = \frac{R_1 R_2 + R_2 R_3 + R_3 R_1}{R_3}$$

In this experiment, you will build a delta configuration, predict its corresponding wye configuration, build the predicted wye, and then verify, by measurement, that the wye is an equivalent circuit to the original delta.

Materials The equipment and components required to perform this experiment are:
- ANDY board
- Digital multimeter
- 1 ea 3.0 kΩ resistor
- 1 ea 3.3 kΩ resistor
- 1 ea 3.6 kΩ resistor
- Three other resistors will be needed, but you must determine their values in the lab procedure. They are assured to be available in the lab kit.

Procedure **Analysis:**

1. Find the equivalent wye configuration of Figure 1(b) for the delta configuration shown in Figure 1(a). Round the values for R$_1$, R$_2$, and R$_3$ to the nearest tenth.

Measurements:

2. Construct the delta and the predicted wye circuits as shown in Figure 1. Note: do not connect any of the nodes (a,b,c) for either circuit to ground, to a power source, or to each other.

3. Using the multimeter, measure the three resistances R_{ab}, R_{bc}, and R_{ac} for each resistor network. Use your computed values from step 1 to select an appropriate resistance scale.

4. Find the percentage difference for the resistance as measured at each set of nodes. Use the delta data for the basis of comparison.

5. Do the experimental resistances between the nodes, as determined in steps 3 and 4, agree with each other (within experimental tolerance) and do they agree with the computed values determined in step 1?

6. Why might the resistances measured between equivalent nodes of the two circuits be different?

7. **Extra Credit:** Using the theory of propagation of errors found in Appendix C, derive an expression for the variance and standard error for R_1 given the variances of R_a, R_b, and R_c. How does your result affect your answer to the question posed in step 6?

Last Revision   11/26/2008

Experiment 8: Mesh Current and Node Voltage Analysis

Developers   JB Webb, RW Hendricks and KM Lai

Objectives   The objectives of this experiment are to build and analyze a circuit using mesh current or node voltage analysis and examine how sources are accumulated together in a circuit using superposition.

Estimated Time For Completion

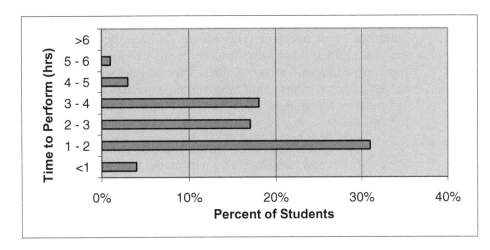

Preparation   Read the sections in your textbook which discuss the node voltage and the mesh current methods, and the sections that discuss the basis for choice between the two. Read Sections 4.2 and 4.3 of Tront (2006) to learn how to perform a sensitivity analysis and how to simulate the effects of resistor tolerances in PSpice. Read the notes on Monte Carlo simulations in PSpice found on the text website at **http://www.lab-in-a-box.net**.

Background   Both the node voltage and the mesh current methods provide systematic procedures for analysis of complex circuits. When used in combination with Kirchhoff's laws and Ohm's law, both methods of analysis will provide a set of simultaneous equations which must be solved. Solving the simultaneous equations for nodal analysis will yield values of the node voltages while solving the simultaneous equations for mesh analysis will yield values of the mesh currents. When the node voltages are known, the mesh currents may be found and vice versa. In either case, the circuit is deemed to be solved when all the node voltages and all the mesh currents are known.

The choice of which method to use for a given circuit is determined by a number of factors. Circuits that contain a number of elements in parallel, supernodes, and/or current sources are usually better suited to nodal analysis. Circuits that contain a number of elements in series, supermeshes, and/or voltage sources are usually best suited to mesh analysis. However, the choice must be tempered by the information required. If only mesh currents are needed, then mesh analysis might be the better choice. Only with experience gained from

113

analyzing a large number of circuits can you become proficient in looking at a circuit and making a good choice.

When analyzing a real circuit, it is important to understand what effect the variation in component values due to their tolerances will have on the node voltages and mesh currents. This information is particularly difficult to obtain analytically except for the simplest of circuits but is easy to obtain via PSpice modeling (Tront 2006). In PSpice, the program is able to simulate a circuit thousands of times, each time changing the value of each component randomly within its given tolerance. This Monte Carlo analysis, named after the famous European principality noted for its gambling casinos, provides the maximum and minimum values of a node voltage that will be seen due to variations in the values of components. This information is related to, but not the same as, the information found from the analysis of errors introduced in Experiments (2) through (6).

In this experiment, you will analyze the circuit shown in Figure 1 using node voltages and mesh currents, will model the circuit in PSpice and examine the effect of component tolerances, and then will build and measure the circuit and show that it performs as predicted within the tolerances of the components.

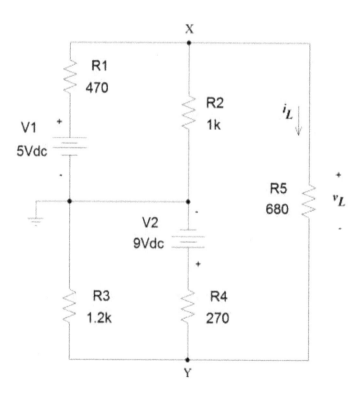

Figure 1: Circuit for verifying various analysis methods.

References	Tront, JG, <u>PSpice for Basic Circuit Analysis</u> (2E), New York: McGraw Hill (2006).

Materials	The equipment and components required to perform this experiment are:

- ANDY board
- Digital multimeter
- PSpice software
- 1 ea 270 Ω resistor
- 1 ea 470 Ω resistor
- 1 ea 680 Ω resistor
- 1 ea 1.0 kΩ resistor
- 1 ea 1.2 kΩ resistor

Procedure	**Analysis:**

1. Using both the mesh current and the node voltage methods, determine v_L and i_L for the circuit shown in Figure 1. Verify that the results from each method agree. Record the results in your laboratory notebook.

Modeling:

2. Using PSpice, model the circuit shown in Figure 1. Display all of the node voltages and branch currents on your circuit diagram. Verify that they agree with the results of step 1. Insert a printout of your results in your lab notebook.

3. Using the Monte Carlo capabilities of PSpice, find the worst case node voltages at X and Y and find the worst case currents through the load resistor, assuming the resistors have a 5% tolerance. Use a flat (rather than Gaussian) distribution for the resistor tolerances.

Measurements:

4. Build the circuit shown in Figure 1. Note that both the +5 V and +9 V supplies are provided by the ANDY board.

5. Using the DMM, measure v_L and i_L. Do the results lie within the bounds predicted by the Monte Carlo analysis of step 3?

6. Calculate the percent deviation from the results computed in step 1.

7. Comment on why the experimental results from step 5 and the calculated results from steps 1 and 2 may differ. Can you improve the agreement between theory and experiment by adjusting some of the ideal values assumed in the calculations? Explain.

8. Modify the calculations of steps 1 through 3 using experimental values for the voltage sources. Do the experimental results of step 5 agree with the modified calculations? Explain.

9. Be sure to save this circuit for use in Experiment 9, if that experiment has been assigned.

Last Revision   1/02/2009

Experiment 9: Superposition and Thévenin Equivalent

Developers   KM Lai, RW Hendricks, and JB Webb

Objectives   The objectives of this experiment are (a) to characterize a linear circuit with multiple sources using superposition and (b) to experimentally determine the Thévenin equivalent of that circuit.

Estimated Time for Completion

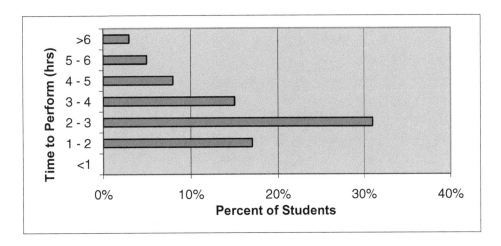

Preparation   Read the sections in your textbook which discuss superposition and Thévenin's theorem. Also read the section of your PSpice manual that describes how to determine the Thévenin's theorem. This is found, for example, on page 47 of Svoboda (2002) or on page 29 of Tront (2006).

Background   If a linear circuit has two or more independent sources, superposition may be used to find the contribution from each individual source to the node voltages and the mesh currents. The superposition principle states that the voltage across an element in a circuit is the sum of the voltage across that element due to each independent source. Also, the current through an element in a circuit is the sum of the currents through that element from each independent source. *Remember, you can only use superposition if all of the elements in a circuit are linear.*

An important and often used circuit theorem is the Thévenin equivalent circuit. A Thévenin equivalent circuit can completely replace a circuit with a single equivalent source and a single equivalent resistance. It is often desirable to use this theorem to eliminate parts of a circuit that are not relevant to the analysis at hand. After applying Thévenin's theorem, other analysis techniques can be applied to the simplified circuit.

In this experiment, which is based on the same circuit built and analyzed in Experiment 8 and shown in Figure 1, you will experimentally verify the

117

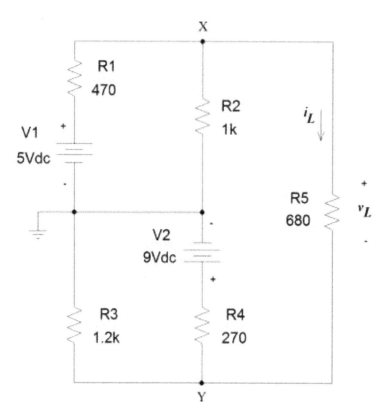

Figure 1: Circuit for verifying the superposition theorem and
Thévenin's theorem.

superposition theorem and you will experimentally determine its Thévenin
equivalent.

References   Svoboda, JA, <u>PSpice for Linear Circuits</u>, Hoboken, NJ: John Wily & Sons
(2002).

Tront, JG, <u>PSpice for Basic Circuit Analysis</u> (2E), New York: McGraw Hill
(2006).

Materials   The equipment and components required to perform this experiment are:
- ANDY board
- Digital multimeter
- PSpice software
- 1 ea 270 Ω resistor
- 1 ea 470 Ω resistor
- 1 ea 680 Ω resistor
- 1 ea 1.0 kΩ resistor
- 1 ea 1.2 kΩ resistor

Procedure

Analysis*:*

1. Using either mesh current or node voltage analysis, determine v_L, i_L and P_L, for the circuit shown in Figure 1 in each of the following cases:

   a) As shown in Figure 1. (You may use the results from Experiment 8 if that experiment was performed.)

   b) With the 9 V power supply removed (replaced with a short).

   c) With the 5 V power supply removed (replaced with a short).

2. Verify that the node voltages and mesh current given in step 1(a) are given by the sums of the voltages and currents found in steps 1(b) and 1(c).

3. Calculate the Thévenin voltage V_{TH} and Thévenin resistance R_{TH} as viewed across the load resistor R5 looking into the circuit at XY. Draw the Thévenin equivalent circuit.

Modeling:

4. Using PSpice, model the circuit shown in Figure 1. Display all of the node voltages, mesh currents, and power dissipation on your circuit diagram. Verify that they agree with the results of step 1(a). Insert a printout of your results in your lab notebook.

5. Repeat step 4 with the 9 V source removed. Verify that the results agree with step 1(b).

6. Repeat step 4 with the 5 V source removed. Verify that the results agree with step 1(c).

7. Following the methodology of Svoboda (p 47) or Tront (p 29, determine the Thévenin equivalent for the circuit. Verify that the result agrees with that of step 3. Insert a printout of your results in your lab notebook.

Measurements (Superposition):

8. Build the circuit shown in Figure 1 with all voltage sources active. Note that both the 5 V and the 9 V sources are provided by the ANDY board.

9. Using the DMM, measure v_L and i_L for the circuit as shown in Figure 1 with both sources active. Calculate the percent deviation from the results computed in step 1(a).

10. Repeat step 9 with the 9 V source removed (replaced with a short). Be sure you disconnect the source before you make a short circuit connection between R_4 and GND. Calculate the percent deviation from the results computed in step 1(b).

11. Repeat step 9 with the 5 V source removed (replaced with a short). Be sure to replace the 9 V source before performing this step and be sure you disconnect the source before you make a short circuit connection between R_1

and GND. Calculate the percent deviation from the results computed in step 1(c).

12. Calculate $v_{L1} = v_{L2} + v_{L3}$, where v_{L2} is the voltage over the load measured in step 10 and v_{L3} is the voltage over the load measured in step 11.

13. Calculate the percent deviation of v_{L1} from v_L determined in step 1(a). Verify that your results confirm the superposition theorem.

14. Calculate $i_{L1} = i_{L2} + i_{L3}$, where i_{L2} is the current through the load measured in step 10 and i_{L3} is the current through the load measured in step 11. Calculate the percent deviation of i_{L1} from i_L determined in step 1(a). Verify that your results confirm the superposition theorem.

15. Calculate P_L, P_{L2} and P_{L3} where P_L is the power dissipated by the load in step 9, P_{L2} is the power dissipated by the load in step 10 and P_{L3} is the power dissipated by the load in step 11. Calculate the percent deviation of these values from those determined in steps 1(a)–(c). Do these results confirm the superposition theorem? Why or why not?

16. Reconnect both sources in the circuit as per Figure 1.

Measurements (Thévenin Equivalent):

17. Remove the 680 Ω load resistor (R₅) from the circuit and measure the open circuit voltage, v_{OC}, between nodes X and Y. This is the Thévenin equivalent voltage.

18. Disconnect both power supplies from the circuit and replace them with short circuits.

> **Note: if you measure a powered circuit with your DMM set for resistance, you may damage your meter!**

19. With the 680 Ω load resistor removed, measure the resistance R_{OC} between nodes X and Y. This is the Thévenin equivalent resistance.

20. Reconnect both power supplies as per Figure 1.

21. With the 680 Ω load resistor removed, measure the current i_{SC} between nodes X and Y. Divide the voltage determined in step 17 by this current. This is also the Thévenin equivalent resistance.

22. Calculate the percent differences between v_{OC} and R_{OC} determined in steps 17, 19, and 21 with the analytical results for V_{TH} and R_{TH} calculated in step 3. Verify that your experimental and analytical estimates of the Thévenin voltages and resistances agree.

23. Draw the Thévenin equivalent circuit for the circuit shown in Figure 1.

Last Revision   1/02/2009

Experiment 10: Measuring Equivalent Resistances

Developer   D Fritz and K Meehan

Objectives   The objectives of this experiment are (a) to measure the source impedance of the function generator and the DC supply on the ANDY board and the input impedance of the digital multimeter and oscilloscope (b) to demonstrate that these voltage sources can deviate from ideal voltage sources and that the accuracy of the voltage measurement can limited by the source and input Thévenin equivalent impedance, respectively, and (c) to determine the range of impedance values that can be used as the equivalent impedance attached to the voltage sources and measured using the digital multimeter and oscilloscope.

Estimated Time for Completion

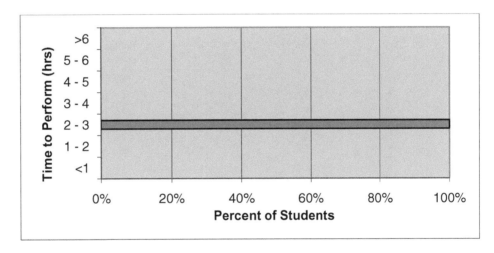

Preparation   Read the sections on a Thévenin equivalent impedance and source transformation in your textbook.

Background   Usually, it is assumed that the voltage sources used in these experiments can supply an unlimited amount of current to the circuit. When measuring the voltage across a component, it is expected that the amount of current flowing through the digital multimeter or oscilloscope is insignificant to the current flowing through the component. However, this is not the case when the equivalent impedance of the circuit approaches (or even worse, is less than) the source impedance of a voltage supply. Nor can you rely on obtaining a valid voltage measurement when the impedance of device under test (DUT) approaches or exceeds the input impedance of the measurement equipment.

To understand the impact of the source impedance on the ability of the voltage source to deliver power to a circuit, consider that a real voltage source can be modeled as an ideal voltage source in series with its source impedance (Fig.1), which is then wired in to the circuit. V_S is the voltage generated within the voltage source while V_{in} is the voltage that is actually applied to the circuit by the voltage source. Z_S is the source impedance, which usually has a large real component and little to no imaginary component. The source impedance is the output impedance of the power supply circuit as well as the impedance of the connectors and wires between the power supply circuit and the circuit on the breadboard. If we assume that $Z_S = R_S$ and that the circuit on the breadboard is a single resistor, RL, then it is easy to see that the circuit in Fig.1 would be a voltage divider, where

$$V_{in} = \frac{R_L}{R_L + R_S} V_S \tag{1}$$

When $R_L \gg R_S$, then $V_{in} \cong V_S$. However, $V_{in} < V_S$ as R_L is on the same order of magnitude or smaller than R_S. This means that the voltage actually applied to the circuit may be less than the voltage that was expected because of this loading effect.

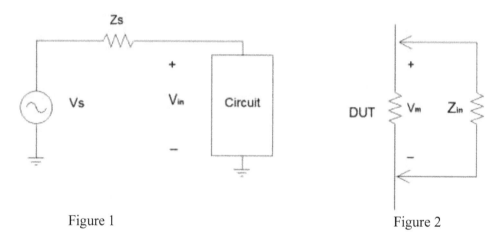

Figure 1   Figure 2

A multimeter or oscilloscope can be modeled as an impedance that is placed in parallel to the DUT (device under test) and, thus, the introduction of the measurement equipment into the circuit acts as a current divider (Fig. 2). If the input impedance of the measurement equipment, Z_{in}, is much larger than the impedance of the DUT, little current is diverted into the measurement device. When Z_{in} is on the same order of magnitude as the impedance of the DUT, the voltage measured, V_m, will be smaller than voltage drop across the DUT without the measurement equipment. As the impedance of an oscilloscope has a resistive and capacitive component to it, the phase angle of the measured voltage will also differ. The real component of Z_{in} for a typical oscilloscope is 1MΩ.

The 10x probe can be used to reduce the measurement error. This probe can be modeled as a 9 MΩ with a trim capacitor in parallel. The effect is to increases the real component of Z_{in} to 10MΩ, which enables more accurate measurement of the voltage across high resistance devices. The trim capacitor is used to compensate for the internal capacitance of the oscilloscope and the parasitic capacitance of the scope cable. The use of the trim capacitor extends the frequency range over which the measured voltage is accurate within a certain percentage. Note that the voltage measured by the oscilloscope will be attenuated by a factor of 10 when the 10x probe is used, which must be taken into account when recording the data.

In this experiment, you will perform several simple measurements to determine the Thévenin equivalent impedance of the source impedance of the 12V supply on the ANDY board and the Velleman function generator using the circuit in Fig. 3. You will also determine the input impedance of the digital multimeter and the Velleman oscilloscope. To limit the current that may flow into the oscilloscope as the resistance of the device under test is increased, you will perform the required measurements on the circuit in Fig.4. From these measurements, you will calculate the range of impedances that can be used with a) the voltage sources without significantly reducing the voltage applied to the circuit and b) the test equipment to obtain reasonably accurate voltage measurements over a specified frequency range. Note that you will also have to specify the frequency range based upon your analysis of the measurements.

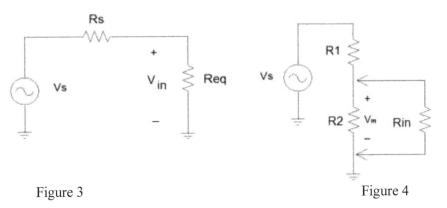

Figure 3   Figure 4

The voltage measured when the DMM is set to AC voltage is root mean squared (RMS) voltage. The relationship between the amplitude, V_m, of a periodic sinusoidal voltage $v(t)$ where $v(t) = V_m\sin(\omega t)$ and the magnitude of the RMS voltage V_{RMS} measured using the DMM is:

$$V_{RMS} = \sqrt{\frac{1}{T}\int_0^T v(t)^2 \, dt} = \frac{\sqrt{2}}{2}V_m = 0.707V_m \qquad (2)$$

where T is the period of the sinusoid and ω is the angular frequency.

$$T = 2\pi/\omega \qquad (3)$$

Note that the DMM does not measure 'true' RMS voltage. The assumption is that the time-varying signal measured is a periodic sinusoidal function. An incorrect value for the root mean squared voltage or current will be displayed if the signal measured using the DMM is not periodic or is not sinusoidal.

The specifications on the Velleman oscilloscope are provided at http://www.vellemanusa.com/us/enu/product/view/?id=524708 and are written on the side of the product box. The specifications for the function generators on the ANDY board are given on page 2 of the RSR/VT A&D "ANDY" Board User Manual and Test Procedure, which can be found on the text website http://www.lab-in-a-box.net. However, no specifications are available for the +12 V source on the ANDY board.

Materials

The equipment and components required to perform this experiment are:
- ANDY board
- Digital multimeter
- USB oscilloscope
- 10 Ω resistor
- 47 Ω resistor
- Four 390 Ω resistors
- One 22 kΩ resistor
- One 33 kΩ resistor
- One 220 kΩ resistor
- One 330 kΩ resistor
- Five 1 MΩ resistors

Procedure

Analysis:

1. Derive the relationship between V_{in} and V_S for the circuit shown in Figure 3 using the nominal source resistance of the Velleman function generator.

2. Using MATLAB, plot V_{in} as a function of the equivalent resistance of the circuit as it varies from 10 Ω to 400 Ω for the circuit shown in Fig. 3. Determine the equivalent resistance of the circuit that causes the voltage applied to the circuit, V_{in}, to be 50% of the magnitude of the ideal voltage, V_s.

3. Generate a second graph in MATLAB of V_{in} as a function of R_S where the equivalent resistance of the circuit is held constant at 130 Ω.

4. Plot the power delivered to the circuit as a function of the equivalent resistance of the circuit, R_{eq}, as it is varied from 10 Ω to 390 Ω, where R_S is equal to the nominal source resistance of the Velleman function generator, using MATLAB. Determine the value of the equivalent resistances at which a) the maximum power is delivered to the equivalent resistor and b) ½ of the maximum power in the circuit is delivered to the equivalent resistor.

5. Derive the relationship for V_m as a function of the resistance of the device under test, R_2, of the circuit shown in Figure 4 where R_{in} is equal to the nominal input resistance of the Velleman oscilloscope. Assume that R_1 is 1.5 times as large as R_2.

6. Repeat the derivation in Step 5 where R_{in} is equal to the nominal input resistance of the Velleman oscilloscope plus the resistance of the 10x probe.

7. Use MATLAB to graph V_m as a function of the $log[R_2,]$ as R_2 varies from 10 kΩ to 10 MΩ when R_{in} is equal to a) the nominal input resistance of the Velleman oscilloscope and b) is equal to the nominal input resistance of the Velleman oscilloscope plus the resistance of the 10x probe. The two curves should be plotted on the same graph.

Modeling

8. Perform a PSpice simulation on the circuit in Figure 3 where V_S is a d.c. voltage source. Set the amplitude of V_S equal to the magnitude of a 2VRMS a.c. source. Obtain a plot of V_{in} and the power dissipated by the equivalent resistance of the circuit, R_{eq}, as R_{eq} varies from 10 Ω to 400 Ω.

9. Perform a PSpice simulation on the circuit in Figure 4 where V_S is a 9V d.c. voltage source. Obtain a plot of V_m and the power dissipated by R_2, as R_2 varies from 10 kΩ to 10 MΩ when R_{in} is equal to a) the nominal input resistance of the Velleman oscilloscope and b) is equal to the nominal input resistance of the Velleman oscilloscope plus the resistance of the 10x probe.

Measurement:

10. Construct the circuit in Figure 3 using the Velleman function generator. Set the function generator to produce a 2V$_{RMS}$ (5.66Vpp) 400Hz sine wave with 0V DC offset. Measure the RMS voltage across resistor R_{eq} using both the oscilloscope and digital multimeter (both set for best accuracy) as you change R_{eq} from a) an open circuit to b) a 390 Ω resistor to c) two 390 Ω resistors in parallel to d) three 390 Ω resistors in parallel to e) four 390 Ω resistors in parallel, to f) a 47 Ω resistor, and lastly to a 10 Ω resistor. Note: Calibrate the Velleman oscilloscope before you begin.

11. Measure the resistance of R_{eq} using the digital multimeter when R_{eq} is equal to a) a 390 Ω resistor, b) two 390 Ω resistors in parallel, c) three 390 Ω resistors in parallel, and d) four 390 Ω resistors in parallel.

12. Calculate the power dissipated by R_{eq} from your measured voltages and resistance values. Plot the points on the MATLAB graphs obtained in Step 2 and Step 4. What is the value of R_{eq} that should be used to obtain the maximum power delivered to the circuit? What is the minimum value of R_{eq} to the voltage applied to the circuit, V_{in}, have at least 50% of the source voltage, V_S?

13. Determine the Thévenin equivalent voltage for the function generator when R_{eq} is an open circuit and the Thévenin equivalent source resistor, R_S when R_{eq} is approximately 100 Ω.

14. Replace the Velleman function generator in the circuit with the +12 V d.c. supply on the ANDY board. Measure the d.c. voltage across resistor R_{eq} using the digital multimeter as you change R_{eq} from a) an open circuit to b) a 390 Ω resistor to c) two 390 Ω resistors in parallel to d) three 390 Ω resistors in parallel, and lastly to e) four 390 Ω resistors in parallel.

15. Calculate the power dissipated by R_{eq} from your measured voltages and resistance values. Plot the points on the MATLAB graphs obtained in Step 2 and Step 4. What is the value of R_{eq} that should be used to obtain the maximum power delivered to the circuit? What is the minimum value of R_{eq} to the voltage applied to the circuit, V_{in}, have at least 50% of the source voltage, V_S?

16. Determine the Thévenin equivalent voltage for the function generator when R_{eq} is an open circuit and the Thevenin equivalent source resistor, R_S when R_{eq} is approximately 100 Ω.

17. Construct the circuit shown in Figure 4 using the +9 V supply on the ANDY board as V_S source. Use the following pairs of resistors for R_1 and R_2: a) R_1 = 33 kΩ and R_2 = 22 kΩ, b) R_1 = 330 kΩ and R_2 = 220 kΩ, and R_1 = 3 MΩ and R_2 = 2 MΩ.

18. Measure V_S and the voltage across R_2 for each pair of R_1 and R_2 using a) the digital multimeter, b) the Velleman oscilloscope with oscilloscope probe provided by the manufacturer where the probe is set to 1X, and c) the Velleman oscilloscope with oscilloscope probe is set to 10X. Remember that the voltage displayed will be attenuated by a factor of 10 when the 10x probe is used, which must be taken into account when you record the data. Note: *DC coupling* should be used and the trigger function on the oscilloscope should be turned *off* during these measurements.

19. Determine the values of R_2 using your measured voltages and the equation for a voltage divider where you have assumed that $R_{in} = \infty$ Ω

20. Measure the resistances of R_1 and R_2 used in Step 17. Determine the percent error in the resistances calculated in Step 19.

    * The formula used to calculate the percent error is:

$$\% \, error = \frac{Calculated \ \ Value - Measured \ \ Value}{Calculated \ \ Value} \times 100\%$$

21. Using your measured and calculated values for R_2 when R_2 = 2 MΩ and recognizing that the calculated resistance is actually $R_{in} \| R_2$, determine the value for R_{in} when a) the 1X probe was used and b) the 10X probe was used to make the voltage measurements.

22. What conclusions can you draw about the effects of the source resistances of the voltage supplies and the input resistances of oscilloscope with respect to the resistance of the circuit or device under test?

Last Revision   9/22/2010

Experiment 11: An Inverting Amplifier Circuit

Developer   RW Hendricks and K Meehan

Objectives   The objectives of this experiment are (a) to investigate the input-to-output relationship of an inverting amplifier circuit, and (b) to verify the difference between the op amp saturation voltages and the power supply voltages.

Estimated Time for Completion

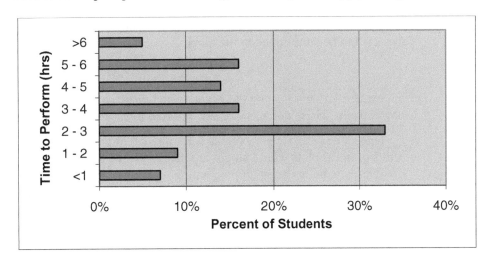

Preparation   Read the sections on an inverting op amp circuit in your textbook. Also, refer to Section 3.12 on op amps in this text and download and read the **LM324 op amp datasheet from National Semiconductor (2008)**.

Background   In introductory analyses of circuits involving operational amplifiers (op amps), several assumptions are usually made. Two of these assumptions are: (1) the op amp has very high open loop gain and (2) the amplifier circuit has infinite input impedance. These imply that the voltage difference between the inverting and the non-inverting op amp inputs is sufficiently small as to be treated as zero. As a consequence, the currents flowing into the inverting input and the non-inverting input are taken as zero. With these assumptions, the summing point constraints can be used.

Because of the very high open loop gain of the op amp, circuits involving op amps become unstable unless there is negative feedback from the output to the inverting input. When a resistor is connected between the output and the inverting input, using the summing point constraints, it is straightforward to show that if the input signal is also connected to the inverting input, the gain, G, of the system is

$$G = \frac{-R_f}{R_i} \qquad (1)$$

where R_f is the feedback resistance and R_i is resistance of the input resistor at the inverting input. The output, v_o, and the input, v_i, are related by

$$v_o = G \cdot v_i \qquad (2)$$

When the product of the input signal and the gain is high enough, the output voltage would be predicted to be greater than the op amp supply voltages. This is impossible and the output signal will saturate. The saturation voltage is V_{CC+} or V_{CC-} depending on the sign of the input voltage. Thus, the output signal is expected to be constrained to the range

$$V_{cc-} \le v_o \le V_{cc+} \qquad (3)$$

where V_{cc-} and V_{cc+} are the negative and positive power supply voltages, respectively. These voltages are also referred to as V+ and V- in some textbooks.

Thus, if one measures v_o versus v_i for a range of gains, one should obtain a series of linear plots whose slopes are the respective gains, G, as shown by Eq (2). This is valid in the op amp operating region given by Eq (3), and then should saturate at either V_{cc+} or V_{CC-}. In practice, the saturation voltage will be different from the power supply voltages because of the design of the op amps. The actual values depend on the op amp and may be found in the op amp data sheet. (see Section 3.12). For example, for the LM324 the operating range is

$$V_{cc-} \le v_o \le V_{cc+} - 1.5 \text{ V} \,, \qquad (4)$$

as stated in the Features section of the National Semiconductor LM 324 datasheet.

In this experiment, you will build a simple, inverting op amp circuit and will measure the DC network function, v_o / v_i over a range of input voltages. From these data, you will determine both the gain of the circuit and the saturation voltages of the op amp. These results will be compared with the op amp data sheet.

In analyzing the acquired data, you will be required to perform several least squares fits of your results to straight line functions by the method of least squares. (See Appendix C.) This procedure, called linear regression, is a built-in function in both Excel and MATLAB for which there are numerous inexpensive paperback and on-line tutorials. Two of the books that we have found to have a good discussion of these methods are those by Stinson and Dodge (2003) and Hanselman and Littlefield (2005).

Caution: Note that several wiring errors can cause excessive heating of the op amp, which will eventual damage the op amp as well as damage the ANDY board. These include (1) connecting -9V to the pin labeled V+ and +9V to the pin labeled ground on the LM 324 datasheet (the two pins used to power the op amp) and (2) connecting the output of the op amp directly to ground, V+, or V-. The temperature increase of the op amp package is sufficient to melt the breadboard under the package. Take care and do not touch the op amp dip package when hot. Remove the power supply to the ANDY board and wait until the package has cooled before replacing the op amp.

References   *Hanselman, D., and B. Littlefield, (2005). <u>Mastering MATLAB 7</u>. Upper Saddle River, NJ: Pearson Prentice Hall.

National Semiconductor (2008). "LM324 - Low Power Quad Operational Amplifier." 16 November 2008 <http://www.national.com/pf/LM/LM324.html>.

Stinson, C. and M. Dodge, (2007). <u>Microsoft Office Excel 2007 Inside Out</u>, Redmond: Microsoft Press.

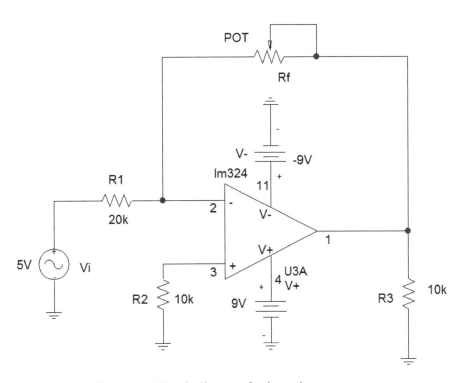

Figure 1: Circuit diagram for inverting op amp.

Materials   The equipment and components required to perform this experiment are:

- ANDY board
- Digital multimeter
- USB oscilloscope
- 1 ea LM324 op amp
- 2 ea 10 kΩ resistors
- 1 ea 20 kΩ resistor
- 1 ea 1 kΩ trim pot
- 1 ea 100 kΩ trim pot

Procedure　　　　**Analysis:**

23. Derive the input-to-output relationship of the amplifier circuit shown in Figure 1.

24. Determine the resistance values of R_f such that the gain of the inverting amplifier, G, is a) -2, b) -3, and c) -4.

Modeling:

25. Model the transient response of the circuit in Figure 1 in PSpice after replacing the trim pot (R_f) with a resistor of fixed value. Plot the output voltage of the op amp (the voltage across R_3) as a function of time where the gain of the op amp circuit is a) -2, b) -3, and c) -4, using the values of R_f calculated in step 2. The input voltage should be a 5V sine wave operating at 1 kHz. Print screen shots of the transient response for each simulation. Each plot should include the trace of the input voltage and the output voltage with 3-5 cycles shown.

Measurements:

26. Download the LM 324 datasheet from the National Semiconductor website. Identify the pins on the op amp dip package after looking at the **Connection Diagram** for the dual in-line package on the datasheet. The pin labeled ground on the datasheet will not be connected to ground and is V- in schematic shown in Figure 1.

27. Construct the inverting amplifier circuit shown in Figure 1. As noted in Section 3.11, it is good practice to short the unused terminal of the trim pot R_f (pin 3) to the wiper (pin 2). Be sure to connect the polarities of the ± 9 V power supplies correctly.

28. Set the voltage of the function generator on the USB oscilloscope to a sinusoidal wave with a 10V peak-to-peak voltage at a frequency of 1 kHz. Use Channel 1 of oscilloscope to measure the input voltage v_i and Channel 2 to measure the output voltage v_o as a function of time.

29. Adjust the trim pot R_f so that gain of the inverting op amp circuit G = -2.0 by using the cursors on the oscilloscope display to measure the output voltage v_o when the input voltage v_i is 1.0 V.

30. Carefully remove R_f from the circuit and measure the resistance between pins 1 and 2. Record the value of R_f and return the trim pot to the circuit.

31. Verify that the gain of the op amp circuit is still -2. Use the cursors on the oscilloscope display to measure the value of the output voltage v_o as the input voltage v_i varies between -5V to 5V in 1V increments.

32. Using the relationship developed in step 1, calculate the gain of the circuit using the known value of R_1 and the measured value of R_r. The careful student will measure R_1.

33. Calculate the percent deviation of the gain determined in step 10 and the actual gain determined by the ratio of the output voltage to the input voltage measured in step 7. Explain any discrepancy.

34. Repeat steps 7-11, setting G = -3

35. Repeat steps 7-11, setting G = -4.

36. Using MatLAB, plot a graph of the output voltage versus the input voltage for the data acquired in step 9 for each value of G.

37. Compute the gain of the amplifier from a least squares determination of the slope of the graph [see Eq (2)]. Note: there are built-in least squares fitting routines in MATLAB as described by Hanselman and Littlefield (2005).

38. Obtain the positive and negative saturation voltages for each gain from the three graphs plotted in step 14.

39. Measure the + 9 V and - 9 V power supplies.

40. Compute the percent deviation[*] of the gain computed in step 10 from that computed in step 15. Do your gain measurements made in step 10 confirm Eq (1) and the measurements made in step 15 confirm Eq (2) over the full range of the input voltage? Explain any discrepancies.

41. Compare the average saturation voltage determined in step 16 with the measured values of the power supplies determined in step 17. Does the saturation voltage depend on the amplifier gain (within experimental error)? Does the saturation voltage agree with that specified in the data sheet? (See Table 17 in Section 3.12 and Eq (3) above.)

[*] The formula used to calculate the percent deviation is:

$$\% \text{ deviation} = \frac{\text{Ideal Value} - \text{Measured Value}}{\text{Ideal Value}} \times 100\%$$

Last Revision   6/09/2010

Experiment 12: A Non-Inverting Amplifier Circuit

Developer   RW Hendricks and K Meehan

Objectives   The objectives of this experiment are (a) to investigate the input-to-output relationship of a non-inverting amplifier circuit, (b) to demonstrate that the operation of an op amp can be modeled as a voltage controlled voltage source via simulation, and (c) to determine the differences between the op amp saturation voltages and the power supply voltages.

Estimated

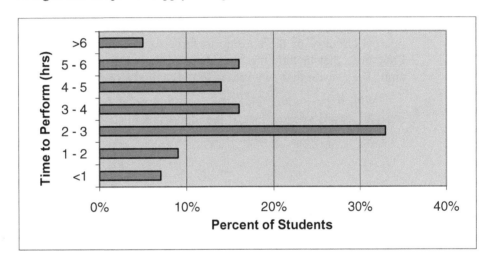

Preparation   Read the sections on a non-inverting op amp circuit in your textbook. Also, refer to Section 3.12 on op amps in this text and download and read the LM324 op amp data sheet from National Semiconductor (2008). Review Experiment 6 on the use of trim pots as voltage dividers.

Background   In introductory analyses of operational amplifier (op amp) circuits, a simple model of an op amp is used as its equivalent circuit (Fig. 1). The output voltage of the op amp, v_o, is proportional to the difference in the voltage between the positive and negative input terminals. where the voltage drop across the input resistance, R_{in}, between the two input terminals,. The proportionality constant, or open loop gain, is A. Therefore, $v_o = Av_d$.

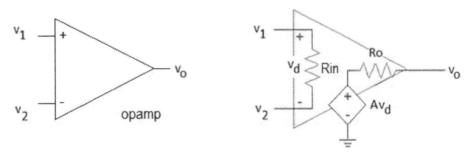

135

Figure 1: Symbol for a simple ideal op amp and its equivalent circuit.

Several assumptions are usually made when applying the equivalent circuit. Three of these assumptions are: (1) the op amp has very high open loop gain, A = ∞, (2) the amplifier circuit has infinite input impedance, R_{in} = ∞ Ω, and the output resistance is zero, R_o = 0 Ω. The first two assumptions imply that the voltage difference between the inverting and the non-inverting op amp inputs is sufficiently small as to be treated as zero. As a consequence, the currents flowing into the inverting input and the non-inverting input are taken as zero. When a circuit element, such as a resistor, is used to connect the output terminal to the negative input terminal of the op amp, the output voltage v_o is generated by the internal circuitry of the op amp to force $v_1 = v_2$ so that v_d = 0V within certain limitations that include the magnitude of the voltages supplied to power the op amp. The resistor that connects v_o to v_2 is called a feedback resistor.

With these assumptions, the summing point constraints can be used. It is straightforward to show that, if the input signal is connected to the non-inverting input of the op amp, the gain, G, of the system is

$$G = \frac{v_o}{v_S} = 1 + \frac{R_f}{R_1} \tag{1}$$

where R_f is the feedback resistance and R_1 is the resistor that ties the negative input terminal of the op amp to ground. The output, v_o, and the input, v_i, are related by

$$v_o = G \cdot v_i \tag{2}$$

When the product of the input signal and the gain is high enough, the output would be predicted to be greater than the op amp supply voltages. This is impossible and the output signal will saturate. Ideally, the saturation voltage is V_{CC+} or V_{CC-} depending on the sign of the input voltage. Thus, the output signal is expected to be constrained to the range

$$V_{cc-} \leq v_o \leq V_{cc+} \tag{3}$$

where V_{cc-} and V_{cc+} are the negative and positive power supply voltages, respectively. Thus, if one measures v_o versus v_i for a range of gains, one should obtain a series of linear plots whose slopes are the respective gains, G, as shown by Eq (2). This is valid in the op amp operating region given by Eq (3), and then should saturate at either V_{cc+} or V_{CC-}. In practice, the saturation voltage will be different from the power supply voltages because of the design of the op amps. In the case of the LM324, the output should be constrained by $V_{cc-} \leq v_o \leq V_{cc+} - 1.5$ V according to the data sheet.

In this experiment, you will build a simple, non-inverting op amp circuit and will measure the DC transfer function, over a range of input voltages. From these data, you will determine both the gain of the circuit and the saturation voltages of the op amp and if the saturation voltages are as specified in the data sheet. In analyzing the acquired data, you will be required to calculate the mean and variance or standard deviation of your results. (See Appendix C.) There are built-in functions in MATLAB to assist you with these calculations that are described in numerous inexpensive paperback and on-line tutorials. Two of the books that we have found to have a good discussion of these methods are those by Stinson and Dodge (2003) and Hanselman and Littlefield (2005).

Caution: Note that several wiring errors can cause excessive heating of the op amp, which will eventual damage the op amp as well as damage the ANDY board. These include (1) connecting -9V to the pin labeled V+ and +9V to the pin labeled ground on the LM 324 datasheet (the two pins used to power the op amp) and (2) connecting the output of the op amp directly to ground, V+, or V-. The temperature increase of the op amp package is sufficient to melt the breadboard under the package. Take care and do not touch the op amp dip package when hot. Remove the power supply to the ANDY board and wait until the package has cooled before replacing the op amp.

References

*Hanselman, D., and B. Littlefield, (2005). Mastering MATLAB 7. Upper Saddle River, NJ: Pearson Prentice Hall.

National Semiconductor, (2006). "LM324 - Low Power Quad Operational Amplifier." 16 November 2008 <http://www.national.com/pf/LM/LM324.html>.

Stinson, C., and M. Dodge, (2007). Microsoft Office Excel 2007 Inside Out, Redmond, WA: Microsoft Press.

Materials

The equipment and components required to perform this experiment are:
- ANDY board
- Digital multimeter
- USB oscilloscope
- 1 ea LM 324 op amp
- 3 ea 10 kΩ resistors
- 1 ea 1 kΩ trim pot
- 1 ea 100 kΩ trim pot

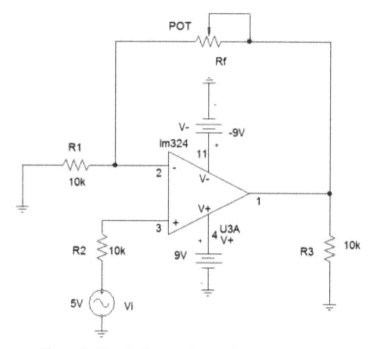

Figure 2: Circuit diagram for non-inverting op amp.

Procedure

Analysis:

1. Derive the input-to-output relationship of the amplifier circuit shown in Figure 1.

2. Determine the resistance values of R_f such that the gain of the non-inverting amplifier G is equal to a) 2, b) 3, and c) 4.

Modeling:

3. Perform a DC Sweep on the circuit in Figure 2 in PSpice after replacing the trim pot (R_f) with a resistor of fixed value. Plot the output voltage of the op amp as a function of the input voltage, which is the plot of DC voltage transfer characteristic, where the gain of the op amp circuit is 4, using the value of R_f calculated in step 2. Replace Vi with a dc voltage source, which should be swept from -5V to +5V.

4. Replace the op amp in the schematic with a voltage controlled voltage source (VCVS). Set the gain of the VCVS to 4 and repeat the DC Sweep to obtain the voltage transfer characteristic of the circuit. Are there any differences between this plot and the plot obtain in step 3?

Measurements:

5. Download the LM 324 datasheet from the National Semiconductor website. Identify the pins on the op amp dip package after looking at the **Connection Diagram** for the dual in-line package on the datasheet. The pin labeled ground on the datasheet will not be connected to ground and is V- in schematic shown in Figure 1.

6. Construct the non-inverting amplifier circuit shown in Figure 2. As noted in Section 3.11, it is good practice to short the unused terminal of the trim pot R_f (pin 3) to the wiper (pin 2). Be sure to connect the polarities of the ± 9 V power supplies correctly.

7. Set the voltage of the function generator on the USB oscilloscope to a sinusoidal wave with a 10V peak-to-peak voltage at a frequency of 1 kHz. Use Channel 1 of oscilloscope to measure the input voltage v_i and Channel 2 to measure the output voltage v_o as a function of time.

8. Adjust the trim pot R_f so that gain of the non-inverting op amp circuit G = 2.0 by using the cursors on the oscilloscope display to measure the output voltage v_o when the input voltage v_i is 1.0 V.

9. Carefully remove R_f from the circuit and measure the resistance between pins 1 and 2. Record the value of R_f and return the trim pot to the circuit.

10. Verify that the gain of the op amp circuit is still 2. Use the X-Y plot option to obtain a plot of the DC voltage transfer characteristic. Calculate the gain from the slope in the linear region of the voltage transfer characteristic.

11. Export the data from the oscilloscope of the measured values of the input and output voltages, which will be used in step 16.

12. Using the relationship developed in step 1, calculate the gain of the circuit using the known value of R_1 and the measured value of R_f. The careful student will measure R_1.

13. Calculate the percent deviation of the gain determined in step 10 and the actual gain determined by the ratio of the output voltage to the input voltage measured in step 7. Explain any discrepancy.

14. Repeat steps 8-13, setting G = 3

15. Repeat steps 8-13, setting G = 4.

16. Import the data saved in step 11 into MatLAB. Compute the average gain of the amplifier and the variance after calculating the ratio of the output voltage v_o to the input voltage v_i while the op amp is in the linear region. Note: there are built-in routines in MATLAB that can be used, as described by Hanselman and Littlefield (2005).

17. Obtain the positive and negative saturation voltages for each gain from the three plots of the DC voltage transfer characteristics.

18. Measure the + 9 V and - 9 V power supplies.

19. Compute the percent deviation* of the gain computed in steps 10, 12 and 16. Do your gain measurements made in step 12 confirm Eq (1) and the measurements made in step 10 and 16 confirm Eq (2) over the full range of the input voltage? Explain any discrepancies.

20. Compare the average saturation voltage determined in step 17 with the measured values of the power supplies determined in step 18. Does the saturation voltage depend on the amplifier gain (within experimental error)? Does the saturation voltage agree with that specified in the data sheet? (See Table 17 in Section 3.12 and Eq (3) above.)

* The formula used to calculate the percent deviation is:

$$\% \text{ deviation} = \frac{\text{Ideal Value} - \text{Measured Value}}{\text{Ideal Value}} \times 100\%$$

Last Revision 6/10/201

Experiment 13: Current Source (Voltage-to-Current Converter)

Developers   NE Eltahir, RW Hendricks, and K Meehan

Objectives   The objective of this experiment is to design, construct, and test the properties of a voltage-controlled current source (VCCS). The conditions under which the output current of the circuit is independent of the load impedance are explored.

Estimated Time for Completion

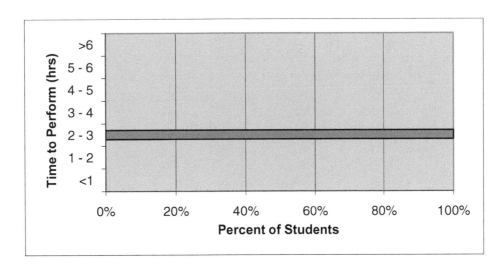

Preparation   Read Sections 3.8 and 3.12 in this text on resistors and on op amps, respectively. Review Experiment 6 on voltage and current dividers. Read the sections on inverting op amp circuits in your textbook. Download and read the LF356 and LM741 op amp data sheets from National Semiconductor (2008), and the description of a VCCS in the application notes from Apex Microtechnology (2007) and by Carter and Brown (2001). The book by Tobey et al. provides some excellent background.

Background   Most electric circuits are characterized by their I–V or current-to-voltage relationships. In many cases, one applies a known voltage (V) to the circuit and observes the resultant current (I) response. However, there are many applications where it is desirable to drive the circuit with a known current and to observe the resultant voltage. For example, such circuits are used to drive signals down long lines, or to drive the coils of a relay. Another application is the characterization of a two-port network as developed in Experiment 36 of this text.

It is the objective of this experiment to construct a simple circuit in which a known output current that is independent of the load is controlled by a known input voltage. Such a circuit is called a voltage controlled current source (VCCS). There are several ways to design a VCCS using one or more op amps (Graeme et al, 1971; Carter and Brown, 2001; Apex Microtechnology, 2007). These circuits may have either floating or grounded loads and may draw varying amounts of power from the controlling circuit. One such circuit is shown in Figure 1.

141

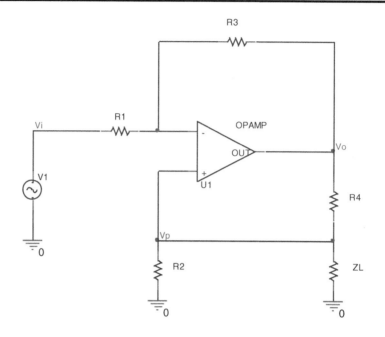

Figure 1: A VCCS circuit with grounded load.

The advantages of this circuit are (a) the load is grounded, and (b) the circuit draws very little current from the source if the input impedance of the circuit is large. Improvements to this circuit involve adding a stabilizer capacitor across R_2 and developing more sophisticated circuits using two op amps in cascade with a common feedback (Graeme et al., 1971). For the purposes of this project, the circuit shown in Figure 1 is sufficient.

From a nodal analysis of the circuit, it is easy to show that

$$i_L = \frac{v_p}{Z_L} = -\frac{R_2 R_3 v_i}{Z_L(R_1 R_4 - R_2 R_3) + R_1 R_2 R_4} \tag{1}$$

If we select the four resistors R_1 through R_4 such that

$$R_1 R_4 = R_2 R_3 \tag{2}$$

then, from Eq (1)

$$i_L = -\frac{v_i}{R_2} \tag{3}$$

and the current through the load is independent of the load and is controlled by the input voltage.

142

This seemingly simple result has four hidden constraints. First, the op amp output current i_o cannot exceed its output current capability. It can be shown that this current is given by

$$i_o = i_L \left(1 + \frac{Z_L}{R_2} \right) \tag{4}$$

and is constrained to lie within the bounds $-i_o^{min} \leq i_o \leq i_o^{max}$ where i_o^{min} and i_o^{max} are found on the specification sheet for the particular op amp in use. We also note that the op amp output current is not independent of the load, but is given by a constant multiplier times the load current.

Second, the control voltage cannot exceed the range of the voltage supplies for the op amps. For the ANDY board, $V_{CC-} \leq v_i \leq V_{CC+}$ or (approximately) $-9 \leq v_i \leq 9$ V.

Third, the resistors R_1 through R_4 must satisfy the constraint of Eq (2) quite precisely. Let us denote the gain of the inverting and non-inverting inputs by the expressions

$$G_n = \frac{R_3}{R_1} \tag{5}$$

and

$$G_p = \frac{R_4}{R_2} \tag{6}$$

Then, if the two gains are mismatched by an amount ε such that

$$G_p = G_n(1 + \varepsilon) \tag{7}$$

substitution of Eqs (5) through (7) in Eq (1) leads to the result that

$$i_L = \frac{-v_i}{\varepsilon(R_2 + Z_L) + R_2} \tag{8}$$

Clearly, for Eq (8) to be equivalent to Eq (3), it is necessary that

$$\varepsilon \left(1 + \frac{Z_L}{R_2} \right) \ll 1 \tag{9}$$

Fourth, it is imperative to assure that the current that flows through each resistor does not exceed the maximum current allowed by the power rating of the resistors. The resistors provided in the Lab-in-a-Box kit and described in Appendix A are all ½ W devices; one should be sure that the current does not produce a power in excess of perhaps ¼ W. Every resistor in the circuit should be checked, not just the loads. These constraints are most easily verified in the PSpice model of the circuit developed in the experimental procedure.

Design Example   Consider the case where a μ741 op amp is used. The approximate operating region for the circuit shown in Figure 1 is constrained by the heavy black lines that form a box as shown in Figure 2. The upper and lower horizontal solid lines represent the maximum positive and negative current outputs of the op amp. Note that although these outputs are symmetric for the μ741, they are sometimes not symmetric (i.e., the maximum negative output current may be less than the maximum positive output current as is seen in Table 17 of Section 3.12 for the LM324 device). Similarly, the solid vertical lines represent the approximate minimum and maximum voltages of the ANDY board DC 9 V power supplies.

Let us select the resistors R_1, R_2, R_3, and R_4 that will allow us to drive a constant current through resistors up to and including the 1.8 KΩ resistors in the component kit. We wish to operate the circuit in a bipolar mode; i.e., we want to be able to drive it with the current flowing in either direction through the resistor. Substituting Eq (3) in Eq (4) and substituting $v_i = -9$ V, $i_0 = 25$ mA, and the desired load resistance, we find the solution to the resulting quadratic equation is $R_2 = 1004.8\,\Omega$. Because R_2 controls the gain of the circuit, we pick $R_2 = 1.0\,\mathrm{k\Omega}$ which gives a transconductance gain of -1 mA/V. The resulting current through the load is given by Eq (3) and is shown by the solid line in Figure 2. We verify from Eq (4) that the op amp current will not saturate for any input voltage from the ANDY board. However, if a larger load resistor is inserted, the op amp output will saturate. Similarly, if R_2 is selected to be 200 Ω, then the load current is given by the dashed line in Figure 2 where the gain is now 5 mA/V. Notice that the output current now saturates the op amp output capabilities at ±5 V.

All of the op amp output current flows through R_4. At maximum current output (±25 mA), and with a maximum power dissipation by the resistor of about ¼ W, we find

$$(25 \cdot 10^{-3})^2 R_4 \leq \frac{1}{4} \tag{10}$$

or $R_4 \leq 400\,\Omega$. We wish to pick a large input resistance R_1 to the circuit so that there will be negligible current draw from the variable voltage supply. If we choose $R_1 = 100\,\mathrm{k\Omega}$, then from Eq (2) we find $R_3 = 40\,\mathrm{k\Omega}$.

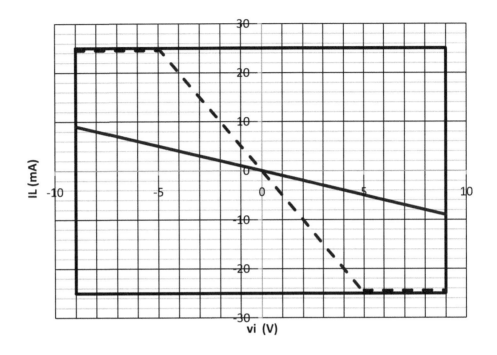

Figure 2: The operating regime of a μ741 op amp on the VT ANDY board.

It is left as an exercise for the student to verify that the power dissipated by each resistor in the circuit is less than ¼ W.

References

Apex Microtechnology (2007). "Application Note 13: Voltage to Current Conversion." 18 December 2008
< http://www.cirrus.com/en/pubs/appNote/Apex_AN13U_C.pdf >

*Carter, B., and T.R. Brown, (2001). Handbook of Operational Amplifier Applications, Application Report SBOA092A. 01 December 2008
<http://focus.ti.com/lit/an/sboa092a/sboa092a.pdf>. (See the section on the current injector on p. 80.)

*Hanselman, D., and B. Littlefield, (2005). Mastering MATLAB 7. Upper Saddle River, NJ: Pearson Prentice Hall.

National Semiconductor, (2004). "LM 741 Operational Amplifier." 16 November 2008 <http://www.national.com/ds/LM/LM741.pdf>.

National Semiconductor, (2004). "LF 356 JFET Input Operational Amplifiers." 01 December 2008 < http://www.national.com/mpf/LF/LF356.html >.

Stinson, C., and M. Dodge, (2007). Microsoft Office Excel 2007 Inside Out, Redmond, WA: Microsoft Press.

Tobey, G.E., J.G. Graeme, and L.P. Huelsman, eds., (1971). Operational Amplifiers: Design and Applications. New York: McGraw-Hill, pp. 225-229.

Materials

The equipment and components required to perform this experiment are:
- ANDY board
- Digital multimeter
- 1 ea LF356 op amp
- various resistors (to be determined)
- various trim pots (to be determined)

Procedure

Analysis and Design:

1. Derive Eq (1), which demonstrates the relationship of the input (control) voltage v_i to the load current i_L of the circuit shown in Figure 1.

2. Plot the operating regime for the LF356 op amp. Obtain the properties of the device from the datasheet given in the references.

3. Determine the maximum load resistance R_L that can be accommodated if we wish to drive the load with a current of up to approximately ± 1.8 mA.

4. Calculate the value of R_2 for which the op amp output current will not saturate over the entire allowable range of $V_{CC-} \leq v_i \leq V_{CC+}$. Pick R_2 such that the transconductance gain is a simple, convenient number. Note that you may need to iterate between steps 3 and 4 to find an acceptable solution.

5. Select resistor R_4. Be sure that it is capable of carrying the full output current of the op amp.

6. Choose resistor R_1 such that the input impedance of the circuit is very large. It must be sufficiently high so that the op amp circuit does not load the voltage divider created in Step 8 below. Hint: R_1 should be about ten times greater than the value of the trim pot selected in Step 8.

7. Select resistor R_3 to meet the constraints of Eq (2).

8. Modify the circuit diagram of Figure 1 such that the control voltage v_i is provided by a voltage divider created from a single trim pot. The control voltage must cover the entire allowable range of input voltage $-9 \leq v_i \leq 9$ V. Pay careful attention to the discussion in Section 3.1 of this text to assure that the trim pot does not overheat.

Modeling:

9. Model your circuit using PSpice. Verify that the power dissipated in each resistor is within the power ratings of the resistor ($\approx \frac{1}{4}$ W).

10. Sweep the load resistor and verify that the load current is independent of the load resistance for all values of the load.

11. Verify the transconductance gain of the circuit by plotting a graph of load current versus control voltage.

12. Verify that your PSpice model is correct by sweeping the input voltages over a range that is somewhat larger than the supply voltages V_{CC-} and V_{CC+} (e.g., $-1 + V_{CC-} \le v_i \le V_{CC+} + 1$ V)

Measurements:

13. Select resistors from your parts box for R_1, R_2, R_3, and R_4. Hint: You may need to use a series of resistors and/or trim pots.

14. Carefully measure the resistance of each resistor (or combination of resistors) and assure that the constraint of Eq (2) is met.

15. **Extra Credit:** Using the method of propagation of errors discussed in Appendix C and the stated accuracy of your DMM in its instruction manual, estimate the standard error of your measurements for each resistor and determine the accuracy with which Eq (2) is satisfied. (Refer to Experiment 5.)

16. Construct the modified voltage-to-current converter circuit shown in Figure 1, using the trim pot selected in Step 8 as a voltage divider for the input and your choices for the resistors R_1, R_2, R_3, and R_4.

17. Vary the input voltage v_i from -9 V to $+9$ V in increasing increments of about 0.5 V. Record the current through the load, i_L, for each v_i. Hint: you may find that it is easier to measure the voltage drop across the load and compute the current from the measured load resistance.

18. Using your choice of a scientific graphing program (i.e. Excel or MATLAB), plot a graph of v_i versus i_L. Be sure to add a trend line to your data points using the method of least squares (see Appendix C).

19. **Extra Credit:** Compute the standard error of the slope and the intercept of the regression (see Appendix C).

20. Select a (negative) input voltage that will produce an output current of $+1.0$ mA through the load. Vary the load resistance R_L by increasing it increments of your choice. Be sure to vary R_L across its full range. Record the current across the load, i_L, for each R_L.

21. Using your choice of a scientific graphing program (Excel or MATLAB), plot a graph of i_L versus R_L. Be sure to add a trend line to your data points using the method of least squares (see Appendix C).

22. **Extra Credit:** Compute the standard error of the slope and the intercept of the regression (see Appendix C).

23. Do the plots from steps 18 and 20 support the predictions of Eq (3)? If not, why not? Comment on the operation of your current source.

Last Revision   1/02/2009

Experiment 14: Series RC Circuit

Developer   RW Hendricks

Objectives   The objective of this experiment is to build a series RC circuit and to measure its response to a step increase and a step decrease in the applied voltage that is provided by a clock signal. Two different time constants are used—one which is short compared to the clock period and one which is long compared to the clock period. An oscilloscope is used to observe the transient nature of both the voltage across and the current through the capacitor as it responds to the step changes in the voltage source.

Estimated Time for Completion

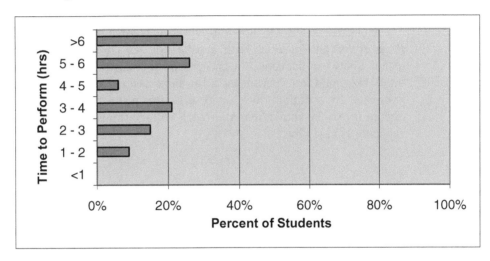

Preparation   Read the sections of your textbook which describe the natural and forced responses of RC networks. Also read Section 3.6 (PC Oscilloscope), Section 3.9 (Capacitors), and Section 3.11 (Trim Pots) of this text. Complete Experiments 13 and 14 prior to beginning this experiment.

Background   Signals applied to a circuit may be DC or AC, may be complex in terms of their underlying frequency components, or may be step changes from one voltage or current level to another. Experiments presented thus far in this book have involved only DC sources—sources whose output voltages are constant with time. We will meet AC sources, in which the signal varies at a single, fixed frequency, starting in Experiment 22. More specifically, we will study the same circuit as used in this experiment when it is excited by an AC source in Experiment 33.

In this experiment we will examine the time response of a series combination of a resistor and a capacitor when it is subjected to a step change in a DC voltage. The step change will be both a step increase and a step decrease as created by a digital clock or by a square wave function generator.

149

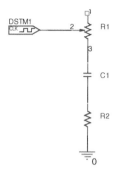

Figure 1: Circuit diagram for RC time constant determination.

Consider the circuit shown in Figure 1. Here, a trim pot (a variable resistor), R_1 is connected in series with a capacitor, C_1. A small current shunt, R_2, is inserted between the capacitor and ground to measure the capacitor current. (See the Background to Experiment 22 for a discussion of current shunts.) The signal is created by a digital clock or by a square wave function generator. For this circuit, it may be shown that after each voltage transition, the voltage across the capacitor is given by

$$v_C(t) = v_f + (v_i - v_f)e^{-t/\tau} \tag{1}$$

where v_i is the initial voltage from the source, v_f is the final voltage, and the time constant, τ, is given by $(R_1 + R_2) \cdot C_1$. In this experiment, we will select the current shunt, R_2, to be sufficiently small compared to R_1 that it can be ignored. In addition, R_1 will be made variable so that the time constant can be adjusted to desired values.

After some interval of time after the application of a step response, which will be used to define the zero of time, the output will essentially be v_f, as is seen from Eq (1). An excellent rule of thumb for this time is 5τ in which case the exponential in the equation becomes $e^{-5} \approx 0.0067$ or about 0.7%. In other words, the output is within 0.7% of its final value in five time constants.

To observe the response of the circuit to both a step increase in voltage and a step decrease, we will apply a variable frequency square wave to the circuit. We will set the magnitude of this signal to 5 V, the magnitude of the clock signal of the ANDY board. From Eq (1), when the input signal makes transition from 0 to 5 V, the circuit response should be given by

$$v_C(t) = 5(1 - e^{-t/\tau}) \tag{2}$$

and when the input signal makes a transition from 5 to 0 V, the circuit response should be given by

$$v_C(t) = 5e^{-t/\tau} \tag{3}$$

The (displacement) current through the capacitor is given by

$$i = C\frac{dv_C}{dt} \qquad (4)$$

where v is the voltage across the capacitor as given in Eq (1). Thus, a step increase in the voltage at $t = 0$ causes a current given by

$$i(t) = \frac{5}{R_1 + R_2}e^{-t/\tau} \qquad (5)$$

while a step decrease in the voltage at $t = 0$ causes a current given by

$$i(t) = \frac{-5}{R_1 + R_2}e^{-t/\tau} \qquad (6)$$

For this experiment to behave as predicted by Eqs (2) through (6), the input signal must be constant at both 0 and 5 V for at least 5τ. Typical expected voltage and current signals for the case where the clock voltage is constant for at least 5τ are shown in Figure 2.

If the condition that the step response of the clock be constant for a period of 5τ following the step transition is not met and the clock undergoes an opposite step transition before the capacitor voltage has reached its final value of either 0 V or 5 V as appropriate, then the response of the circuit must be computed using the instantaneous value of the capacitor voltage as given by Eq (1) at the time of the second transition rather than the step values of 0 and 5 V as were used in deriving Eqs (2) through (6). Such computations are described in your text, usually under the topic of sequential switching, and can become quite complex.

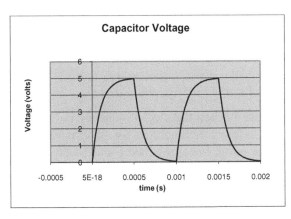
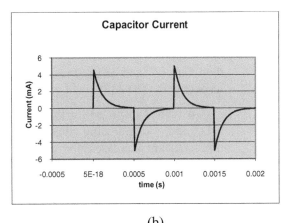

(a)   (b)

Figure 2: (a) voltage signal and (b) current signal expected from the circuit of Figure 1 when the clock frequency is 1 kHz and the circuit time constant is 100 μs.

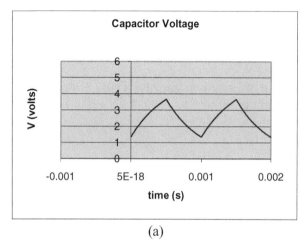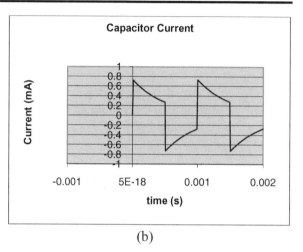

(a)   (b)

Figure 3: (a) voltage signal and (b) current signal expected from the circuit
of Figure 1 when the clock frequency is 1 kHz and the circuit
time constant is 500 μs.

In the present case, if τ > 1/10f, then for a 5 V square wave with a
50% duty cycle, the capacitor voltage is given by

$$v_C(t) = 5 - \frac{5}{1 + e^{-1/(2f\tau)}} e^{-t/\tau} \qquad (7)$$

and

$$v_C(t) = \frac{5}{1 + e^{-1/(2f\tau)}} e^{-t/\tau} \qquad (8)$$

In Eqs (7) and (8), the references for the zero of time are taken at the transition
edges from 0 to 5 V and from 5 to 0 V, respectively. Note that if $\tau \leq 1/10f$,
then Eqs (7) and (8) reduce, within acceptable accuracy, to Eqs (2) and (3)
respectively. The equivalent current equations for this case are easily derived.

A typical response for the circuit of Figure 1 when the clock frequency is 1
kHz and the circuit time constant is 500 μs is shown in Figure 3. As the circuit
time constant increases, the capacitor voltage curve becomes flatter and flatter
and, in the limit as τ approaches infinity, the voltage approaches a constant value
of 2.5 V.

For students using a Behringer sound card and the Zeitnitz PC oscilloscope,
there is the additional complication of AC coupling of the sound card as
described in the information posted on the text website. In this case, it is
necessary that the circuit time constant, τ, be short compared to the sound card
decoupling network time constant so that the latter will not seriously adversely
affect the former. For the time constants of 100 and 500 μs illustrated above, the

clock signal will decay by 3.5% and 17%, respectively. These are considered to be acceptable compromises for illustrating the points of this experiment.

References   *Hanselman, D., and B. Littlefield, (2005). Mastering MATLAB 7. Upper Saddle River, NJ: Pearson Prentice Hall.

Stinson, C., and M. Dodge, (2007). Microsoft Office Excel 2007 Inside Out, Redmond, WA: Microsoft Press.

Materials   The equipment and components required to perform this experiment are:
- ANDY board
- Software oscilloscope
- PSpice software
- 1 ea 10 Ω shunt resistor
- 1 ea 4.7 kΩ resistor
- 1 ea 0.1 µF capacitor
- 1 ea 1 kΩ trim pot

Procedure   **Analysis:**

1. Calculate the time constant of the RC network shown in Figure 4 assuming the trim pot is adjusted to provide the maximum resistance in the circuit.

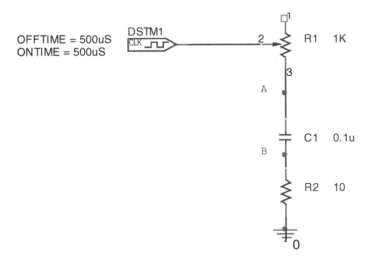

Figure 4: Circuit diagram for RC time constant determination.

2. Using your choice of scientific graphing software (e.g., Excel or MATLAB), plot a graph of $v_C(t)$ given by Eqs (2) and (3) versus t for the time constant calculated in step 1 and the clock signal shown in Figure 4. Also show the clock signal on the same graph. Do not plot the data points for either curve; show only a line connecting the data points. Be sure to compute a sufficient number of data points to obtain a smooth curve. Your graph should show

153

three full clock periods and should appear similar to Figure 2(a). Procedures for plotting such graphs may be found in Stinson and Dodge (2004) for Excel and in Hanselman and Littlefield (2005) for MATLAB. (See the MATLAB code in Appendix D.2 for an outline of how to plot multiple data sets on a single graph.)

3. Using Eqs (5) and (6), plot a graph of $i_C(t)$ versus t for the time constant calculated in step 1. Also show the clock signal on the same graph. Do not plot the data points for either curve; show only a line connecting the data points. Be sure to compute a sufficient number of data points to obtain a smooth curve. Your graph should show three full clock periods and should appear similar to Figure 2(b).

4. Using Eqs (7) and (8), plot a graph similar to that prepared in step 2 for a circuit time constant of 500 μs. Your graph should show at least three full clock periods and should be similar to Figure 3(a).

5. Using Eqs (7) and (8), derive expressions for the steady-state capacitor current for a network time constant of 500 μs. Plot a graph similar to that prepared in step 3. Your graph should show at least three full clock periods.

Modeling:

6. Model the circuit shown in Figure 4 in PSpice for a network time constant of 100 μs. Plot graphs of the capacitor voltage and current similar to those created in steps 2 and 3. Verify that the PSpice waveforms match those plotted in steps 2 and 3. Include screenshots of your waveforms in your report.

7. Model the circuit shown in Figure 4 in PSpice for a network time constant of 500 μs. Plot graphs of the capacitor voltage and current similar to those created in steps 4 and 5. Verify that the PSpice waveforms match those plotted in steps 4 and 5. Include screenshots of your waveforms in your report.

RC Network Measurements (100 μs time constant):

8. Using your digital multimeter, measure the capacitance of the 0.1 μF capacitor.

9. Adjust the resistance of the 1 kΩ trim pot so that the time constant of the circuit will be 100 μs. If the trim pot will not produce sufficient resistance, you may add a small resistor in series with it to increase the total resistance.

10. Build the circuit shown in Figure 4, being careful not to change the trim pot setting. Be sure to use the same terminals of the trim pot as were measured in step 9.

11. Adjust the digital clock to produce a 1 kHz, 5 V square wave.

12. Connect the oscilloscope Channel 1 input via the ×10 attenuator to node A. Trigger the scope on this channel. This signal is the capacitor voltage and should look similar to Figure 2(a). Remember that you must attenuate the voltage because the voltage across the capacitor is too large for the "Line" input of the sound card.

13. Connect the oscilloscope Channel 2 input via the ×1 attenuator to node B. This signal, when divided by the value of the shunt resistor, is the displacement current of the capacitor and should look similar to Figure 2(b).

14. Using the oscilloscope cursors, tabulate five data points on the rising waveform of the voltage across the capacitor and five data points on the falling waveform as seen on Channel 1.

15. Similarly, tabulate five data points on the falling edge of the positive current pulse and five data points on the rising edge of the negative current pulse as measured at node B.

16. Make screenshots of the oscilloscope output and include them in your report.

17. Plot the capacitor voltage data acquired in step 14 on the graph created in step 2. Note that you will have to adjust your data points vertically by ≈2.5 V depending on the true output of your digital clock in order to compensate for the AC coupling of the scope. Plot the data points, but do not connect them with lines. Include this plot in your report. Comment on the agreement between the observed and the expected results.

18. Plot the data for the falling voltage curve acquired in step 14 on a semi-logarithmic graph and determine the network time constant from the least squares slope of this graph [see Eq (3)].

19. Calculate the percent deviation of the experimental time constant from the 100 μs expected value. Explain any significant deviation.

20. Calculate the current in the branch from the data acquired in step 15 and plot it on the graph created in step 3. Plot the data points, but do not connect them with lines. Include this plot in our report. Comment on the agreement between the observed and the expected results.

RC Network Measurements (500 μs time constant):

21. Measure the resistance of the 4.7 kΩ resistor with your DMM.

22. Rewire the circuit to include the 4.7 kΩ resistor in series with the capacitor and the trim pot.

23. Remove the 1 kΩ trim pot from the circuit and adjust its resistance so that the circuit RC time constant will be 500 μs. Be sure to use the measured values for the capacitance and the series resistor as were measured in steps 8 and 21 in your calculations.

24. Replace the trim pot in the circuit, being careful to use the same terminals as were measured in step 23. The circuit should now be wired similar to that of step 10.

25. Using the oscilloscope cursors, tabulate five data points on the rising waveform of the voltage across the capacitor and five data points on the falling waveform as was done in step 14.

26. Similarly, tabulate five data points on the falling edge of the positive current pulse and five data points on the rising edge of the negative current pulse.

27. Make a printout of the oscilloscope screen and include it in your report.

28. Plot the data acquired in step 25 on the graph plotted in step 4. Plot the data points, but do not connect them with lines. Include this plot in your report. Comment on the agreement between the observed and the expected results.

29. Plot the data for the falling voltage curve acquired in step 25 on a semi-logarithmic graph and determine the network time constant from the slope of this graph [see Eq (8)].

30. Calculate the percent deviation of the experimental time constant from the 500 μs expected value. Explain any significant deviation.

31. Calculate the current in the branch from the data acquired in step 26 and plot it on the graph plotted in step 5. Plot the data points, but do not connect them with lines. Include this plot in your report. Comment on the agreement between the observed and the expected results.

Extra Credit Question:

32. Extra credit will be awarded to students who can provide a complete and correct derivation of Eqs (7) and (8). The derivation should start with Eq (1).

Last Revision   1/03/2009

Experiment 15: Metronome Circuit Using a 555 Timer

Developers   R Smith, A Heilesen, and K Meehan

Objectives   The objectives of this experiment are to determine the time required to charge and discharge a capacitor where these times are determined by two different resistor-capacitor networks in an astable multivibrator circuit and to measure the resulting frequency and duty cycle of the square wave output.

Estimated Time for Completion

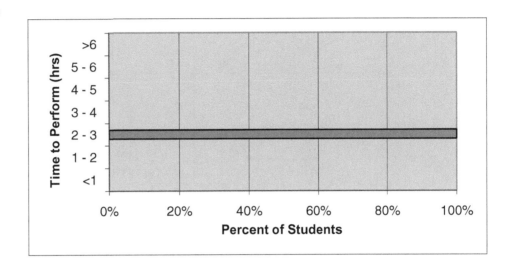

Preparation   Read the section describing RC time constants in your textbook. Also read Section 3.6 (Oscilloscope), Section 3.13 (Trim Potentiometers), Section 3.9 (Capacitors), and Section 3.14 (555 Timers) of this text.

Background   Metronomes produce regular sounds, usually a single frequency tone, beat, or click, which instrument players and singers use to count the meter or tempo of a piece of music. The repetition rate of the sound from a metronome can be adjusted by the musician. The typical range is from 40 to 200 beats per minute (bpm), which translates to a frequency of 0.667 to 3.33Hz.

In this experiment, the square wave output of a 555 timer chip, configured as a astable multivibrator, will be used to drive a speaker to obtain the sound of the beat. The frequency of the astable multivibrator circuit, shown in Figure 1, is determined by the time required to charge a resistor-capacitor network composed of R_a, R_b, and C and to discharge a resistor-capacitor network of R_b and C. Internal to the 555 timer chip are two voltage comparators U1 and U2 (see Fig. 2). These two comparators are designed to keep the voltage across the capacitor V_C, which is also the voltage on pins 2 and 6 of the 555 timer chip, between 1.67 V and 3.33 V. When $V_C = 3.33\ V$, the output of comparator 1 resets the RS flip-flop (U2A) and causes a transistor is activated, which connects ground to pin 7 of

157

the timer chip. This forces the node between R_a and R_b to be equal to 0 V. The capacitor will then discharge the stored charge on its plates through R_b to ground until the voltage on the capacitor decreases to 1.67 V. When $V_C = 1.67\,V$, the second comparator causes the transistor to be turned off, opening a switch between ground and pin 7. This allows a current to flow from V_{CC} through R_a and R_b to charge the capacitor. The output of the 555 timer (pin 3) is the output Q of the RS flip-flop whose state is set and reset by the output of voltage comparator U2 and U1, respectively. Thus, the output from a 555 timer is a logical "1" or close to 5V while the capacitor is charging and is a logical "0" or approximately equal to 0V while the capacitor is discharging.

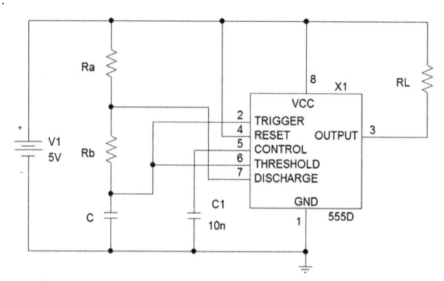

Fig. 1: Schematic for an astable multivibrator with output resistor R_L.

Thus, the time constants of two different resistor-capacitor networks determine the length of time the timer output, t_1 and t_2, is at 5V and 0V, respectively.

$$t_1 = 0.693(R_a + R_b)C \tag{9}$$

And

$$t_2 = 0.693(R_b)C \tag{10}$$

The frequency $f = \frac{1}{T}$, where $T = t_1 + t_2$, and duty cycle $D = \frac{t_2}{T}$ of square wave output of the 555 time is given by:

$$f = 1.44/[(R_a + 2R_b)C] \tag{11}$$

and

$$D = R_b/(R_a + 2R_b) \tag{12}$$

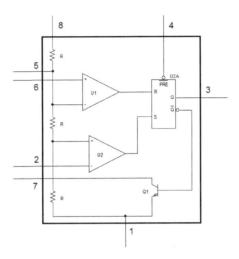

Fig. 2 Schematic of the 555 timer circuitry.

Note that the duty cycle of the square wave will always be less than 50%.

If R_b is held constant and the resistance of R_a is changed, t_1 will be fixed and t_2 will be a function of R_a. If a speaker or buzzer replaces R_L, which is connected between the output of the 555 timer (pin 3) and V_{CC}, then current will flow through the speaker or buzzer only and, hence, sound will only be produced from the metronome when the output of the 555 timer is 0V. The time between tones is determined by only t_2. Therefore, the beats per minute – the frequency of the square wave output from the 555 timer – will be varied by changing the value of R_a.

The resistance of most speakers and piezoelectric buzzers is very small. The resistance of the speaker in the Lab-in-a-Box parts kit is only 8Ω. If only the speaker replaced R_L in Fig. 1, the maximum current that would flow through the speaker, $I = 5V/8\Omega = 0.625$ A, is larger than the 555 timer can supply and the power dissipated by the speaker, $P = (5V)^2/8\Omega = 3.125$ W, would exceed the power rating of the speaker, which is 0.5 W. R_L should be replaced by the series combination of a speaker and a current limiting resistor (Fig. 3). In the circuit to be constructed, R_a is composed of trim pot and fixed resistor to prevent the case where $R_a = 0$ Ω.

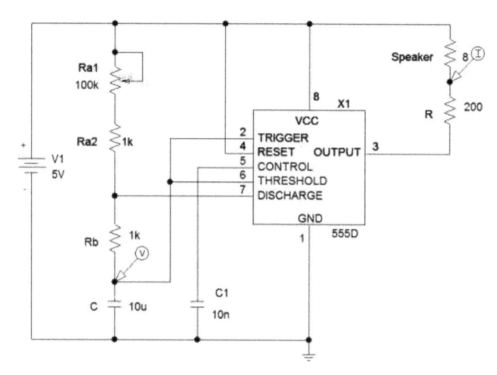

Fig. 3 Schematic of metronome circuit

Materials

The equipment and components required to perform this experiment are:
- ANDY board
- DMM
- oscilloscope
- 1 ea 200 Ω resistor
- 1 ea 1 kΩ resistor
- 1 ea 100 kΩ trim pot
- 1 ea 10 μF electrolytic capacitor
- 1 ea 10 nF capacitor
- 1 ea LM555 timer chip
- 1 ea speaker

Procedure

Analysis:

1. Calculate the maximum and minimum values for R_a that will produce a square wave output with a frequency between 0.667 and 3.33 Hz. Determine the duty cycle of the square wave when f = 0.667 Hz and f = 3.33 Hz.

2. Using MATLAB, plot the output frequency as a function of R_a where the value of R_a is allowed to range between the maximum and minimum resistances calculated in step 1.

3. Using MATLAB, plot the charge and discharge times, t_1 and t_2, as a function of R_a where the value of R_a is allowed to range from the maximum and minimum resistances calculated in step 1.

4. Determine the maximum current and power dissipated by the speaker.

Modeling

5. Plot the voltage across the capacitor C and the current through the speaker for 3-5 periods of the square wave outputted by the 555 timer when $R_{a1} + R_{a2}$ is equal to (a) the minimum resistance and (b) the maximum resistance found in step 1. Record the time required to charge and discharge capacitor C. [Note that the measurements should be made after the operation of the circuit has stabilized and the voltage across the capacitor varies between 1.67 V – 3.33 V. Note that one terminal on the capacitor is always at a higher voltage than the other.

Measurements:

5. Measure the value of resistors R_{a2} and R_b and the value of capacitor C with your DMM.

6. Construct the circuit shown in Figure 3. Be sure to connect the electrolytic capacitor so that the polarity of the capacitor is correct (the positive terminal should be connected to R_b; see Section 3.9.).

7. Set the trim pot R_{a1} to its maximum resistance. Be sure that the unused terminal of the pot is tied to pin 2 as suggested in Section 3.11.

8. Using your oscilloscope, measure the frequency of operation and duty cycle of the output from the 555 timer. Adjust resistance of the trim pot to obtain a frequency of 0.667 Hz. Measure the maximum and minimum voltages across the capacitor C and the values of t_1 and t_2 using the other channel of the oscilloscope. Collect a screen shot of the oscilloscope traces. [Set the trigger on the oscilloscope to stabilize the image if needed.]

9. Remove the trim pot from the circuit. Measure its resistance using the DMM and record the value.

10. Calculate the percent deviation from the expected values of R_{a1}, the duty cycle D, and charging and discharging times of the capacitor t_1 and t_2.

$$\% \; deviation = \frac{Expected-Measured}{Expected} \; x \; 100\%$$

11. Insert the trim pot back into the circuit. Adjust the resistance of the trim pot such that the frequency of the 555 time output is 3.33 Hz. Measure the duty cycle of the output from the 555 timer. Measure the maximum and minimum voltages across the capacitor C and the values of t_1 and t_2 using the other

channel of the oscilloscope. Collect a screen shot of the oscilloscope traces. [Set the trigger on the oscilloscope to stabilize the image if needed.]

12. Calculate the percent deviation from the expected values of R_{a1}, the duty cycle D, and charging and discharging times of the capacitor t_1 and t_2.

13. Reinsert the trim pot into the circuit. Measure voltage across the speaker and calculate the current, assuming that the resistance of the speaker is 8Ω. Calculate the power dissipated by the speaker while the output of the 555 timer is 0V.

14. Calculate the percent deviation from the expected values of the current flowing through the speaker and the dissipated power.

Conclusions

15. Do the measured values of D, t_1 and t_2 differ from the expected values as would be expected from the measured values of R_{a1}, R_{a2}, R_b, and C when (a) f = 0.667 Hz and (b) f = 3.33 Hz. Why or why not?

16. Explain why the calculated values for the current through the speaker and dissipated power are differ from the expected values.

17. Explain why an electrolytic capacitor can be used for capacitor C.

Last Revision   5/29/2011

Experiment 16: A Differentiator Circuit

Developers   RW Hendricks and DA Class

Objectives   The objective of this experiment is to investigate the input-to-output relationship of an op amp differentiator circuit. You will design a simple amplifier that gives an output that is a scaled derivative of the input.

Estimated Time for Completion

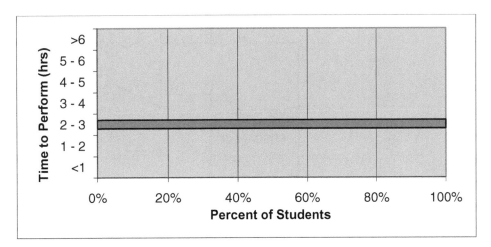

Preparation   Refer to the section on first order op amp circuits in your textbook and to Section 3.12 (Operational Amplifiers) in this text.

Background   A differentiator circuit is an op amp circuit that can be used for analog mathematical calculations to find the derivative of an input signal. The circuit comprises an op amp with an input capacitor and a feedback resistor as shown in Figure 1. A nodal analysis shows that

$$v_o = -R_1 C_1 \frac{dv_i}{dt} \qquad (1)$$

The output has a negative polarity with respect to the input, but a unity gain inverter may be used to change the polarity. Note that this sign change may also be represented by a 180° phase change.

The scaling factor of the derivative ($R_1 C_1$) must be chosen carefully so that the output of the op amp does not saturate. Consider the case where the input is a sine wave of the form

$$v_i = A\sin(\omega t) \qquad (2)$$

where A is the amplitude of the signal and ω is its angular frequency. Then

163

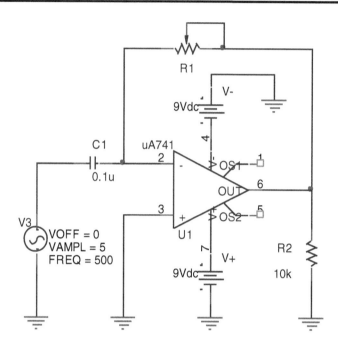

Figure 1: An ideal differentiating op amp circuit.

$$v_o = -R_1 C_1 A\omega \cos(\omega t) \tag{3}$$

The amplitude of the output will be scaled by the factor $\omega R_1 C_1$ (a dimensionless number) from the input. If $\omega R_1 C_1 = 1$, the output will have the same amplitude as the input and will be 90° out of phase with it. Thus, it is seen that, if the amplitude of the output signal is to be a desired fraction of the amplitude of the input signal, the differentiator time constant is frequency dependent. This result will be verified in this experiment. Of course, other relationships will exist for different input signals.

The ideal differentiator shown in Figure 1 (and also shown in many introductory texts) is not without problems and can rarely be implemented in practice. From Eq (3) we see that once a value for $R_1 C_1$ is fixed, the gain for all frequencies above $\omega = 1/R_1 C_1$ increases linearly with ω. Thus, if the input contains electronic noise with high frequency components, those components will be amplified significantly over the signal of interest and the system likely will become unstable. It is thus necessary to modify the circuit to reduce or eliminate such effects. This is done in two ways. First, a series resistor is inserted in the input. The effect of this resistor is to act as an attenuator for the high frequency components. Second, a capacitor is placed in the feedback network. This capacitor provides more feed-back for the high frequency components than for

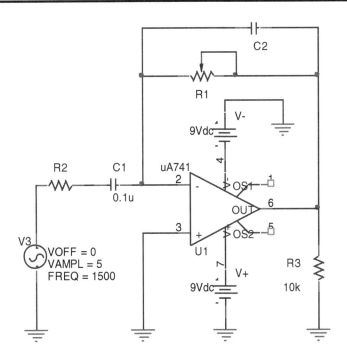

Figure 2: A practical differentiator circuit.

the low frequency components and also acts to stabilize the circuit. In Experiment 34 it will be shown that these modifications, shown in Figure 2, convert the circuit into a bandpass filter. Thus, the circuit operates as a differentiator in the frequency range

$$\frac{1}{R_1 C_1} \leq \omega \leq \frac{1}{R_2 C_1} < \frac{1}{R_1 C_2} \tag{4}$$

The task is to define the values of the four passive components (R_1, R_2, C_1, C_2) that will provide the desired gain at the desired frequency, will suppress the undesired frequencies, and will provide stability to the system.

References

*Boyce, JC, (1988). <u>Operational Amplifiers and Linear Integrated Circuits</u> (2E). Boston: PWS-Kent. p289.

*Hanselman, D., and B. Littlefield, (2005). <u>Mastering MATLAB 7</u>. Upper Saddle River, NJ: Pearson Prentice Hall.

Stinson, C., and M. Dodge, (2007). <u>Microsoft Office Excel 2007 Inside Out</u>, Redmond, WA: Microsoft Press.

Materials

The equipment and components required to perform this experiment are:
- 1 ea ANDY board
- 1 ea DMM

- 1 ea dual trace oscilloscope
- PSpice software
- 1 ea LF356 op amp
- 1 ea 10 kΩ resistor
- 1 ea 10 nF capacitor
- 1 ea 22 nF capacitor
- 1 ea 0.1 μF capacitor
- 1 ea trim pot (value to be determined)
- 1 ea resistor (value to be determined)

Procedure

Analysis:

1. Derive the input-to-output relationship [Eq (1)] of the amplifier circuit shown in Figure 1. Which trim pot is required such that the circuit may be adjusted to have a unity scaling factor for a sine wave at 1500 Hz? Note: for most effective operation, the desired resistance should be near the middle of the range of the trim pot.

2. Calculate the component values required such that the differentiator circuit of Figure 2 will have unity gain at 1500 Hz ($\omega R_1 C_1 = 1$) and will have cut-off or corner frequencies of 3000 Hz ($\omega R_2 C_1 = 1$) and 5000 Hz ($\omega R_1 C_2 = 1$) for the series resistor R_1 and the feedback capacitor C_2, respectively. Use a 0.1 μF capacitor for C_1. Round your remaining component values to the nearest components available in your kit (see Appendix A). Which trim pot is required to achieve the desired amplifier performance? Note: the cutoff frequencies do not correspond to -3 dB frequencies.

Modeling:

3. Using the component values determined in step 1, model the circuit of Figure 1 in PSpice for a 5.0 V amplitude sine wave input signal with frequencies (f) varying from 500 to 3000 Hz in steps of 500 Hz. For each frequency, adjust the value of R_1 to obtain an output signal of 5.0 V. Record screenshots of your schematic and of your PSpice simulation results for 500 Hz. Also record in a table the value of R_1 at each frequency that yields unity gain for the PSpice simulation.

4. Using your choice of scientific graphing program (e.g., Excel or MATLAB), plot a graph (in log-log space) of the value of R_1 determined in step 3 versus f. Do not plot data points, but only plot a line joining the data points. Save your graph for use in step 16. Examine the MALAB file in Appendix D.2 for an example of an easy way to plot such data in MATLAB. Background information may be found in both Stinson and Dodge (2004) for Excel and in Hanselman and Littlefield (2005) for MATLAB.

5. Do your results agree with the condition $\omega R_1 C_1 = 1$? Hint: solve this expression for ω and show that the data should be a straight line of slope -1 when plotted in log-log space. Plot this line on your graph drawn in step 4.

6. Repeat steps 3 through 5 for the circuit in Figure 2 using the component values computed in step 2. Save your graph for use in step 25.

7. What effect do R_2 and C_2 have on the performance of the circuit as compared to the circuit of Figure 1 in the frequency range $500 \le f \le 3500$ Hz?

Measurements: Ideal Differentiator

8. Construct the differentiator amplifier circuit shown in Figure 1. Notes: (a) Be careful to use the center terminal and one end terminal of the trim pot. Following the "good practice" note in Section 3.11, be sure to connect the unused terminal of the trim pot to pin 2 (the wiper) of the trim pot. (b) Use the ANDY board function generator with the shape set to SIN and the OFFSET set to zero for the input signal. Make sure your sine wave amplitude is not zero! (c) Although the circuit diagram calls for a μ741 op amp, use the LF 356 called for in the bill of materials.[†]

9. Connect the output of the function generator to the ×10 attenuator of channel 1 (green) to the oscilloscope and the output of the op amp to the ×10 attenuator of channel 2 (red).

10. Adjust the frequency of the function generator (green trace) to produce a 500 Hz sine wave. Hint: You may observe the signal frequency in the oscilloscope mode or you may change the view by pressing the "Frequency Analysis" tab at the top of the oscilloscope screen. In the spectrum view, you should see a single peak at the frequency of the source. There is a box below the spectrum window that is labeled "main frequency" which will provide a numerical value for the frequency. We generally find that it is easiest to set a desired frequency in the Spectrum mode.

11. Adjust the amplitude of the function generator to 5.0 V. Remember that you are using the ×10 attenuator, so you should read 0.5 V on the oscilloscope screen and interpret that as 5.0 V.

12. Observe the output of the op amp on the oscilloscope (red trace). It should be a sine wave of the same frequency as the function generator but with a phase shift of 90°. Verify the frequency in either the "Oscilloscope" or the "Spectrum" mode of the oscilloscope. Record screenshots to document your results. Measure the phase shift of the two signals using the methodology described in the Background section of Experiment 22.

[†] The PSpice model for the LF356 op amp, available at the National Semiconductor website, has a large number of nodes and the circuits of Figures 1 and 2 will fail in the demo version of PSpice. The model for the μ741 is simpler and is adequate for the purposes of this experiment.

13. Adjust the trim pot R_1 to produce an output signal with a 5.0 V amplitude.

14. Remove the trim pot from the circuit and use your DMM to measure the resistance between the same two terminals as were wired in the experiment. Be sure to turn off the ANDY board before removing the pot. Be careful to not change the setting of the trim pot.

15. Repeat steps 10 though 14 for frequencies of 1000 Hz to 3000 Hz in steps of 500 Hz. Record a screenshot for the signal at 1500 Hz and prepare a table of the R_1 resistance measurements vs. frequency. Suggestion: Examine the resistor values for unity gain at each frequency computed in step 3 before attempting to adjust the trim pot. This will give you a feel for how to adjust the pot. It is easy to miss the target resistance if you adjust the pot too quickly.

16. Plot the potentiometer resistance vs. frequency data obtained in step 15 on the graph created in step 4. Plot only the data points.

17. Do your experimental observations agree with your PSpice models and with the derivation presented in the Background? Comment and/or explain.

Measurements: Practical Differentiator

18. Turn off the ANDY board and add the components R_2 and C_2 to create the circuit shown in Figure 2.

19. Adjust the frequency of the function generator (green trace) to produce a 500 Hz sine wave.

20. Adjust the amplitude of the function generator to 5.0 V.

21. Observe the output of the op amp on the oscilloscope (red trace). It should be a sine wave of the same frequency as the function generator but with a phase shift of $90°$. Verify the frequency in either the "Oscilloscope" or the "Spectrum" mode of the oscilloscope. Record screenshots to document your results. Confirm that the phase shift is $90°$.

22. Adjust the trim pot R_1 to produce an output signal with a 5.0 V amplitude.

23. Remove the trim pot from the circuit and use your DMM to measure the resistance between the same two terminals as were wired in the experiment. Be careful to not change the setting of the trim pot. Be sure to turn off the ANDY board before removing the pot.

24. Repeat steps 19 though 23 for frequencies of 1000 Hz to 3000 Hz in steps of 500 Hz. Record a screenshot for the signal at 1500 Hz and prepare a table of the R_1 resistance measurements vs. frequency.

25. Plot the potentiometer resistance vs. frequency data obtained in step 24 on the graph created in step 6. Plot only the data points.

26. Do your experimental observations agree with your PSpice models and with the derivation presented in the Background? Comment on the effect of these components on the performance of the circuit.

Last Revision   8/07/2011

Experiment 17: A Circuit with Two Ideal Differentiators

Developers   M Hutton and K Meehan

Objectives   The objective of this experiment is to investigate the input-to-output relationship of an op amp differentiator circuit. You will design a simple amplifier that produces an output that is proportional to the derivative of the input.

Estimated Time for Completion

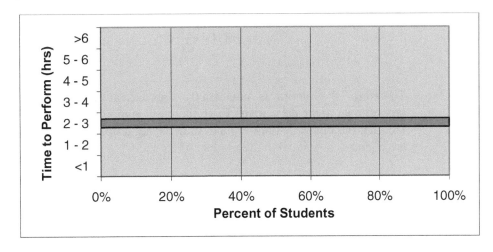

Preparation   Refer to the section on first order op amp circuits in your textbook and to Section 3.11 (Operational Amplifiers) in this text.

Background   In our analysis of circuits, we have been treating op amps as ideal elements. This simplifies our calculations considerably, but we may suspect that the subtleties of the op amp's workings will come back to haunt us when we implement our design in the physical world. This is not an unwarranted concern, but there is another interesting possibility to consider: can we unintentionally design a circuit that is impractical precisely because it performs in a nearly ideal manner?

In this lab, we will experiment with an ideal differentiator circuit. Differentiators along with integrators are used in analog computers. Analog computers were used extensively during the 1940's and 1950's in industrial and military applications to perform mathematical calculations using inputs from electrical and/or electromechanical components in real-time, though very slowly compared to the speeds that calculations can be performed using digital computers today. Mathematically, the first derivative of a function is its slope. If the input to the differentiator circuit was a voltage that is proportional to the location of an object, then the output of a differentiator circuit will be proportional to the velocity of the object since $dx/dt = v(t)$. If the output of the differntiator is used as an input into a second differentiator, then the output of the second differentiator circuit will be the acceleration of the object as $d^2x(t)/dt^2 = dv(t)/dt = a(t)$. Thus, differentiators were used extensively to obtain solutions to complex mathematical functions using data collected in real time until the speed at which the data could be post-processed digitally exceeded

171

that obtained using analog circuitry, which is limited to 100 kHz – 10 MHz. The circuit is fundamentally composed of a resistor, a capacitor, and an op amp. The construction of the circuit is illustrated in Figure 1.

It can be shown that the input / output relationship between Vin and Vout is described by the equation:

$$V_{out} = -R_1 C_1 \frac{dV_{in}}{dt} \tag{1}$$

Therefore, the output is not strictly the derivative of the input, but it is proportional to the derivative. First, there is a sign inversion that results from the fact that the circuit is built around an inverting amplifier. Secondly, the system has a gain that is equal to the product of R_1 and C_1.

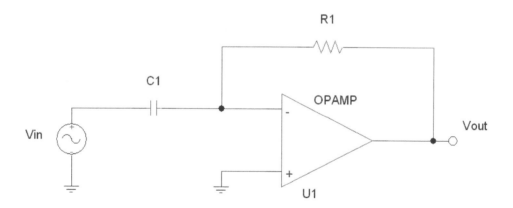

Figure 2: An ideal differentiator circuit

If we assume that the input is sinusoidal, with $V_{in} = \sin \omega t$, the output becomes

$$V_{out} = -\omega R_1 C_1 \cos \omega t \tag{2}$$

which means that the gain is a function of the frequency of the input. The negative sign can be included into the cosine function as a phase shift of either + 180 or -180 degrees, which means that the output voltage can be expressed as

$$V_{out} = \omega R_1 C_1 \cos(\omega t - 180^o) \tag{3}$$

Furthermore, a cosine function can be rewritten as a sine with a phase angle of +90 degrees. Therefore, the equation for the output voltage can rewritten again as

$$V_{out} = \omega R_1 C_1 \sin (\omega t - 90^o) \qquad (4)$$

You will explore this frequency-dependent gain by building a differentiator that can switch between two different feedback resistors. The values of R_1 and R_2 will correspond to two frequencies at which the differentiator will operate with a gain of $\omega R_n C_1 = 1$. A schematic is provided in Figure 2. To clarify, switches U2 and U3 in the schematic represent *one* slide switch in your actual circuit.

- The output of the op amp should be connected to the middle pin of the slide switch.
- Resistor R_1 should be connected to one of the two outside pins.
- Resistor R_2 should be connected to the remaining pin.

A slide switch will generally create a low-resistance connection between its middle pin and the outside pin that the switch is "pointing" to. However, you should check your switch with a multimeter to make sure it operates as you expect it to.

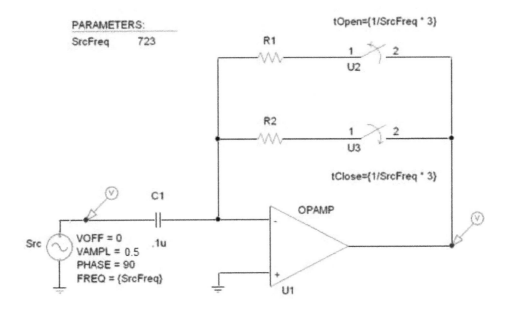

Figure 3 – A differentiator circuit with selectable feedback resistance

In the schematic, you will notice that the tClose and tOpen times of U2 and U3 are described by functions of the SrcFreq parameter. You will not need to be concerned with flipping the actual switch on your circuit at precise times during your experimentation; the formulas are for simulation purposes only. During simulation, R_1 will be connected to the op amp for a length of time equal to 3 periods of the input wave. After that time has elapsed, R_1 will be disconnected and R_2 will be connected. R_2 will remain connected for the rest of the simulation.

Curly braces tell PSpice to compute the value of the expression between the braces and then use that value for simulation. As an example, you could test different values for a fixed resistor by setting its VALUE equal to a curly brace expression and then changing the parameters that affect that expression. This is shown in Figure 3. The resulting current through R1 will be 1mA.

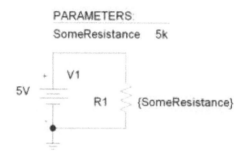

Figure 3 – Simple example of PSpice Parameter

In Figure 2, you will also notice that there is a 90° phase shift on the input signal. The phase shift and the tClose and tOpen times are there to make sure that the PSpice output is as easy to read as possible. Shifting the input 90° causes its derivative (and the output) to have a value of zero on startup. Then, by switching to R_2 at an integer multiple of the period, the derivative will again be zero as the new setting takes effect. This may seem like a needless complication, but it serves as an introduction to a useful feature of PSpice.

Materials

The equipment and components required to perform this experiment are:

- 1 ea ANDY board
- 1 ea DMM
- 1 ea dual trace oscilloscope
- PSpice software
- 1 ea LF356 op amp
- 1 ea 0.1µF capacitor
- 1 ea slide switch
- 2 resistors (values to be determined)

Procedure   **Analysis:**

1. Use KCL to derive the input-to-output relationship of the circuit shown in Figure 1. Your final result should look like Equation (1).

2. Calculate the value of R_1 needed for $\omega R_1 C_1 = 1$ when the frequency of the input is 7.23 kHz. Use 0.1 µF for C_1. Using the results of this calculation, determine the gain when the frequency of the input signal is decreased to 723 Hz.

3. Calculate the value of R_2 needed for $\omega R_2 C_1 = 1$ when the frequency of the input is 723 Hz. Using the results of this calculation, determine the gain when the frequency of the input signal is increased to 7.23 kHz.

4. Your analysis in step 1 should show that there is a linear relationship between frequency and gain in an ideal differentiator with sinusoidal input. Do you expect this frequency-dependent relationship hold for other types of periodic input? Consider a triangle wave as the input voltage, for example. Will the output of the differentiator change if the amplitude of the triangle wave is first set to vary from 0V to 5V and then is changed to vary from -2.5V to 2.5V?

Modeling:

5. Using the component values determined in steps 2 and 3, model the circuit with the ideal operational amplifier OPAMP as shown in Figure 2 using PSpice. Change the value of VPOS attribute in the OPAMP component to 9V by double clicking on the device to open the PartName popup window. Change the value of VNEG to -9V. Take a screenshot of your circuit.

6. Perform a transient analysis of your circuit with SrcFreq = 723, Final Time = 9ms, and Step Ceiling = 50us. Graph the input and output voltages. Save the graph.

7. Perform a transient analysis of your circuit with SrcFreq = 7230, Final Time = 0.9ms, and Step Ceiling = 5us. Save the graph.

8. Predict what will happen when you actually build this circuit. Be specific about what you expect from each of the four combinations of input frequency and feedback resistance. You do not have to write your predictions in the pre-lab report.

Measurements:

9. Construct the circuit shown in Figure 2 using an LF 356 operational amplifier.

10. Set your function generator for sine wave output at 7.23 kHz. Set your slide switch so that R_1 is connected to the circuit. Record the input and output waveforms on your oscilloscope at 1 V/div and 20 µs/div. Make sure that you are triggering based on the input voltage.

11. Set your oscilloscope to 3 V/div (or another close value) on both channels and then change the position of the switch so that R_2 is connected. Record the waveforms. Determine the amplitude of the output voltage and its phase angle with respect to the input signal.

12. Calculate the percent deviation from the expected amplitude and phase angle.

$$\% \, deviation = \frac{Expected - Measured}{Expected} \, x \, 100\%$$

13. Set your slide switch so that R_2 is connected to the circuit. Record the input and output waveforms on your oscilloscope at 1 V/div and 20 µs/div. Make sure that you are triggering based on the input voltage. Determine the amplitude of the output voltage and its phase angle with respect to the input signal.

14. Calculate the percent deviation from the expected amplitude and phase angle.

15. Set the slide switch back to the R_1 position, set the oscilloscope to 1 V/div and 0.2 ms/div. Change the frequency of the function generator output to 723 Hz. Record the waveforms. Determine the amplitude of the output voltage and its phase angle with respect to the input signal.

16. Calculate the percent deviation from the expected amplitude and phase angle.

17. Move the slide switch to the R_2 position. Change the voltage/division scale on the oscilloscope appropriately and record the waveforms. Determine the amplitude of the output voltage and its phase angle with respect to the input signal.

18. Calculate the percent deviation from the expected amplitude and phase angle.

$$\% \, deviation = \frac{Expected - Measured}{Expected} \, x \, 100\%$$

19. Use your function generator to experiment with various waveforms (e.g., the triangular wave) as the input voltage to the differentiator with the switches set to select either R_1 or R_2.

Conclusion:

20. What was the primary complication you encountered when operating your differentiator? If the components of your system were perfect, would it resolve the issue?

Last Revision   5/29/2011

Experiment 18: An Integrator Circuit

Developers   RW Hendricks and DA Class

Objectives   The objective of this experiment is to investigate the input-to-output relationship of an op amp integrator circuit. You will design a simple amplifier that gives an output that is a scaled integral of the input. The stability of the circuit will be explored.

Estimated Time for Completion

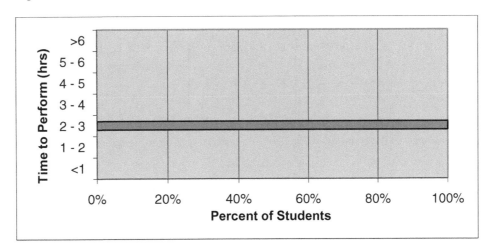

Preparation   Refer to the section on first order op amp circuits in your textbook and to Section 3.12 in this text.

Background   An integrator circuit is an op amp circuit that can be used for analog mathematical calculations to find the integral of an input signal. It is the analog of the differentiator circuit developed in Experiment 17. The circuit comprises an op amp with an input resistor and a feedback capacitor as shown in Figure 1. A nodal analysis shows that

$$v_o(t) = v_o(0) - \frac{1}{R_1 C_1} \int_0^t v_s(t) dt \qquad (1)$$

In general, the circuit is started from a quiescent state in which $v_o(0) = 0$. This can be accomplished by shorting the feedback capacitor and then removing the short at $t = 0$. In this case, we note that the output has a negative polarity with respect to the input. A unity gain inverter may be used to change the polarity.

As with the differentiator studied in Experiment 17, the choice of time constant $R_1 C_1$ is important. As an example, consider a source signal that is a

179

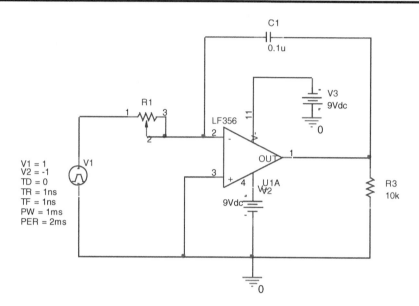

Figure 1: An ideal integrating op amp circuit.

bipolar square wave described by the following expression

$$v_s(t) = A\left(1 - 2u\left[t - T/2\right]\right) \quad 0 \leq t \leq T \tag{2}$$

where A is the amplitude of the wave and $u(t)$ is the Heaviside operator. Substitution of Eq (2) in Eq (1) yields

$$v_o(t) = \begin{cases} \dfrac{-At}{R_1 C_1} & 0 \leq t \leq T/2 \\[2ex] \dfrac{-A(T-t)}{R_1 C_1} & T/2 \leq t \leq T \end{cases} \tag{3}$$

This is the equation of a triangular wave. Thus, we have a seemingly simple way to create a triangular wave form on the ANDY board simply by integrating the output of the square wave function generator.

The choice of the $R_1 C_1$ time constant is dependent on the frequency of the signal. Examination of Eq (3) shows that if the amplitude of the output pulse is to be the same as the amplitude of the input, then

$$R_1 C_1 = \frac{T}{2} = \frac{1}{2f} \tag{4}$$

For a pulse train with a frequency of 500 Hz, then $R_1 C_1 = 10^{-3}$ if the output amplitude is to be the same as the input amplitude. Note that Eq (4) is valid only for the square wave pulse and must be rederived for other pulse shapes.

As with the differentiator circuit in Experiment 17, the ideal circuit put forth in introductory texts and shown in Figure 1 is not without its problems. First, if there is any DC component to the signal, the output will saturate the op amp. Consider a small offset of ΔV dc volts. The output due to this offset will be

$$v_o(t) = \frac{-1}{R_1 C_1} \int_0^t \Delta V dt = \frac{-\Delta V \cdot t}{R_1 C_1} \tag{5}$$

If the offset is only -100 μV dc, then for a 500 kHz pulse train with a 1 ms time constant as discussed above, the op amp will saturate at the positive rail in

$$t = \frac{v_o \cdot R_1 C_1}{\Delta V} = \frac{9 \cdot 10^{-3}}{100 \times 10^{-6}} = 90 \text{ s} \tag{6}$$

This is hardly acceptable; offsets of this magnitude are within the error of operation of the ANDY board and signals cannot be controlled to these levels. In addition to offset biases in the input signal, leakage currents in the op amp also get integrated and cause such "run-away" behavior of the op amp. The solutions to these problems are threefold.

1. A resistor is placed on the inverting input to reduce the leakage current. This resistor is of about the same value as the input resistor, R_1.

2. A feedback resistor is placed in parallel with the feedback capacitor. This causes some leakage of the offset bias and improves the stability of the circuit. The value of this resistor is typically $R_2 = 10 R_1$.

3. A switch (usually an FET) is also placed in parallel with the feedback capacitor. This switch is closed before the start of integration to drain the capacitor and then is opened at the start of integration. It is used to assure that the initial output voltage of the circuit is zero, as is assumed in the discussion following Eq (1).

A circuit that implements these ideas is shown in Figure 2. Here, resistor R_2 and switch S_1 are added to the feedback network, while resistor R_4 is added to suppress device leakage currents.

There is yet another complication, even for the circuit of Figure 2. The feedback current in R_2 causes a shift in the output predicted by Eq (3). In about $5 \cdot R_2 C_1$ seconds the output drifts so as to be symmetrical about 0 V. This offset is best compensated by adding a unity gain adder circuit after the integrator output. One adder input signal is the integrator output. The other is a variable offset voltage formed by a 10 kΩ trim pot connected across the positive and negative power supplies. The design of this part of the circuit is left as an exercise for the student.

In this experiment, you will build and test both of these circuits for generation of triangular pulse trains at different frequencies.

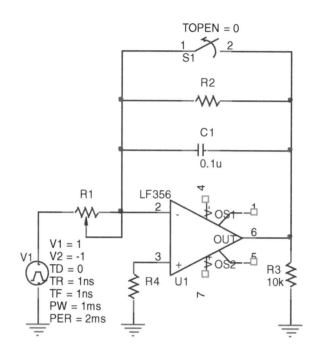

Figure 2: A practical op amp integrator circuit.

References   *Boyce, JC, (1988). <u>Operational Amplifiers and Linear Integrated Circuits</u> (2E). Boston: PWS-Kent. p284.

*Hanselman, D., and B. Littlefield, (2005). <u>Mastering MATLAB 7</u>. Upper Saddle River, NJ: Pearson Prentice Hall.

Stinson, C., and M. Dodge, (2007). <u>Microsoft Office Excel 2007 Inside Out</u>, Redmond, WA: Micrcrosoft Press.

Materials   The equipment and components required to perform this experiment are:
- 1 ea ANDY board
- 1 ea dual trace oscilloscope
- 1 ea DMM
- PSpice software
- 2 ea LF356 op amp
- 1 ea 10 kΩ resistor
- 1 ea 0.1 uF capacitor
- 1 ea 10 kΩ trim pot
- 1 ea 100 kΩ trim pot
- 2 ea resistors (values to be determined)
- 1 ea SPDT switch

Procedure

Analysis:

1. Derive the input-to-output relationship of the amplifier circuit shown in Figure 1 as given in Eq (1). Which trim pot is required to have a unity gain over the desired operating frequency of 500 Hz to 3000 Hz? Note that the output of the circuit is negative. If a positive sawtooth is desired, you may use a unity gain op amp inverter circuit following the output of the integrator.

2. Select the values of the components required such that the integrator circuit of Figure 2 will have a gain of unity at 1500 Hz. Determine the values of R_1, R_2, and R_4 based on the information provided in the Background. R_1 should be a trim pot, or a combination of a trim pot and a fixed resistor with sufficient range to allow the frequency of the output pulse train be varied from 500 Hz to 3000 Hz and still maintain unity gain at the operating frequency.[†] Use a 0.1 µF capacitor for C_1. Round your remaining component values to the nearest components available in your kit (see Appendix A).

Modeling:

3. Using the component values determined in step 1, model the circuit of Figure 1 in PSpice. Use a bipolar ±1.0 V amplitude pulse train as the input signal with frequencies (f) varying from 500 to 3000 Hz in steps of 500 Hz. For each frequency, adjust the value of R_1 to obtain an output signal of amplitude -1.0 V. Tabulate the values of R_1 for each frequency. Hint: instructions for sweeping a trim pot in PSpice may be found on the book website at **http://www.lab-in-a-box.net.**

4. Using your choice of a scientific graphing program (e.g., Excel or MATLAB), plot a graph (in log-log space) of the value of R_1 versus f. Do not plot data points, but only plot a line joining the data points. Save your graph for use in step 17.

5. Do your results agree with the condition $R_1 C_1 = T/2$? Hint: rearrange this expression and plot it on the graph created in step 4.

6. Repeat steps 3 through 5 for the circuit in Figure 2 using the component values computed in step 2. Save your graph for use in step 27.

7. What effect, if any, do R_2 and R_4 have on the performance of the circuit as compared to the circuit of Figure 1 in the frequency range $500 \leq f \leq 3500$ Hz? Hint: to model the circuit of Figure 1 using the circuit of Figure 2, let

---

[†] You may have a series resistor, R_s, and a potentiometer, R_{pot}. Thus, $R_1 = R_s + R_{pot}$. You are required to have unity gain from 500 Hz to 3000 Hz. Find the values of R_s and R_{pot} that satisfy the constraints

$$R_{(low)} = \frac{1}{2 f_{low} C_1} \text{ and } R_{(high)} = \frac{1}{2 f_{high} C_1}$$

R_2=100G and R_4=0.001. Explain the drift of the sawtooth output versus time in the circuit of Figure 2.

Measurements (Ideal Integrator):

8. Construct the integrator amplifier circuit shown in Figure 1. Notes: (a) Use the - 9 V and + 9 V supplies of the ANDY board to power the op amp. See Figure 28 in Section 3.12 for the pinouts of the LF356 op amp. (b) Use the ANDY board function generator with the shape set to SQ and the OFFSET set to zero for the input signal. (c) Be careful to use the center terminal and one end terminal of the trim pot. Following the "good practice" notes in Section 3.11, tie the unused terminal of the trim pot to the wiper of the pot. (d) Use two terminals of the SPDT switch to short the inverting input of the op amp to the output and discharge the feedback capacitor before measuring the output waveform. Remove the wire to start making measurements. [See Figure (2).]

9. Connect the output of the function generator to the ×10 attenuator of Channel 1 (green) to the oscilloscope and the output of the op amp to the ×10 attenuator of Channel 2 (red).

10. Adjust the frequency of the function generator (green trace) to produce a 500 Hz square wave. You may observe the signal frequency in the oscilloscope mode or you may change the view by pressing the "Frequency Analysis" tab at the top of the oscilloscope screen. In the latter view, you should see a single peak at the frequency of the source. You can determine the frequency by reading the "main frequency" just below the frequency distribution.

11. Adjust the amplitude of the function generator to ± 1.0 V. Be very careful to adjust the voltages to be as symmetric as possible. Remember that you are using the ×10 attenuator, so you should read 0.1 V amplitude on the oscilloscope screen and interpret it as 1.0 V.

12. Observe the output of the op amp on the oscilloscope (red trace). It should be a triangular wave of the same frequency as the function generator. Verify the frequency in either the "Oscilloscope" or the "Spectrum" mode of the oscilloscope. Record a screenshot of your output.

13. Adjust the trim pot R_1 to produce an output signal of amplitude 1.0V.

14. Record your observations of the ease/difficulty with which you are able to construct and operate this circuit. Do you observe the result predicted by Eq (3)?

15. Remove the trim pot from the circuit and use your DMM to measure the resistance between the same two terminals as were wired in the experiment. Be sure to turn off the ANDY board before removing the pot. Be careful not to change the setting of the trim pot. Record the frequency and the value of the trim pot in a table.

16. Repeat steps 10 though 15 for frequencies of 1000 Hz to 3000 Hz in steps of 500 Hz.

17. Plot the data obtained in steps 15 on the graph created in step 4. Plot only the data points.

18. Do your experimental observations agree with your PSpice models and with the derivation presented in the Background? Comment and/or explain.

Measurements (Practical Integrator):

19. Turn off the ANDY board and add the components R_2 and R_4 to create the circuit shown in Figure 2. Use a SPDT switch for the switch. Slide the switch to short the capacitor before starting each measurement.

20. Adjust the frequency of the function generator (green trace) to produce a 500 Hz square wave.

21. Adjust the amplitude of the function generator to ± 1.0 V.

22. Observe the output of the op amp on the oscilloscope (red trace). It should be a triangular wave of the same frequency as the function generator. Verify the frequency in either the "Oscilloscope" or the "Spectrum" mode of the oscilloscope. Record a screenshot of your output.

23. Adjust the trim pot R_1 to produce an output signal of amplitude 1.0V.

24. Record your observations of the ease/difficulty with which you are able to construct and operate this circuit in comparison with the circuit of Figure (1).

25. Remove the trim pot from the circuit and use your DMM to measure the resistance between the same two terminals as were wired in the experiment. Be sure to turn off the ANDY board before removing the pot. Be careful to not change the setting of the trim pot. Record the frequency and the value of the trim pot in a table.

26. Repeat steps 20 though 25 for frequencies of 1000 Hz to 3000 Hz in steps of 500 Hz.

27. Plot the data obtained in steps 24 and 25 on the graph created in step 6. Plot only the data points.

28. Do your experimental observations agree with your PSpice models and with the derivation presented in the Background? Comment and/or explain.

29. Comment on the effect of the addition of R_2 and R_4 on the performance of the circuit. Do you observe the result predicted by Eq (3)?

Measurements (Improved Design):

30. Modify the circuit shown in Figure 2 by adding a summing amplifier in which a variable offset voltage is added to the output of the integrator. The offset should be variable between -9 V and +9 V. This offset can be used to

compensate for any integrated DC bias that is introduced from the input signal. Remove the load resistor R_3 from output of the op amp in the circuit shown in Figure (2) and put it on the output of the summing amplifier. The gain of each input to the summing amplifier should be 1.0. Hint: the variable input can be made with a 10 kΩ trim pot. Show a circuit diagram for your proposed solution.

31. Construct the circuit proposed in step 30. Adjust the offset so that the output of the summer is as predicted by Eq (3). Using your DMM, measure the offset voltage. Explain your result.

Last Revision   1/03/2009

Experiment 19: Design A Voltmeter

Developers   DR Moore, KM Lai, JB Webb, and RW Hendricks

Objectives   The objective of this experiment is to design and construct a simple graphical DC voltmeter (a "voltage tester") that uses an LED bar graph as an output indicator. The circuit will also display the polarity of the voltage.

**Estimated Time
for Completion**

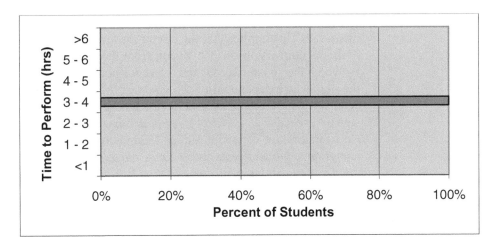

Preparation   Read the sections of your textbook which cover the basic properties of op amps. Also read Section 3.11 on trim pots, Section 3.12 on op amps, and Section 3.13 on LEDs in this text.

Background   Simple and inexpensive voltage testers are available on the market that display a visible light output in the form of a bar graph that is proportional to the applied voltage. In this experiment, you will design a circuit that will control a ten-segment LED bar graph in which the number of illuminated lights will be proportional to the applied DC voltage. The polarity of the voltage will also be displayed

Specifications The project should be designed in three sections.

1. Section 1 should be a voltage divider network that will generate a continuously variable output between - 9 V and + 9 V and should be driven by the ANDY board ± 9 V supplies. A trim pot is ideal for providing control. This part of the circuit will be used for testing and validation of the proposed circuit for the voltmeter.

2. Section 3 should be a polarity detector. It should consist of a single LED that will glow when the detected voltage is negative and be extinguished when the voltage is positive. It is not necessary to display negative voltages; it is presumed that the user can reverse the leads of the tester. The LED may be one of the LEDs in the LED bar graph or may be a separate LED.

3. Section 3 should be the voltmeter itself. This circuit should include up to nine LEDs that will turn on in 1 V increments as the voltage is increased from 0 to + 9 V. The LEDs should all be off if the applied voltage is negative. A voltage divider circuit can be used to provide the reference voltages that are for comparison with the applied voltage and thus to determine if an LED should be on or off. However, to provide uniform LED intensity, when the LED is lit, it should have a constant applied potential and should draw a fixed current, regardless of the voltage being measured. This implies that the circuit must contain some form of analog to digital conversion—a conversion from the analog value of the amount by which the signal exceeds the reference point to a digital "on" in which the output is independent of the value of the analog signal. This can be achieved with a comparator, a device whose output is one voltage if the signal exceeds a threshold and another voltage is it does not. Comparators are discussed under **Design Suggestions** in the following paragraphs. Note: *if you try to drive the LEDs directly from a voltage divider, you will burn out some of the LEDs very quickly.* Do not do this!

Design the voltmeter so that it reads increasing voltage levels from left to right. Low voltage levels should light up only the leftmost bars of the LED bar graph. As the voltage level increases, more bars should light up towards the right side. High voltage levels should light up the rightmost bars of the LED bar graph and all bars to the left. A picture representing one possible layout of the voltmeter bar graph is shown in Figure 1. Note that all LEDs that are lit should glow with the same intensity. You may use either the left-most or the right-most LED for the polarity indicator, or you may use a separate LED. For example, in Figure 1 the eight right-most LEDs are related to the voltage and the two left-most LEDs are unused. One of these could be used for the polarity.

Design Suggestions

The seemingly simplest approach to designing a circuit that meets the specifications for Section 3 involves driving each LED with the output from a voltage divider network. However, this design will fail and you will burn out LEDs because, as the applied voltage increases, the lowest voltage LED (say the LED for 1 V) will greatly exceed the drive voltage required by the LED. You may solve this problem by using an op amp as a buffer between the voltage divider and the op amp. To assure that the op amp output is independent of the input, it must be used as a comparator. This is done as follows.

Low voltage level

Medium voltage level

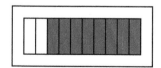
High voltage level

Figure 1: LED colors for home-made voltmeter.

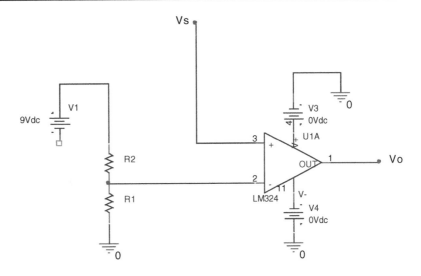

Figure 2: A simple voltage comparator

Consider the circuit shown in Figure 2. In this circuit, R_1 and R_2 form a voltage divider to provide a reference voltage to the inverting input to the op amp. The signal (voltage level) of interest, V_s, is applied to the non-inverting input. Note that the op amp is operated in open loop; there is no feedback. If V_s is greater than the reference voltage, the output of the op amp is driven to the + 9 V rail; if it is less than the reference, it is driven to the - 9 V rail. Thus, if the op amp output is used to drive the LED, when the output is positive, the LED will be lit. However, be sure to put the appropriate current limiting resistor in the circuit as discussed in Section 3.12. If the output is negative, the op amp will be driven in reverse bias, which has no effect on the device.[†]

The circuit does have limitations. "Real" comparators, such as the TI LP2901, will have output voltages that are different from the power rails; often these are 0 and 5 V. Second, the circuit above has some hysteresis; the op amp switches from output high to output low at different voltages when the signal is increasing as compared to when it is decreasing. However, this effect is rather small and is of no significance for this experiment.

Design Report Your design report, which may be written in a format of your own choosing, should be self-contained. It should indicate the objectives of the project, the design principles used, the feature set included, and test results to demonstrate its performance. A complete circuit diagram must be included; diagrams generated in PSpice are more than satisfactory. There should be some form of rudimentary "user manual"—how does a user use the device/circuit you have designed? A good design will show an analysis of the circuit, either analytical or in PSpice, that assures that all devices are working within proper specifications.

[†] Driving an op amp to the rails as is done in Figure 2 is generally not considered to be good practice, but will suffice for the present discussion.

Experiment 19

Validation   The design will be validated by demonstrating that when an arbitrary voltage between - 9 V and + 9 V is applied to the circuit, (a) the polarity LED will light correctly, and (b) that when a positive voltage is applied, as measured by a DMM, the correct number of LEDs will light. The student is to write the validation procedure for the design and then verify that the design performs per the validation checksheet and per the design specifications.

Materials   The (typical) equipment and components required to perform this experiment are:
- 1 ea ANDY board
- 1 ea digital multimeter
- 1 ea trim pot
- 3 ea LM324 Quad op-amp chips
- 1 ea LED bar graph
- 1 ea red LED (optional)
- Various resistors

Procedure   **Design**

1. Develop a voltage divider circuit that uses a trim-pot to regulate input voltage in the range of – 9 V to + 9 V. Build this circuit on the ANDY board

2. Design a voltage divider circuit of ten resistors that will step the 9 V supply from the ANDY board down to 0 in nine equal steps of 1 V each. The voltage from these resistors should be connected to the inverting terminals of the op-amps. The positive terminals of these op-amps should be connected to the applied voltage (the voltage developed in step 1).

3. Devise the current limiting step for the LED array. An op-amp will clip to rail voltage any time the applied voltage is larger than the voltage at that point in the ladder. Therefore, use the equations developed in the LED section (3.13) of this manual to limit the current through each LED.

Construction and Test

4. Build and test the circuit you designed in Steps 1 through 3. Gather sufficient data to demonstrate the correct operation of the circuit.

Report

5. Prepare a report for your project per the specifications above. Be sure to include a validation checksheet of your own design. Using obtained in Step 4, validate your design.

Last Revision   12/04/2008

Experiment 20: Design a Logic Probe

Developers   SL Karty and RW Hendricks

Objectives   The objective of this experiment is to design and construct a simple logic probe that, depending on the input voltage, lights one of three LEDs. These LEDs will indicate "logic low," "logic high," or intermediate and undetermined states.

Estimated Time for Completion

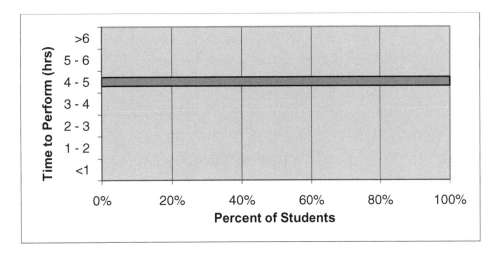

Preparation   Read the Background section of Experiment 19: Design A Voltmeter, paying careful attention to the operation of a voltage comparator. Also read Sections 3.11(Trim Pots), 3.12 (Op Amps), and 3.13 (Light Emitting Diodes) in this text.

Background   In digital electronics, it is necessary to know if a logic level is high, low, or undetermined. For our purposes, logic high is defined as a voltage greater than 2.2 V, while logic low is defined as a voltage less than 0.8 V. An undetermined or undefined level is either a voltage between 0.8 and 2.2 V or an unconnected (floating) node. In Experiment 19 you configured and used op amps as comparators in voltage reference circuits. This experiment builds on Experiment 19 by combining those comparator circuits in a more complex configuration.

In this project, you will design and build a simple logic probe. It will consist of a circuit that will turn on one of three LEDs depending on the state of the target node.

A question arises as to how to handle unconnected (floating) nodes. A simple procedure is to force a floating input to a fixed voltage that lies between the upper value of a logic low (0.8 V) and the lower level of a logic high (2.2 V). In fact we will use the term "centering voltage" as the average of these two voltages—in our case $(0.8 + 2.2) / 2 = 1.5$ V. This can be accomplished by

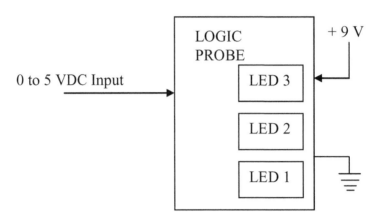

Figure 1: Block diagram of a logic probe

connecting the 1.5 V output of a very high resistance voltage divider and the input. The voltage divider resistors are then called "centering" resistors.

Specifications   Design a logic probe as shown in the block diagram of Figure 1 with a signal input lead, a ground lead, and a power input lead. The logic probe should have three output LEDs. Only one LED at a time should light when the input is a steady DC level between zero and +5 V. LED 1 should light when the input voltage is below 0.8 V. LED 2 should light (a) when the input is open (floating) or (b) when the input voltage is between 0.8 and 2.2 V. LED 3 should light when the input voltage is above 2.2 V. All voltage levels have a tolerance of approximately ±12%.

Your design should use only one LM324 chip. You may use all four of the LM324's op amps. Extra credit will be awarded for designs that use only two op amps.

You may use either the +5 V ANDY board supply or the +9 V supply. Figure 1 illustrates a probe that uses the +9 V supply.

Your report must include details of your design, a validation checksheet that demonstrates how you will verify the correct operation of your circuit, and experimental data that demonstrates the operation of your logic probe.

Materials   The equipment and components required to perform this experiment are:
- 1 ea ANDY board
- 1 ea digital multimeter
- 1 ea 100 kΩ trim pot
- 1 ea LM324 quad op-amp chip
- 3 ea red LEDs
- various resistors

Procedure

Part A: Circuit Design

1. Design two resistive voltage dividers to develop the reference levels. One end of each voltage divider must be grounded and the other end connected to either the +5 VDC or +9 VDC supply on the ANDY board. One voltage divider should have a total series resistance greater than 100 kΩ and must develop reference voltage levels of 0.8 volts and 2.2 volts. The second voltage divider should have a total series resistance greater than 1 MΩ and should develop a voltage level of approximately 1.5 volts. The second divider serves to generate the centering voltage and should be connected to the logic probe's input as a bias. When the signal input is open, the bias voltage will center the signal to the LEDs, causing LED2 to light.

2. Using a single supply voltage (+9 V is recommended) can simplify your design, but you may use any of the voltage supplies on the ANDY board. However, you must be sure that the voltage supplied to the LM324 meet its minimum power supply requirements (see Tabale 17 in Section 3.12.) The positive VDC supply can be connected to the LM324 positive voltage supply input terminal (pin 11). The LM324 negative voltage supply input terminal (pin 4) can be connected to ground.

3. Use PSpice to design your circuit. Use 1N4002 (D1N4002) rectifier diodes instead of LEDs in the PSpice simulation if your version of PSpice does not include LEDs.

4. Both the PSpice simulation and your circuit design must use an appropriate current-limiting resistor in series with each LED (or diode) (see Section 3.13 on LEDs).

5. **Hint:** Remember that op amps can sink current as well as source current.

Part B: PSpice Simulation and Analysis

6. Use "Enable Bias Voltage Display" to be sure you have calculated the correct resistances in your voltage dividers. You must disconnect the logic probe input (so that only the internal centering resistors are connected to the input) before you check the input bias voltage. Each time you change the resistances, run a new simulation to update the bias voltages before you check them.

7. Recommended PSpice simulation settings are: Analysis tab > Analysis type: Time Domain (Transient) > Run to time: 0.2 seconds > Start saving data after: 0 seconds > Maximum step size: 0.005 seconds. Run new simulations for steps 3 and 4.

8. To check the operation of the logic probe in PSpice, drive it with an AC sine wave with an amplitude of 2.5 volts, an offset of 2.5 volts, and a frequency of 10 Hz. Provide one or more screenshots of the signal at each LED to verify correct operation of the circuit. Using a sine wave for the input (rather than a

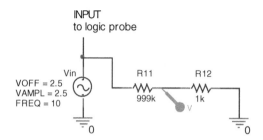

Figure 2: Test input to logic probe for PSpice simulation

square wave) makes it easier to see the switching points of the comparators.

9. Put a PSpice voltage probe on the input to the circuit and PSpice voltage probes on the outputs from the op amps (comparators).

10. Put a PSpice voltage probe on the input to the circuit and at least one PSpice differential voltage probe across the series combination of an LED and its current limiting resistor.

11. Put a PSpice current probe on the anode of each LED (or diode) to see when the LED is conducting. If the LED never conducts, it might be installed backwards. To display the input voltage along with the output current (on the same scale), the input voltage going into the PSpice voltage probe must be reduced. For PSpice simulation only (not in the circuit that you will build in Part C), add two resistors in series across the input to the circuit (Figure 2). The two resistors in Figure 2 divide input voltage by 1,000 for the PSpice voltage probe. The reduced input voltage is small enough for PSpice to graph it together with the smaller LED currents on the same scale.

Part C: Circuit Construction and Testing

12. Construct the circuit designed in Part A and confirmed in Part B.

13. To demonstrate the logic probe circuit, use a 100 kΩ trim pot (Figure 3) instead of the input sine wave used in the PSpice simulation. Connect the voltmeter between the trim pot wiper and ground to monitor the input voltage. Demonstrate that the three LEDs turn off and on at the correct voltages by rotating the trim pot.

14. Record the turn-on and turn-off voltages for each LED on your validation sheet. You should check for hysteresis in these voltages.

15. Validate your design by demonstrating your circuit to your instructor. She will check the observed voltage levels with those recorded on the validation sheet.

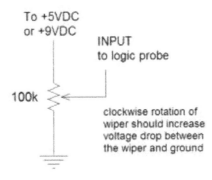

To +5VDC
or +9VDC

INPUT
to logic probe

100k

clockwise rotation of
wiper should increase
voltage drop between
the wiper and ground

Figure 3: Input test circuit for logic probe validation

Lab Report

Your lab report may be written in a format of your choosing. Your report should explain the design principles you used and must include additional schematic diagrams for each of the following steps showing the locations of any PSpice voltage and/or current probes with the following PSpice screen snapshots:

1. Schematic diagram showing the bias voltages (Procedure Part B, step 6).

2. PSpice graph of logic probe input voltage versus the output voltages from the op amps (Procedure Part B, step 7). The graph should cover the entire range of voltages that illustrate all three logic levels.

3. PSpice graph of logic probe input voltage versus the voltage across the series combination of an LED and its current limiting resistor using at least one PSpice differential voltage probe (Procedure Part B, step 8).

4. PSpice graph of reduced logic probe input voltage (using the circuit in Figure 2) versus the current through each of the three LEDs (Procedure Part B, step 9).

In addition to the PSpice graphs described above, you should also include tabulated, numerical data from the graphs described in steps 7–9 in the procedure above.

Finally, your report should contain a table of the turn-on and turn-off voltages for each LED and a discussion of the hysteresis of these voltages. If there is significant hysteresis, how might you modify your design to eliminate these effects?

Last Revision   12/04/2008

Experiment 21: Design A Traffic Arrow

Developers SL Karty, RW Hendricks, KM Lai, and JB Webb

Objectives The objective of this experiment is to design a simple blinking traffic arrow in which the lights turn on in sequence from the tail to the arrowhead.

Estimated Time for Completion

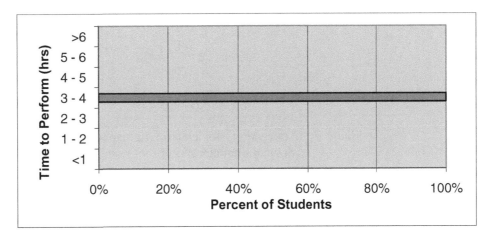

Preparation Read the background for Experiment 19: Design A Voltmeter and for Experiment 20: Design A Logic Probe. Also read the paragraph on using electrolytic capacitors in Section 3.1 (Lab Safety), Section 3.12 (Operational Amplifiers) and Section 3.13 (Light Emitting Diodes) in this text.

Background Consider an array of LEDs laid out to represent a simple arrow as shown in Figure 1. Six LEDs are the minimum required for an effective representation; more may be used. The arrow may be designed to point either to the left or to the right (as shown). The layout is identified in four sections. The objective of the experiment is to design a circuit that will illuminate each section in sequence, moving from left to right for the right-pointing arrow. Once lit, each section

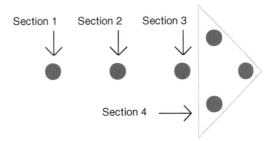

Figure 1: Layout of traffic arrow LEDs.

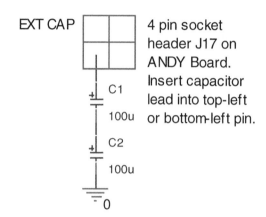

Figure 2: Connections for electrolytic capacitors required to slow down digital clock

should remain lit. After the entire arrow is lit, all the LEDs should turn off and the cycle should restart again. The sequencing time for turning on each section is to be selected so that the arrow appears to move from left to right. This means that the illumination time and sequences must be consistent with the ability of the human eye to resolve each flash of an LED individually. Research suggests that the sequencing time between sections should be no less than 20–40 ms; substantially longer times may be appropriate. With four sections, this implies that one cycle for the array shown in Figure 1 should be no less than 120–160 ms; longer times may be appropriate.

To accomplish the desired sequencing of the various sections, it is suggested that the digital clock (CLCK) on the ANDY board be used. However, as designed, the minimum clock frequency is about 70 Hz—a frequency well above the maximum suggested above. To slow down the clock, connect two 100 µF electrolytic capacitors (in series) to the EXT CAP socket header on the ANDY board. (See Figure 4 in Section 3.3.) The correct polarity of the capacitors is shown in Figure 2. **Note:** it is critical to wire electrolytic capacitors with the correct polarity as discussed in Section 3.1 of this text. Failure to wire the capacitors correctly could result in an explosion of the devices. The positive lead of capacitor C1 should be plugged into either the top-left or bottom-left pin of the EXT CAP socket header (J17). The negative lead of capacitor C2 must be connected to ground. Adding capacitance allows the CLK FRQ potentiometer to be adjusted for longer clock periods. A period of between 4 and 8 seconds is recommended, although other periods can be used. Because the period is too slow for some oscilloscopes to measure, use a watch with a second hand to measure the period. Look at the bi-polar LED located on the ANDY board between the CLK and EXT CAP socket headers (See Figure 4 in Section 3.3) to time the period from when the LED lights green, changes to red, then changes back to green.

The digital clock output from any pin of the CLCK socket header (J16) is a square wave with approximately a 50% duty cycle. The output is high (4.7 V) when the LED is red, and low (0.3 V) when the LED is green.

Specifications

The traffic arrow is to be built on the ANDY board with red LEDs. The arrowhead may point in either direction. Each of the three (or more) LEDs in the shaft of the arrow is a separate section; the three LEDs in the arrowhead are a single section. A suggested LED layout is shown in Figure 1. In operation, each LED section should light in sequence from the tail to the head approximately one-half to one second apart. The student may adjust this timing to a visually suitable value. After the arrowhead section lights, all the LEDs should go out simultaneously. After several seconds, the cycle should repeat.

Materials

The (typical) equipment and components required to perform this experiment are:
- 1 ea ANDY board
- 7 ea red LEDs
- Various resistors
- 3 each 100 µF electrolytic capacitors
- 1 ea LM324 quad op amp

Procedure

Part A: Circuit Design Using PSpice

1. Use PSpice to help design your circuit and to draw the circuit's schematic diagram. Use Figure 3 as the basis for the schematic. **Note:** The diagram in Figure 3 is not consistent with the layout of Figure 1. One section of Figure 1 has been deliberately omitted in Figure 3. Use the fourth op amp of the LM324 to include the missing section. You may add additional sections as desired following the same procedures. Use PSpice to check your calculation for the resistance of R4 with 100 µF for capacitor C3. Place PSpice voltage probes on both sides of R4, and at the outputs of op amps A, B, and C in order to view the waveforms at these points. After verifying that your choice for the resistance of R4 gives you a workable RC time constant (with C3), run PSpice simulations to determine the voltage across C3 versus time. Use

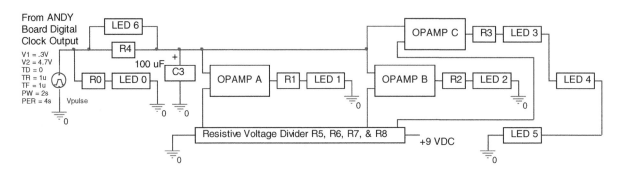

Figure 3: Detailed block diagram of traffic arrow circuit.

the following parameters for Vpulse in PSpice to simulate the digital clock output from the ANDY board: V1 = 0.3V, V2 = 4.7V, TD = 0, TR = 1 μs, TF = 1μs, PW = 2s, PER = 4s. Recommended PSpice simulation settings: Analysis tab > Analysis type: Time Domain (Transient) > Run to time: 5 seconds > Start saving data after: 0 seconds. Run a new simulation each time you change a component or its value, and also before you check the bias voltages.

2. After calculating the resistance of R4, you need to determine the voltage reference levels for each of the op amps. Once the levels are determined, you can calculate the values of the resistors in the voltage divider. Calculate the values of the resistors (R5 through R8) based on the voltage levels across C3 at the times you want each LED to light. Use "Enable Bias Voltage Display" to be sure you have calculated the correct resistances in your voltage divider. Each time you change the resistances, run a new simulation to update the bias voltages before you check them. Set the reference voltage level from the resistive voltage divider to the level at the time that you want each LED to light.

3. **Note:** If your version of PSpice does not include LEDs, use 1N4002 (D1N4002) rectifier diodes instead of LEDs in the PSpice simulation. Both the PSpice simulation and your circuit design must use appropriate current-limiting resistors in series with the LEDs (see Section 3.13 on LEDs). Calculate the values of R0, R1 = R2, and R3.

4. Using a single voltage supply can simplify your design, but you may use any of the voltage supplies on the ANDY board. The +9 VDC supply is recommended. The +9 VDC supply should be connected to the LM324 positive voltage supply input terminal (pin 11). The LM324 negative voltage supply input terminal (pin 4) should be connected to ground.

5. Use the digital clock output from the ANDY board as a timing signal for triggering the turn-on time of the LED sections. Use the CLK FRQ

potentiometer on the ANDY board to adjust the delay before the sequence restarts.

6. LED 6 is used only as a diode and must be connected so it conducts only when the digital clock output is low. What is the function of LED 6?

Part B: Circuit Construction

8. You may design a different circuit as long as it uses approximately the same number of components as (or fewer than) the design in Figure 3. Alternate designs must include a schematic diagram and a circuit description, and must meet the same validation requirements. All designs are limited to the parts listed in Appendix A.

9. Hint: If an LED never lights, it might be installed backwards.

10. Test the circuit and adjust your calculations in steps 1 and 2 and in your schematic diagram. Your final schematic diagram should be identical to the operating circuit presented for validation.

11. Demonstrate that your circuit operates as specified during validation.

Design Report

The design report, which may be written in a format of your choosing, should be self-contained. At a minimum, the report must include the following:

1. A statement of the objectives of the project

2. A description of the design principles used and the feature set included

3. A schematic diagram of the circuit

4. A PSpice analysis showing the bias voltages and the locations of any PSpice voltage and/or current probes. A screen snapshot of the PSpice waveforms showing the pulse generator voltage versus the voltage at the junction of R4 and C3 should be included. The waveforms must also show the output voltages from the op amps. Be sure to answer the question in Procedure Part A, step 6.

5. Test results that demonstrate the performance of the design.

Validation

The design will be validated by demonstrating that the LEDs light in the prescribed sequence and at the prescribed time (approximately one-half to one second apart).

Last Revision 1/03/2009

Experiment 22: Introduction to Phasors

Developers WC Headley, SL Karty, and RW Hendricks

Objectives The objectives of this experiment are to measure the current phasor for a resistive, capacitive, and inductive load and to demonstrate the function of a current shunt.

Estimated Time for Completion

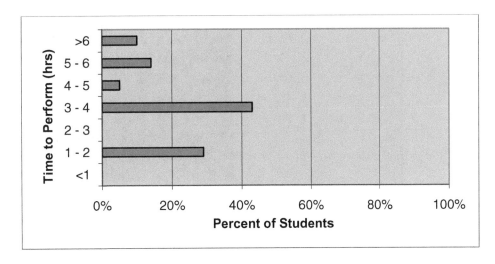

Preparation Read the chapter on phasors in your textbook. Also read Section 3.6 of this manual describing the oscilloscope.

Background A critical parameter in AC measurements is the phase difference (in degrees) between signals. An oscilloscope has the capability of showing the relationship between signals in the time domain. Thus, on an oscilloscope one may determine the increment of time by which one signal leads or lags another. The time cursors of the software oscilloscope may be used to measure this time difference, Δt. Using this time difference and knowing the period of the signals, one can find the phase shift of the circuit using the formula

$$\varphi = \frac{\Delta t}{T}(2\pi) \text{ (in radians)} \tag{7}$$

When measuring the time difference, one must make sure to take the closest identical points on the two graphs. Consider Figure 1. The time cursors have been placed on the zero crossing of each signal, making sure that the closest two zero crossings were used. If, for example, the red waveform represents current and the green waveform represents voltage, it is seen that the red waveform (current) leads the green waveform (voltage) because the red waveform reaches

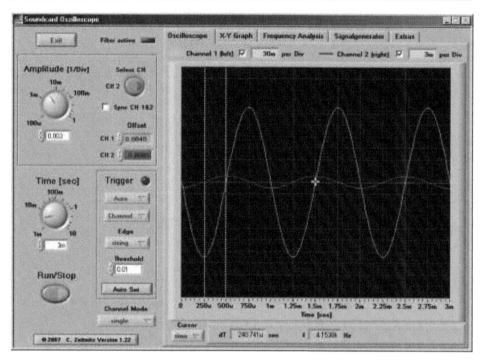

Figure 1: Correct way to measure the phase shift for a capacitive load.

its zero crossing before the green waveform. (Download color images of Figure 1 from the text website a **http://www.lab-in-a-box.net** to see these effects.)

Current measurements are difficult to make on an oscilloscope. One simple method is to measure the voltage drop across a calibrated resistor that is inserted into the branch in which it is desired to measure the current. This resistor must be small enough to have negligible effect on the circuit impedance, but large enough to provide a sufficient signal to be measured on the oscilloscope. Because the oscilloscope has only a single voltage probe, and because that probe is referenced to ground, this shunt resistor must connect the branch to ground. In the experiment performed here, a 10 Ω resistor has been chosen. Let R_s be the resistance of the shunt resistor and let A_a be the value of the input attenuation (1.0 or 10.0). Then, for a measured voltage V_s across the shunt, the current I_s through the shunt is

$$I_s = \frac{A_a V_s}{R_s} \qquad (8)$$

If one measures the voltage (in volts) through the 10× attenuator circuit across a 10 Ω shunt, the current (in amperes) is numerically identical to the observed voltage. Or, if one measures the voltage through the 1× attenuator across a 10 Ω shunt, the current is numerically 1/10 of the observed voltage.

Depending on the input voltages and the circuit impedances, one needs to take care in selecting the choice of oscilloscope inputs (1× or 10×) and the value of the shunt resistor. Clearly, one must select values that will allow the measurement of the desired signals on the oscilloscope. The authors recommend reasonable values for the shunt resistors for the signals to be measured in each of the experiments in this text.

Materials

The equipment and components required to perform this experiment are:
- 1 ea ANDY board
- 1 ea dual trace oscilloscope
- 1 ea 10 Ω resistor (shunt resistor)
- 1 ea 100 Ω resistor (shunt resistor)
- 1 ea 1 kΩ resistor
- 1 ea 10 nF capacitor
- 1 ea 100 mH inductor

Procedure

Analysis:

1. Find the angular frequency (ω) of the circuit shown in Figure 2.

2. Determine the impedance of the element if the element is:
   a. a 1 kΩ resistor
   b. a 100 mH inductor

   Show that the 10 Ω shunt has only a small effect on the impedance of the circuit by plotting the impedances in the complex plane. Calculate the percent change in the magnitude and phase angle of the impedance from that of the element alone. It is not necessary to include the internal DC resistance of the inductor in the computations for this step.

3. Repeat the calculations in step 2 for an 10 nF capacitor using a 100 Ω shunt.

4. Determine the current phasor for the current through each element. Reference the phase of all signals to a function generator phase of 0° at t = 0. For these calculations, you may ignore the shunt.

Measurements:

5. Construct the circuit shown in Figure 2 using a 1 kΩ resistor as the element.

6. If you are using:

   a. a software oscilloscope - Connect the output of the function generator to the 10× attenuator input of channel 1 and connect the 1× input of channel 2 to the current shunt. This will be sued to show the voltage-to-current relationship of the element.

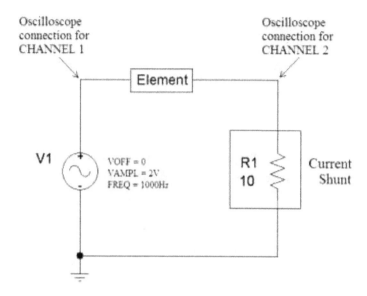

Figure 2: Circuit for determining phasor for various loads.

    b. a hardware oscilloscope – Connect channel 1 of the oscilloscope to the output of the function generator and connect channel 2 to the current shunt. This will be used to show the voltage-to-current relationship of the element.

7. Set the function generator to produce a 1 kHz sine wave with an amplitude of 2.0 V (4.0 V peak-to-peak).

8. Using the voltage cursors of your oscilloscope to determine the peak-to-peak voltage across the shunt resistor, (10 Ω for the resistor and the inductor and 100 Ω for the capacitor), determine the amplitude of the current through the 1 kΩ resistor using Eq (2) as given in the Background. Suggestion: In those cases where the signals have significant jitter, it is much easier to use the cursors to find peak voltages and make time measurements if you stop data acquisition prior to making the measurements.

9. Using the time cursors of your oscilloscope, determine the time shift of the current through the 1 kΩ resistor from the voltage across it. Place the cursors on the waveforms' corresponding zero crossings for taking time measurements. To eliminate jitter in the signal, it is best to stop data acquisition before making the measurements.

10. Starting with Eq (1) given in the Background, $\varphi = 2\pi\Delta t / T$ radians, show each step involved in converting the Δt measurement into a phase angle. This "calculation of the phase difference from time" should end with the last step of $\varphi = \Delta t \cdot f \cdot 360^{o}$. Using the measured time shift from step 9,

calculate the phase of the current relative to the voltage. Be careful to correctly assign the sign.

11. Calculate the current phasor (both amplitude and phase). Is the current through the element leading, lagging, or in phase with the applied voltage?

12. Calculate the percent error of the experimental results from the calculated result for both the amplitude and the phase.

13. Make a printout of the oscilloscope window or copy and paste it into your electronic laboratory notebook. Clearly label that device under test (DUT) is the resistor, identify the current and voltage waveforms, and attach or include the figure to your notebook.

14. Measure the resistance of the 100 mH inductor.

15. Replace the 1 kΩ resistor with the 100 mH inductor.

16. Repeat steps 8 through 13. Be sure to label the printout or scope image with the inductor as the DUT.

17. You will likely notice that the phase angle for the inductor is significantly less than 90°. Repeat the calculations of steps 2(b) and 4 but include the internal resistance of the inductor in series with the coil. Then, compare the experimental observation from step 11 with the new analytical results by repeating step 12.

18. Replace the 100 mH inductor with a 10 nF capacitor and replace the 10 Ω shunt with a 100 Ω shunt.

19. Repeat steps 8 through 13. Be sure to label the printout or scope image with the capacitor as the DUT.

20. **Extra Credit:** Submit PSpice screenshots using the configurations you used for the oscilloscope screenshots and calculate the percent error between the experimental and the PSpice results.

Last Revision   1/04/2009

Experiment 23: Phasor Analysis and Kirchhoff's Current Law

Developers　　　WC Headley, SL Karty, and RW Hendricks

Objectives　　　The objective of this experiment is to use phasor analysis to solve an AC circuit using Kirchhoff's current law (KCL).

Estimated Time for Completion

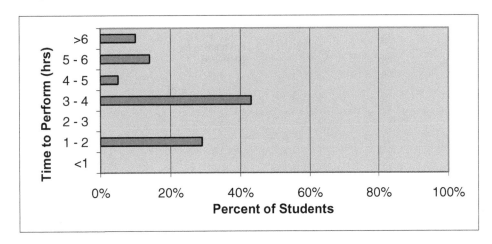

Preparation　　　Read the sections in your textbook concerning phasors and Kirchhoff's Laws in the frequency domain. Experiment 22 should be completed before performing this experiment.

Background　　　As is shown in most textbooks on circuit analysis, if the impedance of each circuit element is written in phasor notation, Kirchhoff's Laws as developed for DC circuit analysis apply for a given frequency AC signal. Thus, to analyze an AC circuit, the first task is to write the impedance of each circuit element for the given frequency. The implicit assumption is that the excitation signal, be it a voltage or a current source, operates at a single fixed sinusoidal frequency. In this experiment, you will build a simple circuit (shown in Figure 1) with two parallel branches in which there are combinations of resistors, inductors, and capacitors. First, you will solve the circuit in PSpice to obtain an estimate of the various node voltages and branch currents. Then you will measure the circuit as built and compare the experimental results with the modeled results.

Materials　　　The equipment and components required to perform this experiment are:
- 1 ea ANDY board
- 1 ea dual trace oscilloscope
- PSpice software
- 2 ea 10 Ω resistors (shunt resistors)
- 1 ea 470 Ω resistor

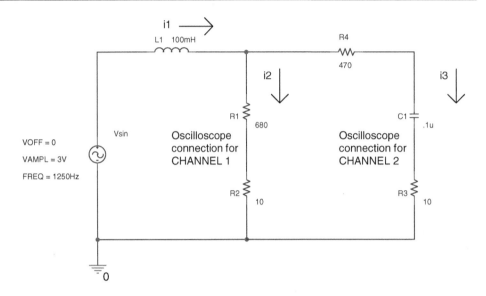

Figure 1: Circuit for verification of Kirchhoff's current law in the frequency domain.

- 1 ea 680 Ω resistor
- 1 ea 0.1 μF capacitor
- 1 ea 100 mH inductor

References   Tront, JG, (2006). PSpice for Basic Circuit Analysis (2/E), New York: McGraw-Hill. p39.

Procedure   **Modeling:**

1. In PSpice, construct the circuit shown in Figure 1.

2. Using transient analysis, make plots of i_1, i_2, and i_3 on the same graph. Run the transient analysis for 3 ms with a step size of 1 μs. Also, to avoid plotting data before the system has reached a steady state, start saving data after 1 ms.

3. Using this graph, determine the current phasors i_1, i_2, and i_3. You may do this using the cursor functions in PSpice (Tront 2006). For the purposes of this lab, reference the phase of all signals to an i_3 phase of 0° at t = 0.

4. Print out a copy (or save an electronic copy) of the graph and label each current waveform.

Measurements:

5. Build the circuit shown in Figure 1.

6. Place a 10 Ω current shunt in both the i_2 branch and the i_3 branch. Be sure that one leg of each shunt is grounded.

7. On the software oscilloscope, produce the waveforms for i_2 and i_3.

8. Using the oscilloscope, determine the current phasor for i_2 and i_3 using the same phase reference as in step 3. Do the experimental values match those found in step 3?

9. Use Kirchhoff's current law and phasor addition to find i_1. Does this value match the value found in step 3?

Last Revision   12/05/2008

Experiment 24: Using Nodal or Mesh Analysis to Solve AC Circuits

Developers   WC Headley, SL Karty, and RW Hendricks

Objectives   The objectives of this experiment are to use either nodal or mesh analysis to solve an AC circuit, to build and measure the circuit, and to examine the effects of using measured rather than nominal component values in the analysis.

Estimated Time for Completion

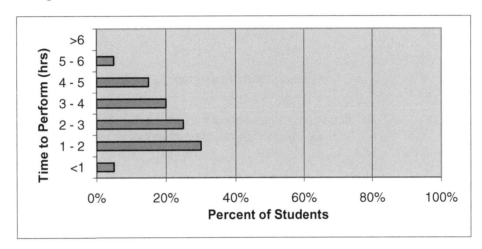

Preparation   Read the sections of your textbook concerning nodal and mesh analysis for sinusoidal steady state signals.

Background   As shown in your circuits text and was verified in Experiment 23, if one replaces all of the capacitors and inductors in a circuit by their complex impedances, one may apply Kirchhoff's laws to solve the circuit exactly as was done for DC circuits. Thus, the techniques of both nodal and mesh analysis apply exactly as before. In this experiment, you will analyze a simple circuit (shown in Figure 1) involving resistors, inductors, and capacitors to predict some node voltages. You will then build this circuit and measure the same node voltages, and then compare the experimental results with the analytical results.

It is highly likely that your experimental results will deviate significantly from the analytical values. These deviations may result from:

1. erroneous selection of components or miswiring of the circuit (always double check your component values and your wiring!),

2. experimental errors in the measurements (such as your inability to perfectly match the oscilloscope cursors to the signal traces),

3. deviations of the true component values from their nominal values, or

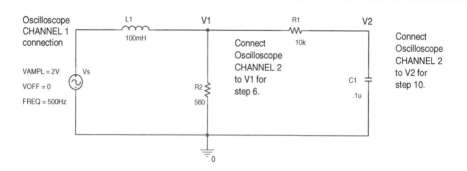

Figure 1: Circuit diagram for node and mesh analysis.

4. deviations of component performance from the ideal model due to effects such as internal resistance of an inductor, leakage currents in a capacitor, etc.

In this experiment, you will measure some of these deviations and will refine your model to account for any such deviations. You will then compare your experimental results with the predictions of the refined model and find significant improvement in the agreement.

In performing this experiment, you will make numerous calculations using complex algebra. These calculations become very tedious and the results are prone to computational errors. You are strongly encouraged to use MATLAB to perform these calculations. We have found the texts by Gilat (2008) and Hunt et al. (2006) have good coverage of the MATLAB Symbolic Toolbox which is required for symbolic calculations such as those necessary to solve AC problems. Other programs that also have symbolic processing capabilities include Mathematica and Maple. If you use such software, be sure to copy your derivations into your laboratory notebook for submission with your report.

References

Gilat, A., (2008). MATLAB: An Introduction with Applications (3/E). Hoboken, NJ: John Wiley & Sons.

*Hunt, BR, RL Lipsman, and JM Rosenberg, (2006). A Guide to MATLAB for Beginners and Experienced Users (2E). Cambridge: Cambridge Univ. Press.

Materials

The equipment and components required to perform this experiment are:
- 1 ea ANDY Breadboard
- 1 ea dual trace oscilloscope
- 1 ea 560 Ω resistor
- 1 ea 10 kΩ resistor
- 1 ea 100 mH inductor
- 1 ea 0.1 μF capacitor

Procedure

Analysis:

1. Draw the frequency-domain equivalent of the circuit shown in Figure 1.

2. Using the circuit drawn in step 1 and your choice of analysis method, find V_1 and V_2. Express V_1 and V_2 in both rectangular and phasor form. For the purposes of this lab, reference the phase of all signals to a function generator phase of $0°$ at t = 0. If PSpice is used, submit PSpice screen snapshots showing the voltage traces at V_1 and V_2 as well as the magnitude and phase of the signals at these nodes.

Measurements:

3. Construct the circuit in Figure 1.

4. Observe the function generator output (V_s) on Channel 1 of the oscilloscope. Set the function generator to the voltage and frequency given in Figure 1.

5. Connect node V_1 to the Channel 2 input of the oscilloscope.

6. Using the oscilloscope cursors, find the magnitude and phase of V_1.

7. Compute the percent error between the calculated (step 2) and measured (step 6) magnitude and phase of V_1.

8. Make a printout of the oscilloscope window or copy and paste it into your electronic laboratory notebook. Be sure to label the waveform for V_1.

9. Change the connection to the Channel 2 input of the scope from V_1 to V_2.

10. Repeat steps 6 to 8 for V_2.

11. Measure the resistance of the 560 Ω and 10 kΩ resistors, and measure the internal resistance of the inductor coil. Also measure the capacitance of the capacitor.

12. Repeat step 1 using the measured values and inserting a series resistor with the inductor to account for its internal resistance.

13. Repeat step 2 to find refined values for V_1 and V_2.

14. Compute the percent error of the experimentally observed values for V_1 and V_2 obtained in step 6 with the refined values obtained in step 13.

15. Which correction to the component values had the biggest impact on improving your results? Why?

Last Revision   1/04/2009

Experiment 25: Simulated Inductance (The Gyrator)

Developers   AR Young, MC Green, SL Karty, and RW Hendricks

Objectives   The objectives of this experiment are to model a circuit element that simulates an inductor using only resistors, capacitors, and an op amp, and to compare the experimental results with simple circuit theory. This circuit is known as a gyrator.

Estimated Time for Completion

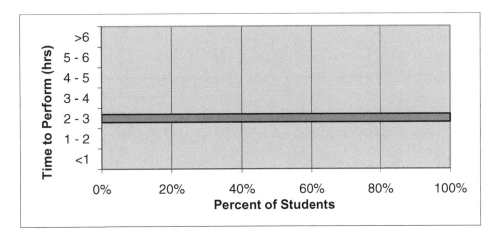

Preparation   Read the sections in your text book which discuss both the AC and DC properties of op amps and the sections that discuss passive filters. Also read Section 3.12 (op amps) in this text.

Background   A filter is a circuit that passes signals of desired frequencies and attenuates signals of other (undesired) frequencies. Lowpass filters pass frequencies below a critical frequency called the corner (or cutoff) frequency and attenuate frequencies above the corner frequency. Highpass filters pass frequencies above the corner frequency and attenuate frequencies below it. A bandpass filter is a combination of a lowpass and a highpass filter that will pass only frequencies within a given desired band. Finally, a bandstop filter is a combination of a lowpass and a highpass filter that will pass all frequencies except those within a prescribed band.

An example of a simple first-order passive highpass filter is illustrated in Figure 1(a) and involves only one resistor and one inductor. This filter works perfectly well when size and cost are not major issues. However, inductors are relatively large and expensive electrical components. They also tend to pick up noise. In order to alleviate these problems, a variation of the circuit was developed by Tellegen in 1948 (Tellegen, 1948; Elliott, 2000; Wikkipedia, 2006). This circuit is commonly known as a gyrator and is illustrated in Figure 1(b).

217

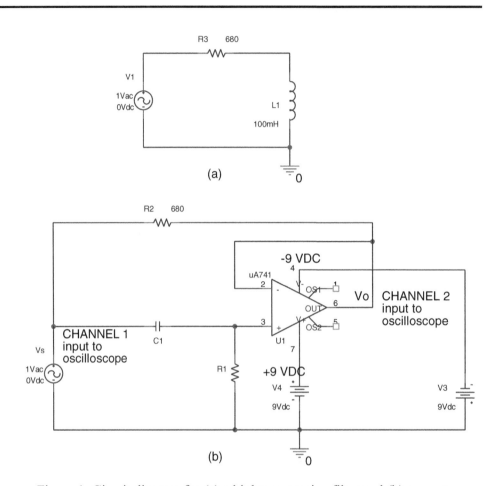

Figure 1: Circuit diagram for (a) a highpass passive filter and (b) a gyrator.

The gyrator does not include any inductors; however, it is still able to maintain the properties of a real inductor because it produces a +90° phase shift of the output signal when compared to the input. The gyrator circuit uses a capacitor and inverts its effects, therefore making it behave as an inductor. Also, when a load is applied to the input of the circuit through resistor R_1, the op amp will ignore it since the change is coupled directly to the input through the capacitor. This simulates high impedance, which is a property of an ideal inductor. It can be shown that the reactance of the circuit is $j\omega R_1 R_2 C_1$, which is purely inductive. Thus, the simulated inductance is given by the expression

$$L = R_1 R_2 C_1 \tag{1}$$

Although the gyrator behaves as though it is a real inductor, it is not an exact replacement. The simulated inductor does not have the same energy storage as, and cannot respond like, an inductor since there is no coupling involved. Therefore, the use of a gyrator has excellent applications as far as eliminating the cost and noise restrictions of a large inductor and is very useful as far as integrated circuits are concerned, but it can never completely replace the real component.

References

Elliott, R., (2000). "Audio Designs with Op Amps." 05 December 2008 <http://sound.westhost.com/dwopa.htm#inductor>.

Tellegen, B.D.H., (1948). Philips Res. Rep. **3**, pgs 81-101.

Wikipedia, (2008). 05 December 2008 <http://en.wikipedia.org/wiki/Gyrator>.

Materials

The equipment and components required to perform this experiment are:
- 1 ea ANDY board
- 1 ea dual trace oscilloscope
- 1 ea 100 mH inductor
- 1 ea 680 Ω resistor
- 1 ea LF356 op amp
- 1 ea resistor *(to be determined)*
- 1 ea capacitor *(to be determined)*

Procedure

Analysis:

1. Derive the transfer function for the circuit in Figure 1(b).

2. Calculate the values of R_1 and C_1 so that the gyrator matches the RL filter in Figure 1(a). Use only components in the parts list given in Appendix A.

Modeling:

3. Simulate the RL circuit in Figure 1(a) in PSpice. Use an AC Sweep to plot the frequency response of the circuit from 10 Hz to 10 kHz. Cut and paste a copy of this graph into your electronic laboratory notebook.

4. Using the Trace feature in PSpice, use the cursors to calculate the corner frequency of the circuit.

5. Simulate the gyrator circuit in Figure 1(b) in PSpice. Use an AC Sweep to plot the frequency response of the circuit from 1.0 Hz to 10 kHz. Cut and paste a copy of this graph into your electronic laboratory notebook.

6. Using the Trace feature in PSpice, use the cursors to calculate the corner frequency of the circuit.

7. Comment on the similarities and/or differences between the curves generated in steps 3 and 5, and the corner frequencies calculated in steps 4 and 6.

Measurements:

8. Construct the gyrator shown in Figure 1(b) and simulated in step 5.

9. Connect the oscilloscope inputs with Channel 1 measuring the function generator output and the Channel 2 measuring the filter output. Be sure to use proper attenuation on the scope input to avoid saturating the sound card input.

10. Set the frequency of the function generator to its lowest value (~67 Hz) and set the amplitude of the function generator to 1 V. Record the magnitude and phase of the output signal.

11. Gradually increase the frequency of the circuit until the output reaches a maximum. Determine the amplitude of the output at this point.

12. Set the voltage cursors at the -3 dB point from the signal maximum.

13. Decrease the input signal frequency from the maximum output until the signal just touches the cursors. Record the frequency.

14. Comment on the significance of the measurement of step 13.

15. Compute the percent deviation of the observed corner frequency measured in step 13 from the design value computed in step 6.

16. Plot the observed amplitude transfer function as a function of frequency. Compare this with the PSpice simulation of the gyrator generated in step 5.

Last Revision   1/04/2009

Experiment 26: The Wien-Bridge Oscillator

Developers   RF Cooper, WC Headley, SL Karty, and RW Hendricks

Objectives   The objective of this experiment is to demonstrate the properties of a Wien-bridge RC oscillator.

Estimated Time for Completion

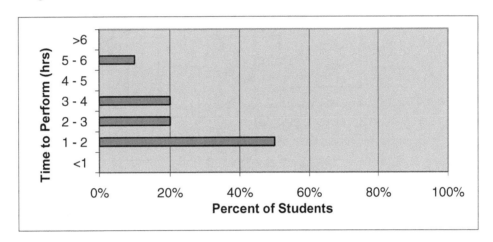

Preparation   Read the discussion of the Wien bridge oscillator in Alexander and Sadiku (2008), Educypedia (2008), or Wikipedia (2008).

Background   An oscillator is a circuit that converts a DC input to an AC output. There are a wide range of oscillator types as described in the Educypedia (2008). This experiment investigates the sinusoidal output of a Wien bridge oscillator. Sinusoidal oscillators consist of an amplifier in a positive feedback loop with a frequency-selective network. The amplifier can be a transistor amplifier or an operational amplifier. The frequency of the oscillator is determined by the frequency-selective network. The criteria for an oscillator to produce sinusoidal oscillations are that the magnitude of the loop gain equal unity and the phase of the loop gain equal zero at the frequency selected for oscillation.

Wien-bridge oscillators are noted for high stability and low distortion. This oscillator, shown in Figure 1, will oscillate at the frequency

$$f_o = \frac{1}{2\pi RC} \tag{1}$$

when the gain, G, is

$$G = \frac{V_o}{V_2} = 1 + \frac{R_f}{R_g} = 3 \tag{2}$$

221

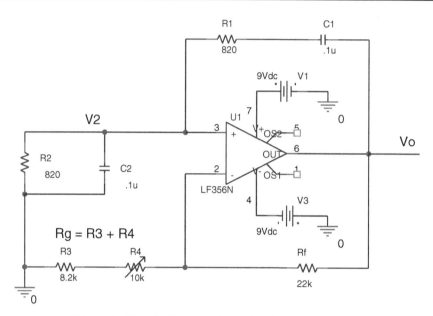

Figure 1: Circuit diagram for Wien bridge oscillator.

In Eqs (1) and (2), $R = R_1 = R_2$ and $C = C_1 = C_2$. For oscillations to start, the gain must be slightly greater than three. This implies the value of R_f/R_g should be slightly greater than 2. The amplitude of oscillation is a very sensitive function of the gain. When the gain just exceeds 3.0, the output will saturate, the signal will go "rail-to-rail," and will begin to appear to be a square wave.

References

Alexander, C.K., and N.O. Sadiku, (2009). <u>Fundamentals of Electric Circuits</u> (4/E), New York: McGraw-Hill, p439.

Educypedia (2008). 05 December 2008 <http://www.educypedia.be/electronics/analogosciltypes.htm >.

Wikipedia, (2008). 05 December 2008 <http://en.wikipedia.org/wiki/Wien_bridge_oscillator >.

Materials

The equipment and components required to perform this experiment are:
- 1 ea ANDY Breadboard
- 1 ea digital multimeter
- 1 ea dual trace oscilloscope
- 1 ea LF356N operational amplifier
- 1 ea 8.2 kΩ resistor
- 1 ea 22 kΩ resistor
- 2 ea 820 Ω resistors
- 1 ea 10 kΩ trim pot
- 2 ea 0.1 µF capacitors

Procedure **Analysis:**

1. Determine the expected frequency of oscillation generated by the Wien-bridge oscillator shown in Figure 1.

Measurements:

2. Using a digital multimeter, measure the actual resistances of the 22 kΩ resistor, the 8.2 kΩ resistor, and the trim pot at its highest resistance value.

3. Using the measured values of the resistances, calculate the gain (V_o / V_2) of the circuit. What do you expect the output to be?

4. Using the digital multimeter, measure the resistance of the trim pot at its lowest resistance value.

5. Using the resistances of the resistors found in step 2 and the trim pot value measured in step 4, calculate the gain of the circuit. What do you expect the output to be?

6. Construct the circuit in Figure 1. Set the trim pot to its highest value.

7. Observe the op amp output on your oscilloscope. Does the output agree with your answer from part 3?

8. Slowly decrease the resistance of the trim pot until the output becomes a stable sinusoidal wave. When you reach the point of oscillation, be sure to wait a few seconds to allow the oscillator to stabilize.

9. Set the two time cursors to display the frequency of the oscillator.[†]

10. What is the value of the output frequency? Calculate the percent difference from the computed answer from step 1.

11. Print out, or make an electronic copy, of the oscilloscope screen. Be sure that the frequency of the waveform is displayed.

12. Using the digital multimeter, measure the resistance of the trim pot. Note: be sure that you do not change the setting of the trim pot by inadvertently turning the knob.

13. Using the measured resistance of the trim pot at oscillation, and the measured resistance of the 8.2 kΩ and the 22 kΩ resistors, calculate the gain of the circuit. Calculate the percent deviation from a gain of 3.0.

14. Continue to slowly decrease the resistance of the trim pot. Record your observations of both the frequency and the amplitude of the oscillator. Describe the results of using too high or too low a resistance for R_g.

15. Set the gain such that you have a stable oscillation. Replace the + 9 V supply with a + 5 V supply. Leave the - 9 V supply unchanged. Record your

---

[†] A slight disturbance in the resistance can cause the oscillator to go unstable.

observations. It may be helpful (although not required) to use a PSpice model to determine the expected output amplitude and waveform (as the supply voltage is changed). Multiple PSpice simulations of the circuit with different resistance values for Rg may be needed if PSpice is used because the gain adjustment is so sensitive.

16. Explain your observations in steps 14 and 15.

17. **Extra credit:** Design and build an oscillator that operates at 1.0 kHz (±5%). Record all component values for your design. Print out, or make an electronic copy, of the oscilloscope screen. Be sure that the frequency of the waveform is displayed. Hint: Two standard value components in series can be used to make a non-standard value.

Last Revision   12/05/2008

Experiment 27: Complex Power in AC Circuit Analysis

Developers   DR Moore, WC Headley, SL Karty, and RW Hendricks

Objectives   The objectives of this experiment are: (1) to measure the average power, the apparent power, the power factor, and the complex power associated with a circuit that is stimulated by an AC source and in which the load has a reactive component (inductor), and (2) to measure the power factor correction provided by a capacitor when the load is inductive.

Estimated Time for Completion

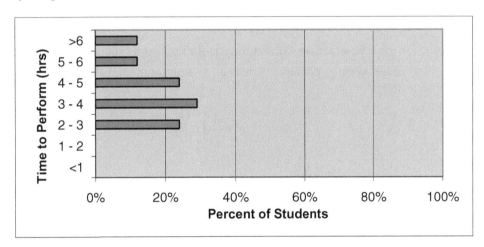

Preparation   Read the sections of your text that that discuss average power, apparent power, power factor, and complex power in AC circuits. You will also use the MATLAB m-file `complexpowerlab.m` found in Appendix D.2. Please study this file to be sure you understand the nature of the computations performed by the program.

Background   The instantaneous power absorbed by a circuit element is given by $p(t) = v(t) \cdot i(t)$. For a sinusoidal voltage and current of frequency ω, magnitude V_m and I_m, and phase θ_v and θ_i respectively, the power may be expressed as

$$p(t) = \frac{1}{2} V_m I_m \cos(\theta_v - \theta_i) + \frac{1}{2} V_m I_m \cos(2\omega t + \theta_v + \theta_i) \qquad (1)$$

This expression comprises two terms. The first is time invariant and depends on the phase difference between the voltage and the current. The second is time varying with a frequency double that of either the voltage or the current.

   The average power, measured in watts (W), is the average of the instantaneous power over one period, and is given by

225

$$P = \frac{1}{T}\int_0^T p(t)dt = \frac{1}{2}V_m I_m \cos(\theta_v - \theta_i) \tag{2}$$

Thus, we see that the lead term in Eq (1) is the average power, P, and that the instantaneous power oscillates around that average with a frequency 2ω. Since both the instantaneous voltage and the instantaneous current are experimentally observable, and since the software oscilloscope is capable of displaying the product of the two, it is thus possible to observe the instantaneous power directly and to obtain the average power by simple movements of the oscilloscope cursors.

The effective current, I_{eff}, is defined to be the DC current that delivers the same average power to a resistor as a periodic time-varying current. This implies that

$$P = \frac{1}{T}\int_0^T i^2 R\, dt = I_{eff}^2 R \tag{3}$$

Solving, we find

$$I_{eff} = \sqrt{\frac{1}{T}\int_0^T i^2 dt} \equiv I_{rms} \tag{4}$$

where I_{rms} is defined as the root mean square, or *rms*, value of the current. Following similar logic, the *rms* value of the voltage is given by

$$V_{eff} = \sqrt{\frac{1}{T}\int_0^T v^2 dt} \equiv V_{rms} \tag{5}$$

Substituting the expressions for the instantaneous current into Eq (3), we find that the *rms* current is

$$I_{rms} = \frac{I_m}{\sqrt{2}} \tag{6}$$

Similarly, the *rms* voltage is

$$V_{rms} = \frac{V_m}{\sqrt{2}} \tag{7}$$

Substituting Eqs (6) and (7) into Eq (2) yields

$$P = V_{rms} I_{rms} \cos(\theta_v - \theta_i) \qquad (8)$$

We define two new quantities. First, the apparent power, S, is defined as

$$S = |\mathbf{S}| \equiv V_{rms} I_{rms} \qquad (9)$$

This definition is a logical analogy with the power delivered by a DC current to a resistor. The units of apparent power are *volt-amperes* (VA) to distinguish it from the average power, which has the units of watts (W). Second, the power factor, pf, is defined as

$$\text{pf} \equiv \cos(\theta_v - \theta_i) \qquad (10)$$

which is dimensionless. The angle $\theta_v - \theta_i$ is known as the power factor angle. From this, we see that the average power is the product of the apparent power and the power factor. If we write the voltage and the current in phasor notation, we find

$$\mathbf{Z} = \frac{\mathbf{V}}{\mathbf{I}} = \frac{V_m}{I_m} \angle(\theta_v - \theta_i) \qquad (11)$$

From this, we learn that the power factor angle is also the phase angle of the impedance.

The concept of complex power is introduced in order to express power relations as simply as possible. The complex power, *S*, is defined as

$$\mathbf{S} = \frac{1}{2} \mathbf{V} \mathbf{I}^* = \mathbf{V}_{rms} \mathbf{I}^*_{rms} \qquad (12)$$
$$= V_{rms} I_{rms} \cos(\theta_v - \theta_i) + j V_{rms} I_{rms} \sin(\theta_v - \theta_i)$$

where **I*** is the complex conjugate of the current phasor. We note that the first term is the average power, P, as defined in Eq (8). We define the second term as

$$Q = V_{rms} I_{rms} \sin(\theta_v - \theta_i) \qquad (13)$$

The real power, P, is the average power (in watts) delivered to the load while the reactive power, Q, is the energy exchanged between the source and the reactive part of the load. This energy is the energy stored or removed from the capacitors or inductors. The units of the reactive power are *volt-ampere reactive* (VAR). Finally, we see that the apparent power, S, is given by

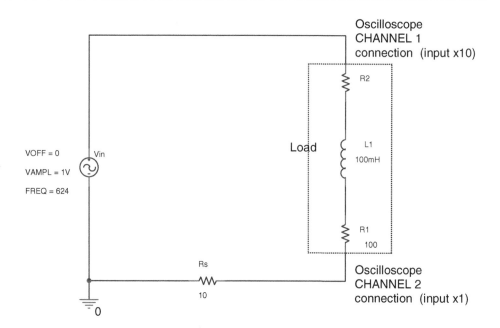

Figure 1: Circuit diagram for experiment with inductive reactance.

$$|\mathbf{S}| = \sqrt{P^2 + Q^2}$$
$$= V_{rms} I_{rms}$$

(14)

as was defined in Eq (9).

The complex power, as defined by the product of the voltage phasor and the complex conjugate of the current phasor as in Eq (12), contains all of the power information for the load.

There is a significant economic consideration associated with all of this—namely, the utilities charge industrial customers for the apparent power, S (the amperes used at a given voltage), while it is only the real power, P, that is useful. There is a great incentive to find a way to increase the power factor to near unity and thus pay only for the useful power. This can be accomplished in the following way. If the load is inductive (as is usual in most applications), one places a capacitor in parallel with the load; if the load is capacitive, one places an inductor in parallel with it.

Consider an inductive load in which an inductor, L, is in series with a resistor, R_2, as shown in Figure 1. The internal resistance of the inductor is given by R_1. In this case, the impedance, Z, of the circuit is $Z = R_1 + R_2 + j\omega L$. If the voltage is $\mathbf{V} = V_m \angle 0$, then the current is given by

$$\mathbf{I}_m = \frac{V_m}{Z}$$

$$= \frac{V_m}{R_1 + R_2 + j\omega L} = \frac{V_m \cdot (R_1 + R_2)}{(R_1 + R_2)^2 + \omega^2 L^2} - \frac{jV_m\omega L}{(R_1 + R_2)^2 + \omega^2 L^2} \tag{15}$$

From Eq (12), the complex power is given by

$$\mathbf{S} = \frac{1}{2}\mathbf{V}_m\mathbf{I}_m^*$$

$$= \frac{1}{2}\frac{V_m^2(R_1 + R_2)}{(R_1 + R_2)^2 + \omega^2 L^2} + \frac{1}{2}\frac{jV_m^2\omega L}{(R_1 + R_2)^2 + \omega^2 L^2} \tag{16}$$

The real power, P, and the reactive power, Q, are

$$P = \frac{1}{2}\frac{V_m^2(R_1 + R_2)}{(R_1 + R_2)^2 + \omega^2 L^2}$$

$$Q = \frac{1}{2}\frac{V_m^2\omega L}{(R_1 + R_2)^2 + \omega^2 L^2} \tag{17}$$

while the phase angle between the current and the voltage is

$$\phi = \frac{180}{\pi}\tan^{-1}\left(\frac{-\omega L}{R_1 + R_2}\right) \tag{18}$$

If a capacitor, C, is placed in parallel with the load, it is left as an exercise for the student to show that

$$P = \frac{1}{2}\frac{V_m^2(R_1 + R_2)}{\omega^2 L^2 + (R_1 + R_2)^2}$$

$$Q = \frac{1}{2}\frac{V_m^2\omega(L - C(\omega^2 L^2 + (R_1 + R_2)^2))}{\omega^2 L^2 + (R_1 + R_2)^2} \tag{19}$$

In order to compensate for the inductive load, the value of the capacitor that must be placed in parallel across the load is given by setting the numerator of Q to zero and solving for C. This condition assures that the composite load has only a real component. Note that C does not appear in the expression for P, which is identical to the expression for P without the capacitor as given in Eq (17), thus showing that the addition of the capacitor has no affect on the real power delivered to the load.

In this experiment, which is performed at a fixed frequency, you will observe on the oscilloscope the magnitude and phase of the current through a load impedance relative to a 1 V reference source, as well as the instantaneous power, p(t). These measurements will allow you to calculate the three different types of power in two different ways. The first way is based on a known voltage phasor (1 V at $0°$). You will measure the current magnitude and phase angle through the circuit, and be able to determine the various forms of power from these results. You will also be able to derive the three kinds of power from the observed p(t) waveform. These results must agree with each other within an experimental tolerance of approximately $\pm15\%$. Finally, you will compare your experimental results with an analytical solution for the circuit. The mathematical computations for this experiment are easy, but tedious. A MATLAB m-file is included to help ease these repetitive calculations. The program will compute the desired properties twice, once based on the current/voltage waveform and once based on the p(t) waveform. If the results from these independent experiments do not agree, you will be informed and must redo the measurements. The source code for this program is shown in Appendix D.1. You may download the m-file from the text website at **http://www.lab-in-a-box.net.** We have found the reference on MATLAB by Hanselman and Littlefield (2005) to be very helpful.

References

*Hanselman, D., and B. Littlefield, (2005). Mastering MATLAB 7. Upper Saddle River, NJ: Pearson Prentice Hall.

Materials

The parts and components required to perform this experiment are:
- 1 ea ANDY board
- 1 ea dual trace oscilloscope
- MATLAB m-file complexpowerlab.m (Appendix D.1)
- 1 ea 10 Ω resistor (shunt resistor)
- 1 ea 220 Ω resistor
- 1 ea 470 Ω resistor
- 1 ea 820 Ω resistor
- 1 ea 0.1 µF capacitor
- 1 ea 100 mH inductor

Procedure

Analysis:

1. Calculate the impedance of the load for the circuit shown in Figure 1 for the three resistors $R_2 = 220$, 470, and 820 Ω. Use a value of 100 Ω for R_1, the internal resistance of the inductor.

2. Calculate the real, the reactive, and the apparent power as well as the power factor for the circuit with each resistor. Record your results in Table 1.

3. Calculate the phase angle between the current and the voltage for the circuit with each resistor. Record your results in Table 2.

Table 1: Calculated Power

Load	Real Power (mW)	Reactive Power (mVAR)	Apparent Power (mVA)	Power Factor (pf)
220 Ω				
470 Ω				
820 Ω				
820 Ω ∥ 0.1 μF				

Table 2: Calculated current and phase angle.

Load	Current Magnitude (mA)	Current Phase Angle (deg)
220 Ω		
470 Ω		
820 Ω		
820 Ω ∥ 0.1 μF		

4. Calculate the phase angle between the current and the voltage for the circuit with each resistor. Record your results in Table 2.

5. Calculate the value of the compensating capacitor required to shift the power factor to unity with $R_2 = 820\ \Omega$.

6. Using a scientific graphics program of your choice (e.g., Excel or MATLAB), plot a graph of the instantaneous power, p(t) for each value of R_2. Make a copy of each graph and record it in your lab notebook.

Measurements:

7. Using your DMM, measure the internal resistance of the 100 mH inductor.

8. Construct the circuit shown in Figure 1 using $R_2 = 220\ \Omega$ in series with the 100 mH inductor. This combination comprises the load.

9. Connect Channel 1 of the oscilloscope to node A as shown in Figure 1 and set the attenuation factor to ×10.

10. Connect Channel 2 of the oscilloscope to node B. Set the Channel 2 attenuation to ×1.

11. Set the function generator to the values shown in Figure 1.

12. Using the oscilloscope cursors, measure the amplitude and phase of the current, taking the voltage as the reference for the zero of phase angle. Record your phase angle in degrees (not radians!) in the Table 3 below. Be careful with the sign!

13. Change the Channel Mode on the oscilloscope to display the CHN1*CHN2 product. This product is the instantaneous power, p(t).

    Using the cursors, determine the maximum and minimum values of the instantaneous power, and determine its frequency. Be very careful to account for the attenuation factor of the voltage and the effect of the shunt resistor. Record your data in Table 3.

Table 3: Experimental values of current and power.

Load	Current Magnitude (mA)	Current Phase Angle (deg)	p(t)$_{max}$ (mW)	p(t)$_{min}$ (mW)	p(t) Frequency (Hz)
220 Ω					
470 Ω					
820 Ω					
820 Ω ‖0.1 µF					

14. Replace the 220 Ω load resistor with the 470 Ω and repeat steps 11 through 13. Be sure to turn off the ANDY board power when changing the resistor.

15. Replace the 470 Ω load resistor with the 820 Ω and repeat steps 11 through 13.

16. Modify the circuit shown in Figure 1 by inserting a 0.1 µF capacitor in parallel with the load (from node A to node B). Leave $R_2 = 820$ Ω and repeat steps 11 through 13.

17. Install the m-file complexpowerlab.m in the Work directory of MATLAB. A listing of this file is found under Experiment 27 in Appendix D.1. The file may be downloaded from the text website found at **http://www.lab-in-a-box.net**.

18. Run the program and input your measurements presented in Table 3. You must run the program separately for each resistor. Record the real, reactive and apparent power and the power factor for each circuit as requested in Table 4. Copy the MATLAB voltage/current waveform for each resistor to its corresponding step number above.

Table 4: Power parameters derived from experimental data.

Load	Real Power (mW)	Reactive Power (mVAR)	Apparent Power (mVA)	Power Factor (pf)
220 Ω				
470 Ω				
820 Ω				
820 Ω ‖0.1 µF				

19. Verify that the real power in the compensated circuit is the same as in the uncompensated circuit.

20. Compute the percent deviation of the measured phase angle, the apparent power, the average power, and the reactive power from the analytical results computed in steps 2 and 3.

21. **Extra Credit.** Create four PSpice screen snapshots using the circuit in Figure 2: one screen snapshot with no changes to Figure 2; one screen snapshot without capacitor C_1; and two screen snapshots without C_1, one for each of the other two values for resistor R_2 (220 and 470 Ω). Describe how the circuit in Figure 2 operates. Do PSpice and MATLAB give you the same information?

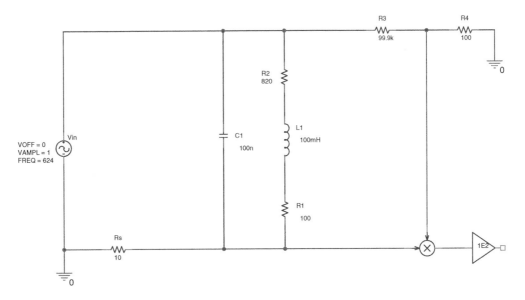

Figure 4: PSpice model for analyzing the circuit in Figure 1.

To do this PSpice analysis, attach a current probe to the right side of R_s; attach a PSpice voltage probe to the output of 1E2; attach another PSpice voltage probe between R_3 and R_4. The PSpice graphs from Figure 2 show p(t) as the smallest wave-form, V_{in} (which always has a peak value of 1 volt), and the current through R_s. The scales have been adjusted for the correct numeric values so p(t) is read out directly in mW, Vin is in volts (not mV), and the current through Rs is in mA.

Last Revision   1/04/2009

Experiment 28: A Three Phase Power Supply

Developers   JJ Hartwell Jr and RW Hendricks

Objective   The objective of this experiment is to build a balanced Y-connected three-phase power supply.

Estimated Time for Completion

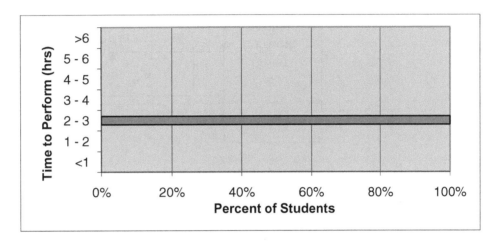

Preparation   Read the sections in your textbook that introduce three phase power. Also read sections 3.11 and 3.12 in this text which cover the use of trim pots and op-amps, respectively.

Background   The subject of three-phase power is discussed in almost every introductory text in electrical circuits, primarily because the great majority of electrical power generated throughout the world today is produced and transmitted in three phase circuits. A simple block diagram of three-phase voltage source is shown in Figure 1. The three lines (a, b, c) are the load lines and the line n is the neutral. The voltages on the three load lines, relative to the neutral, are

$$
\begin{aligned}
\mathbf{V}_{an} &= V_p \angle 0^o \\
\mathbf{V}_{bn} &= V_p \angle -120^o \\
\mathbf{V}_{cn} &= V_p \angle 120^o
\end{aligned}
\tag{1}
$$

If the phases are exactly 120° out of phase and the phase voltages are all exactly V_p, then the sources is said to be *balanced* and it can be shown that

$$
\mathbf{V}_{an} + \mathbf{V}_{bn} + \mathbf{V}_{cn} = 0
\tag{2}
$$

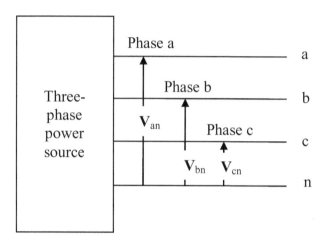

Figure 1: A balanced three-phase power source.[†]

[†] After Irwin and Nelms (2008), p559.

The configuration shown in Figure 1 is known as a "Y" and is particularly well suited to study in the Lab-in-a-Box series of experiments because the PC oscilloscope has only a single input probe and all signals are measured relative to ground. Thus, the implementation of a "Y" configuration will allow us to measure the three voltages $(\mathbf{V}_{an}, \mathbf{V}_{bn}, \mathbf{V}_{cn})$ directly with the scope if the neutral is at ground potential. This is a condition that is easily met. The alternative three-phase configuration, the "Δ" configuration, is not as well-suited to Lab-in-a-Box because the voltages that can be measured are the line-to-line voltages which can only be made with a single-input scope by making two measurements, each with respect to ground, and taking their differences. However, note that this difference can be done automatically in the Velleman and Zeitnitz oscilloscopes.

As noted by Irwin and Nelms (2008), the control circuitry for high-voltage, three-phase equipment often operates at much lower voltages than the power circuits. Thus, for testing purposes it is valuable to have a low-voltage, three-phase circuit which can be used to emulate the high-voltage circuits. In this experiment, we will design and build a simple circuit using op amps that will implement the balanced source configuration of Figure 1. Such a circuit has been presented by Irwin and Nelms (2008, pp 577–580) as an engineering design problem. We will implement that design exactly in the present experiment.

A block diagram of the circuit is shown in Figure 2 and comprises three parts: a signal magnitude adjuster; a phase angle adjuster; and a phase $\mathbf{V}_{bn}$ generator. We implement the first block as a simple voltage divider that assures that the input voltage (to be provided by the ANDY board function generator) is

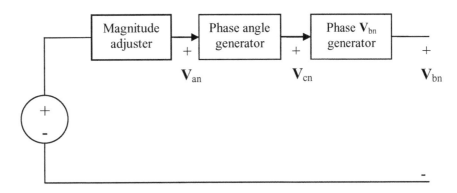

Figure 2: Block diagram of proposed circuit.[†]

[†] After Irwin and Nelms (2008), p578.

an AC signal which has an amplitude between 2.0 and 4.0 V. The second block shifts the input signal by $+120°$ and is created by inverting a signal that is $60°$ lagging. The third block is implemented by adding the first two signals and then inverting the sum to make it $120°$ lagging.

A circuit which will accomplish these functions is shown in Figure 3. It takes a single phase sinusoid as its input and outputs three sinusoids $120°$ apart, each of equal magnitude and with the same frequency as the input. The circuit consists of three primary stages and utilizes a magnitude adjuster (see trim pot in circuit) to set the voltage for the rest of the circuit. In the second stage, an output with a phase angle is produced (V_{CN}), and in the third stage V_{BN} is produced by inverting the sum of V_{AN} and V_{CN}. A more thorough explanation of this circuit is available in Irwin's text, but we review the important results here.

The function generator on the ANDY board provides a variable frequency sine wave with amplitudes varying up to 10 Vp-p. This output amplitude varies with the load and must be determined experimentally. We wish to control the

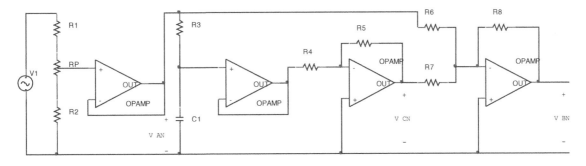

Figure 3: A circuit to emulate a three-phase power source.[†]

[†] After Irwin and Nelms (2008), p580.

amplitude of this signal between 4.0 Vp-p and 8.0 Vp-p by using a trim pot. This can be accomplished using the voltage divider $R_1 - RP - R_2$ as shown in Figure 3. The signal from the potentiometer is then isolated from the rest of the circuit with the first op amp. The output of this op amp is the reference phase V_{an}.

The reference phase is phase shifted by some variable phase angle by the voltage divider $R_3 - C_1$. The maximum phase shift possible with this network is -90°. If the input signal is shifted by -60° and then inverted, we will obtain a signal that is phase shifted by +120°. This can be accomplished if

$$\omega C_1 R_3 = \tan(60^o) = 1.732 \tag{3}$$

The phase shift is accomplished at the input to the second op amp. However, if the constraint of Eq (3) is met, the output of the second op amp is

$$\mathbf{V}_2 = \frac{\mathbf{V}_1}{2.0} \angle -60^\circ \tag{4}$$

This requires that when the output of the second op amp is inverted, the signal must also see a gain of ×2 at the third op amp. Thus, $R_5 = 2R_4$. This assures that the output of op amp three is V_{cn}. However, if the the conditions of Eq (3) are not precisely met, not only will the output of the third op amp not be phase shifted by 120°, but its amplitude will not be exactly the same as that of the input signal. I.e, the denominator of Eq (4) depends on the constraint given by Eq (3).

Using the result of Eq (2), we can create $V_{bn} = -V_{an} - V_{cn}$ by summing the two signals just created in an inverting, unity gain summing amplifier as is done at the fourth op amp. To accomplish this, we requires that $R_8 = R_7 = R_6$.

Construction of the circuit shown in Figure 3, subject to the various constraints described in the above discussion, should provide outputs that meet the requirements of the balanced three phase source described generically in Figure 1.

Implementation Hints

Some suggestions for implementing the circuit shown in Figure 3 that you may find helpful are given below.

1. It is imperative that our simulator behave as a balanced source. Thus, the amplitudes of the three phases must be identical and their respective phase angles given in Eq (1) must be satisfied. The relative phase angles are controlled by Eq (3) while the relative amplitudes are controlled by Eq (4). You may find it helpful to select the value of the feedback resistor R_5 such that you can include a small trim pot in series with it so that you may precisely control the gain of op amp three and thus the amplitude of V_{cn} relative to V_{an}.

2. Similarly, you may wish to add a small trim pot in series with R_8 in order to control the amplitude of V_{bn} relative to the other two phases.

3. Finally, you may wish to include a small trim pot in series with R_3 to control the phase angle of V_{cn} relative to V_{an} accurately. This is important because the tolerance of the capacitor is not tight and it is much easier to trim the resistor than the capacitor.

4. If you implement suggestions 1 and 2 above, you should add a small fixed resistor in series with R_4 whose value is such that you are assured that you can both increase and/or decrease the gain of the third op amp as required to match the amplitude of V_{an}.

5. In a similar fashion, you may want to add trim pots in front of R_6, R_7, and/or R_8 as necessary.

6. Since the values for resistors R_4 and R_6 can be selected arbitrarily, we suggest that you set them each to 10 kΩ. The various constraints then imply that $R_4 = R_6 = R_7 = R_8 = 10$ kΩ and $R_5 = 20$ kΩ. A conveneient value for C_1 is 122 nF. This can be made by placing a 0.1 μF and a 0.022 μF capacitor in parallel.

Reference   Irwin, J.D., and R.M. Nelms, <u>Basic Engineering Circuit Analysis (9/E)</u>, Hoboken: John Wiley & Sons, (2008), pp. 577-580.

Materials   The equipment and components required to perform this experiment are:
- ANDY Board
- DMM
- PC oscilloscope (or equivalent)
- 4 ea LM741 op-amps
- 1 ea 1.8 kΩ resistor
- 4 ea 10 kΩ resistors
- 1 ea 18 kΩ resistor
- 1 ea 0.1 μF capacitor
- 1 ea 0.022 μF capacitor
- various resistors and trim pots to be selected

Procedure   **Analysis:**

1. Select a trim pot for the input control. Be sure its end-to-end resistance is sufficient to not overheat under the applied load (see Section 3.1).

2. Determine the values for resistors R_1 and R_2 so that a 5 V input signal will be controlled between 2.0 and 4.0 V when the trim pot is turned through its entire range.

3. Determine the appropriate value of R_3 for a 400 Hz input signal.

Measurements:

4. Build the input voltage divider for the circuit.

5. Set the function generator to a 400 Hz sine wave using the ANDY board function generator slide switch and frequency control pot. Turn the amplitude to its maximum setting.

6. Measure the amplitude of the function generator output signal.

7. Adjust resistors R_1 and R_2 as necessary to assure that the minimum and maximum output signals from the amplitude control pot are 2.0 and 4.0 V, respectively.

8. Construct the rest of the circuit shown in Figure 3. Select three equal, and large (1 MΩ), resistors to apply loads across the three outputs V_{an}, V_{bn}, and V_{cn}. Note: these load resistors are not shown in the circuit diagram of Figure 3.

9. Adjust the frequency control pot R_3 to produce a 400 Hz signal at the output of the second op amp. Note: set this frequency as closely as possible to the frequency of the function generator.

10. Measure the phase angle difference between V_{an} and the output of op amp 2. Adjust the trim pot associated with R_3 so that this phase angle is exactly -60°.

11. Adjust the gain of the feedback network on op amp 3 to assure that the amplitude of V_{cn} is the same as that of V_{an}.

12. Measure the phase angle difference between V_{an} and V_{cn}. Verify that it is +120°.

13. Measure the phase angle difference between V_{bn} and V_{an}. Verify that it is -120°.

14. Adjust the resistances associated with the summing amplifier (op amp four) such that the amplitude of V_{bn} is the same as the amplitudes of V_{an} and V_{cn} .

15. Create two screenshots of the oscilloscope traces that verify the phase and magnitudes of V_{bn} and V_{cn} relative to V_{an}. Save them in your lab report.

16. **Save the circuit for use in Experiment 29 if it has been assigned.**

Last Revision   1/04/2009

Experiment 29: Three-Phase Loads

Developers   JJ Hartwell and RW Hendricks

Objective   The objective of this experiment is to explore complex three-phase impedances, power factors, and power factor corrections.

Estimated Time for Completion

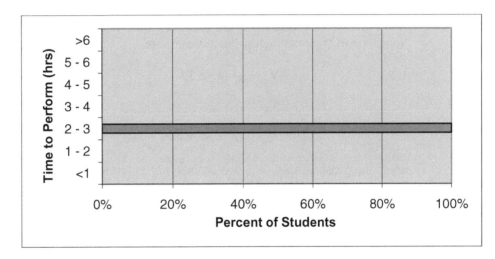

Preparation   Read the section in your textbook that introduces three phase power. Also review Experiment 27 (Complex Power in AC Circuit Analysis) and Experiment 28 (Three-Phase Power Supply).

Background   As with the three phase source described in Experiment 28, a three-phase load may be represented either as a "Y" or as a "Δ." And, as in Experiment 28, due to

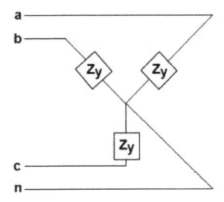

Figure 1: A wye (Y)-connected load.[†]

[†] After Irwin and Nelms (2008), p580.

241

the nature of the PC oscilloscope, we shall examine only the "Y" representation in this experiment. A wye-connected load is shown in Figure 1. Note that the load lines labeled (a, b, c) and the neutral (n) are identical to those in Figure 1 of Experiment 28. If the impedances on each line are identical, the load is said to be balanced.

If a balanced load is supplied by a balanced source, and if the characteristics of the lines connecting them are identical, then it is easily shown (Irwin and Nelms, p 561) that the line-to-line voltages are

$$\left. \begin{array}{c} \mathbf{V}_{ab} = \sqrt{3}\,V_p\angle 30^o \\[4pt] \mathbf{V}_{bc} = \sqrt{3}\,V_p\angle -90^o \\[4pt] \mathbf{V}_{ca} = \sqrt{3}\,V_p\angle -210^o \end{array} \right\} \tag{1}$$

where the phase voltage, V_p, was defined in Experiment 28. Also, we see that the line current in phase a is

$$\mathbf{I}_a = \frac{\mathbf{V}_{an}}{\mathbf{Z}_Y} = \frac{V_p\angle 30^o}{\mathbf{Z}_Y} \tag{2}$$

with similar results for phases b and c shifted by the appropriate amounts. From these results, it is thus straightforward to show that the current in the neutral is

$$\mathbf{I}_n = (\mathbf{I}_a + \mathbf{I}_b + \mathbf{I}_c) = 0 \tag{3}$$

The result of Eq (3) implies that, for a balanced Wye-Wye system, the neutral line could be removed as no current passes through it.

Of course, a number of things can disturb the balance of the system. Let us, for now, assume that the source always remains balanced and that the only sources of imbalance arise in either the load lines or in the loads themselves. For example, it is not only possible, but not uncommon for one of the three load lines to break (go open circuit). This assures that the current in the neutral will not be zero. Similarly, one of the legs of the load may either break (go open circuit) or short out, again forcing currents through the neutral. In this experiment, we shall examine some of these effects.

Finally, the load on each phase line may be reactive thus causing a phase shift of the line voltage with respect to the line current for that phase. The complex power associated with a single phase circuit was studied in Experiment 27. The details of that experiment apply directly to each line of the three phase circuit. In a commercial system, a great deal of care must be taken to ensure that a consumer's load is within proper specifications regarding power factor. Most utilities now monitor a consumer's power factor and if it drops below 0.8 several utilities will divide the power usage by that power factor (i.e., raise the consumer's power bill.) As was done in Experiment 27, in this experiment we

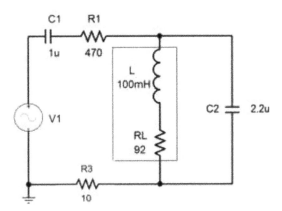

Figure 2: Complete circuit, with power factor correcting capacitors in parallel with inductance (single phase of 3 phase system shown above).

will examine the effects of compensating an inductive load with capacitors on each load line.

A circuit that simulates and inductive load on one line of a three phase circuit is shown in Figure 2. The dashed line shows the 100 mH inductor provided in the lab kit which has a self-resistance of about 92 Ω . The 1 μF capacitor and the 470 Ω resistor complete the load and assure a significant lagging current in the line. The 10 Ω resistor is a current shunt and will be used to measure the current in the neutral line. The 2.2 μF capacitor will be used to adjust the power factor to unity. Note that when you build the remaining two lines, you should connect one end of each inductor to a common node and use only a single current shunt, otherwise you will be unable to measure the sum of the line currents required in Eq (3).

Reference Irwin, J.D., and R.M. Nelms, <u>Basic Engineering Circuit Analysis (9/E)</u>, Hoboken: John Wiley & Sons, (2008), pp. 560–561.

Materials The equipment and components required to perform this experiment are:
- Andy Board
- 1 ea DMM
- 3 Phase Power Supply (built in Experiment 28)
- 1 ea PC oscilloscope
- 1 ea 10 Ω resistor
- 3 ea 470 Ω resistors
- 3 ea 100 mH inductors
- 3 ea 1.0 μF capacitors
- 3 ea 2.2 μF capacitors

Procedure

PSpice Modeling:

1. Using only three AC sources, create a three phase voltage source that models Figure 1 of Experiment 28. Set the phase voltages to 3.0 V and the frequency to 400 Hz. Complete the circuit by using three 1 kΩ resistors as loads on the three load lines (a, b, c).

2. Verify that the current in the neutral line is zero as predicted by Eq (3).

3. Simulate a broken load line by removing line c from the model. Describe the current in the neutral line. Include a screenshot for your report.

4. Remove the three resistive loads and from the model created in step 1 above and install three complex loads as shown in Figure 2. Do not include the compensating capacitors C_2 at this time.

5. Estimate the power factor for each line. Are they the same?

6. Verify that the current in the neutral line is zero, as predicted by Eq (3).

7. Simulate a broken load line by removing line c from the model. Describe the current in the neutral line. Include a screenshot for your report.

8. Using the component values for C_1, R_1, R_L, and L in Figure 2, calculate the value of C_2 required to compensate the load. You may ignore the contribution of the shunt resistor.

9. Insert the three compensating capacitors C_2 calculated in step 8 in each line as illustrated in Figure 2.

10. Estimate the power factor for each line. Is it close to 1.0? If not, check your calculations of step 8 and rerun the model.

Measurements:

11. Check the circuit for the three-phase simulator built in Experiment 28 for correct operation. Be sure the frequency is 400 Hz. Set the phase voltages at 3.0 V. Be sure the phase angles between the three lines are correct.

12. Install three 1 kΩ resistors as loads for the three phase lines (a,b,c). Install a single 10 Ω resistor as a current shunt as illustrated in Figure 2. Note: this requires that the three load resistors have a common node with the shunt resistor and that the other node for the shunt be grounded.

13. Measure the current through the shunt resistor. Do your observations agree with the PSpice model results from step 2 above? If not, why not? Include a screenshot of your results to verify your conclusions.

14. Remove line c and repeat step 13. Do your results agree with the predictions of the PSpice model results from step 3 above. If not, why not? Include a screenshot of your results to verify your conclusions.

15. Remove the three resistive loads installed in step 12 and install the three reactive loads shown in Figure 2. Do not install the three compensating capacitors C_2 at this time. Be sure that the three reactive loads join in a common node with the current shunt resistor as was done for the resistive loads in step 12 above.

16. Measure the current in the shunt resistor. Do your results agree with Eq (3) and with the PSpice model predictions of step 6 above? Include a screenshot to verify your conclusions.

17. Estimate the power factor for each line. Do your results agree with your calculations in step 5 above? Explain any discrepancies.

18. Simulate a broken line by removing the phase c line to the load. Observe the current through the shunt resistor. Do your results agree with your simulation results of step 7? Explain. Include a screenshot to verify your conclusions.

19. Install the three compensating capacitors C_2 and repeat steps 16 and 17. Have you correctly compensated the load on each line? Include screenshots as necessary to verify your results.

Last Revision   1/04/2009

Experiment 30: Transformer Dot Markings and Turns Ratios

Developers   WC Headley, SL Karty, and RW Hendricks

Objectives   The objective of this experiment is to introduce the student to the dot notation for identifying the polarity of the terminals of a transformer and to the basic voltage and phase relationships between the primary and secondary terminals of an iron-core transformer.

Estimated Time for Completion

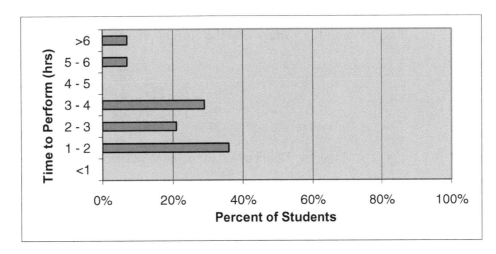

Preparation   Read the sections of your textbook that discuss the dot notation for mutual inductance and the sections that discuss ideal transformers.

Background   An ideal transformer is one in which there are a large number of turns of wire for each of the primary and secondary windings, both of which are wound on a common magnetic core, and for which there is perfect coupling between the primary and secondary coils. In such a case, the voltages across and currents through the primary and secondary coils are related by the expressions

$$\frac{V_2}{V_1} = \frac{I_1}{I_2} = a \tag{1}$$

where V_i and I_i are the voltage and current phasors and $a = N_2 / N_1$ is the turns ratio of the transformer. When $a = 1$, as is the case for the transformer used in this experiment, the transformer is called an isolation transformer.

To analyze a circuit with a transformer, it is important to have a standard notation that identifies the polarity of the terminals of the transformer. This may be done as follows:

1. Arbitrarily place a dot on one terminal of the primary winding and one terminal of the secondary winding. If there are multiple secondary

windings, as is the case with the transformer used in this experiment, place a dot on one terminal of each winding.

2. If the voltage phasors are both positive or both negative at the dotted terminals, use $+a$ in Eq(1). Otherwise, use $-a$.

3. If the current phasors both enter the transformer at the dotted terminals, use $-a$ in Eq (1). Otherwise, use $+a$.

This convention is summarized in Figure 1 where positive a would be used for both the voltage and the current phasors.

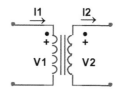

Figure 1: Dot notation for defining polarities of transformer terminals.

In this experiment, the terminals of an audio isolation transformer are unmarked. The transformer has three taps on the primary side—the middle terminal is a center tap that provides access to the middle of the winding and may be used, for example, to provide a DC offset to the coil. This transformer also has two independent, but nominally identical, secondary windings. These may be used to provide two independent outputs, or the windings may be connected together to provide twice as many turns as with a single winding.

The objective of this experiment is to determine the turns ratio of each winding and to determine where the dot markings should be placed to assure that that the notation shown in Figure 1 is valid.

Materials

The equipment and components required to perform this experiment are:
- 1 ea ANDY board
- 1 ea dual trace oscilloscope
- 1 ea audio transformer part TM028

Procedure

Measurements:

1. Insert the TM028 transformer into the ANDY board such that the side with three terminals (the primary coil) is facing the bottom of the board and the side with four terminals (the secondary coils) is facing the top and with the transformer straddling the center trough of the board. Be sure that each terminal is in a separate column of the breadboard so that there are no inadvertent shorts between any pair of terminals. A good place to put the transformer is towards the left side of the ANDY board, near the function generator.

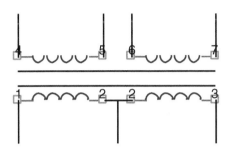

Figure 2: Diagram for transformer properties identification.

2. Number the transformer terminals as shown in Figure 2 on sketches in your lab notebook. Terminal 2 is the center tap of the primary coil while terminals 4/5 and 6/7 identify the two independent secondary coils.

3. Connect the function generator to terminal 1 and ground to terminals 3 and 5. Also connect the function generator to the 10× attenuator input of Channel 1 of the PC oscilloscope. Connect terminal 4 to the 10× attenuator input of Channel 2 of the PC oscilloscope.

4. Set the function generator to 2 V peak-to-peak and 100 Hz.

5. Using the cursors, measure the magnitude and the phase of the voltage across the secondary coil as compared to the voltage across the primary coil. Determine the turns ratio from these data and record your answers in Table 1.

6. Repeat steps 3 to 5 using the connections as shown in Table 1.

7. Arbitrarily put a dot on pin 1. Based on the data in Table 1, determine the dot location for each secondary coil.

8. Again, with a dot on pin 1, based on the data in Table 1, determine the dot location when pins 5 and 6 are shorted.

9. Using an indelible marker or nail polish, put a dot on the terminals as identified in steps 7 and 8.

10. Label Figure 2 to show where the phasing dots are placed. Include Figure 2 in your lab notebook.

11. Include the following three labeled figures of oscilloscope waveforms in your lab notebook. The first figure should show a 1:1 turns ratio out-of-phase condition, (with an explanation of what it would look like if it were in phase). The second figure should show an intermediate turns ratio difference in an in-phase condition. The last figure should show the maximum turns ratio difference in an out-of-phase condition.

Table 1: Transformer Characteristics Table

Primary Side			Secondary Side				
FG	GND		Chan 2	GND	Short	Turns ratio	Phase
1	3		4	5	—		
1	3		5	4	—		
1	3		6	7	—		
1	3		7	6	—		
1	2		7	6	—		
1	2		6	7	—		
1	2		5	4	—		
1	2		4	5	—		
1	2		4	7	5–6		
1	2		7	4	5–6		
1	3		7	4	5–6		
1	3		4	7	5–6		

Last Revision 1/04/2009

Experiment 31: Properties of a Real Transformer

Developers   K Meehan and RW Hendricks

Objectives   The objective of this experiment is to determine the values for the components used to model a real transformer and calculate the frequency response of the transformer using this model.

Estimated Time for Completion

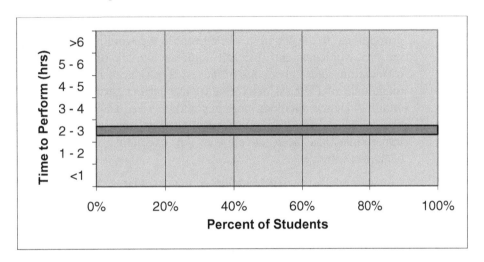

Preparation   Perform Experiment 30 (Transformer Dot Markings and Turn Ratios).

Background   Most introductory electric circuits texts only discuss ideal, and sometimes linear, transformers. In an ideal transformer, it is assumed that all of the flux passing through the primary coil links with the secondary coil (i.e., there is no self-inductance) or that there are no losses in either of the coils due to the resistance of the wires or due to the hysteresis of the B-H curve of the core material. In the ideal case, the voltages and currents of the primary and secondary sides of the transformer are related by Eq (1) of Experiment 30. In this case, one may prove that the input power (P_{in}) and the output power (P_{out}) of the transformer are equal. Similarly, it can be shown that the input and output reactive power (Q) and the input and output apparent power (S) are also equal.

Real transformers are constructed using materials that have less than perfect properties for the application. The wire used to make the windings for the primary and secondary sides of the transformer has nonzero resistance. Currents known as eddy currents can be induced within the core of the transformer. Energy is required to change the orientation of the magnetic domains within the core, which results in hysteresis in the magnetization curve. The magnetic flux induced by the current flowing through the primary winding may not be coupled to the secondary winding (and visa versa), which leads to an effect known as

251

self-inductance. Though not a problem that will be observed with the transformers used in these experiments, in many transformers vibrations of the wire windings and contraction due to the induced magnetic field of the laminated materials in core that may occur. Needless to say, these and other losses act to reduce the efficiency of the transformer.

Each of these losses has a different dependence on the operating conditions – the magnitude and frequency of the current and voltage applied on one winding and induced on the other. For example, the resistive loss of the wire windings is proportional to the square of the current in the winding and can be assumed to be frequency independent. The self-inductance in one of the windings, as you might expect from your knowledge of inductors, produces a voltage that depends on the magnitude of the first derivative of the current flowing through that particular winding. Hence, this loss increases with the frequency of operation. All of these effects have been evaluated quantitatively and an electrical model of the transformer has been developed. An excellent review has been given by Chapman (2002).

A model of a real transformer that simulates the effect of these losses by using a number of components is shown in Figure 1. In this figure, R_P is the resistance of the primary coil, R_S is the resistance of the secondary coil, X_P is reactance of the primary coil and X_S is the reactance of the secondary coil. X_P and X_S describe the self-inductances of each coil, respectively ($X_P = \omega L_P$ and $X_S = \omega L_S$), while X_M is the is the reactance of the core excitations and R_C is the core-loss resistance associated with the core-loss currents.

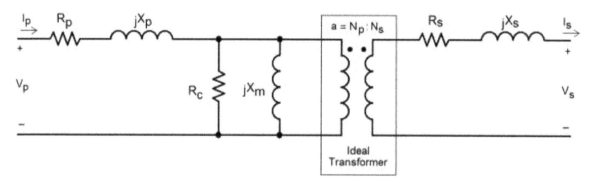

Figure 1. Model of a real transformer. The variables are defined in the text.

A more useful model of a transformer converts the model shown in Figure 1 to an equivalent circuit that does not include an ideal transformer. The values of the impedances in the equivalent circuit are scaled to reflect the magnitude of the voltages and currents at the terminals of primary and secondary windings of the ideal transformers resulting from the turn ratio, a. The equivalent circuit of a

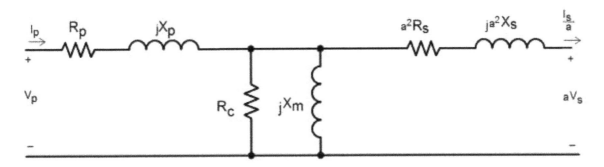

Figure 2: Equivalent circuit of a real transformer using the primary voltage and currents as the reference.

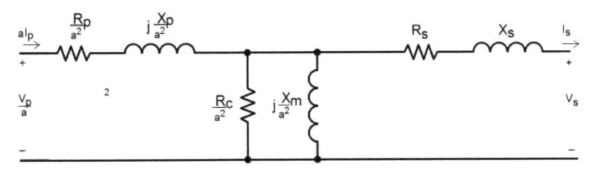

Figure 3: Equivalent circuit of a real transformer using the secondary voltage and current as the reference.

real transformer referenced to the voltage on the primary winding is shown in Figure 2 and the equivalent circuit referenced to the voltage of the secondary winding is shown in Figure 3.

Further simplifications can be made to reduce the complexity of the equivalent circuits. If the voltage drops across R_p and jX_p are much smaller than the voltage drop across the R_c and jX_m, the circuit can be rearranged such that the parallel network of R_c and jX_m is moved before R_p and jX_p. This simplification is acceptable when I_S is much greater than I_p. An equivalent resistance and impedance, R_{eq} and jX_{eq}, can then replace R_p and R_s and jX_p and jX_s, respectively where

$$\left. \begin{aligned} R_{eq} &= R_p + a^2 R_s \\ X_{eq} &= X_p + a^2 X_s \end{aligned} \right\} \tag{1}$$

for the equivalent circuit referenced to the primary voltage and current (Figure 4a) and

$$R_{eq} = R_p / a^2 + R_s \left.\begin{array}{c}\\\\\end{array}\right\}$$
$$X_{eq} = X_p / a^2 + X_s$$
(2)

for the equivalent circuit referenced to the secondary voltage and current (Figure 4b).

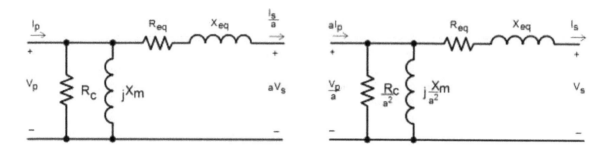

Figure 4. Simplified equivalent circuit for real transformer.

Two sets of measurements are performed – an open circuit test and a short circuit test – to determine the values of the components, R_p, R_s, R_c, X_{eq}, and X_m. Unfortunately, it is not possible to determine the values of X_p and X_s from these measurements. The first set of measurements is made using the digital multimeter to obtain values for R_p and R_s, assuming that R_c is shorted by jX_m. The second set of measurements is made when a 1kHz voltage is applied to the input of the transformer. An analysis of the amplitude and phase angle of the current flowing into (or out of) the winding as compared to that of the voltage applied to that winding will yield the values for R_c, R_{eq}, X_m, and X_{eq}. Note that you must make these measurements at one set of terminals, either the primary windings or the secondary windings, to obtain the values for the equivalent circuit referenced to the primary side (Figure 2) or to the secondary side (Figure 3), respectively.

Let's consider the equivalent circuit referenced to the primary side of the transformer. From a brief analysis of Figure 2, it is obvious that the DC resistance measured is R_p in the open-circuit test. The resistance measured in the DC short-circuit test is R_{eq}, the combination of R_p and $a^2 R_s$ in series. When a reasonably high frequency input voltage is applied to the primary side of the transformer, we need to consider the effects of R_c and jX_m.

From Figure 4, it is clear that only R_c and jX_m influence the current that flows that into (and out of) the terminals of the primary side of the transformer. The admittance of the equivalent circuit measured across the primary side terminals in the open-circuit test is given by

$$Y_{OC} = \frac{I_{OC}}{V_{OC}} \angle -\theta = \frac{1}{R_c} + \frac{1}{jX_m}$$
(3)

In Eq (3), I_{OC} is the current that flows into the primary windings (I_p) when a voltage, V_{OC} (V_p), is applied to the primary side of the transformer and no load is connected to the secondary side. $\cos^{-1}\theta$ is called the power factor (PF).

When the two terminals on the secondary side of the transformer are shorted together (the short-circuit test), R_c, jX_m, and the series combination of R_{eq} and jX_{eq} are in parallel. We assumed that R_p and jX_p are small in comparison to R_c and jX_m to obtain the equivalent circuit in Figure 4a. If the turn ratio of the transformer, a, is small, then we can also assume that R_{eq} and jX_{eq} are small. Thus, the impedance measured in the short-circuit test can be approximated to be

$$Z_{SC} = \frac{V_{SC}}{I_{SC}} \angle \theta = R_{eq} + jX_{eq} \qquad (4)$$

where I_{SC} is the current that flows into the primary windings (I_p) when a voltage, V_{SC} (V_p), is applied to the primary side of the transformer and a short is connected across the terminals on the secondary side.

NOTE: It is critical that a low voltage is used when performing the short-circuit test. Since R_{eq} and jX_{eq} are much smaller components compared to R_c and jX_m, a large voltage applied to the primary side of the transformer during this measurement could force a large current to flow through the secondary windings, which can lead to overheating and damage the transformer.

References Chapman, S.J., (2002). <u>Electric Machinery and Power System Fundamentals</u>, New York: McGraw-Hill. pp.102-110.

Materials The equipment and components required to perform this experiment are:
- 1 ea ANDY board
- 1 ea digital multimeter
- 1 ea PC Oscilloscope
- 1 ea 10 Ω resistor
- 1 ea TM028 audio transformer

Procedure

Measurements

1. Connect the two secondary windings of the transformer in series before making the open-circuit and short-circuit measurements.

2. Using the digital multimeter, measure the resistance across the terminals of the primary side of the transformer with no load connected to the secondary terminals.

3. Using the digital multimeter, measure the resistance across the terminals of the primary side of the transformer when a short circuit is connected to the secondary windings as shown below.

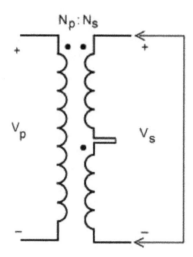

4. Remove the short circuit from the secondary side of the transformer.

> NOTE: Do not apply an arbitrary voltage to the primary side of the transformer before the short circuit is removed as this may cause a large current to flow through the secondary windings, causing them to overheat and permanently damage the transformer.

5. To measure the amplitude and phase of the AC current during the open-circuit and short-circuit tests, wire a 10 Ω current shunt in series with the primary windings of the transformer. The voltage across the resistor will be used to sense the current flowing through the primary side of the transformer. The resistor should be placed on the output terminal of the primary side of the transformer.

6. Set the frequency of the sinusoidal source on the Velleman function generator to 1kHz. The amplitude of the function generator should be set such that the power rating of the 10 Ω resistor and/or the current rating of the transformer is not exceeded.

7. With no load attached to the secondary side of the transformer, perform the AC open-circuit test. Measure the amplitude of the voltage across the 10 Ω resistor and determine the phase angle of this voltage with respect to the voltage from the function generator.

8. Set the voltage of the function generator to zero and then remove the function generator from the circuit. Connect a short from one of the secondary windings to the other secondary winding. Verify that you have not accidently connected a terminal of the secondary side of the transformer to the primary side of the transformer as this will cause a large current to flow through the primary windings when power is reapplied, which could cause a dangerously large amount of current to flow through the transformer.

9. Reattach the function generator to the primary side of the transformer. Slowly increase the voltage of the function generator to maximum allowable voltage, based upon the power rating of the 10 Ω resistor and the maximum current rating of the transformer. Measure the phase angle between the applied voltage and the current flowing through the primary side of the transformer.

10. Calculate the values of the components, R_p, R_s, R_c, R_{eq}, X_m, and X_{eq}.

PSpice Analysis

11. Using the simplified equivalent circuit, Figure 4a, determine the frequency response of the transformer from 1Hz to 100kHz.

12. Determine the 3dB frequency.

13. Using the transfer characteristic function on PSpice, find the ratio of $\mathbf{V}_s / \mathbf{V}_p$ at 1 Hz, 1000 Hz, and 100 kHz. These ratios are equal to an effective turn ratio, a', for the real transformer. What conclusions can you draw from this, given that the turn ratio is unity.

Verification

14.

Last Revision   1/04/2009

Experiment 32: Hybrid Couplers

Developers   RW Hendricks and SL Karty

Objectives   The objective of this experiment is to construct a hybrid coupler from two transformers, measure its isolation, and determine the effects of varying the values of the resistive loads on its ports.

Estimated Time for Completion

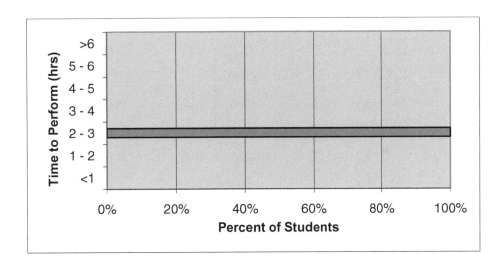

Preparation   Perform Experiment 30 (Transformer Dot Markings and Turns Ratios) on both TM028 transformers.

Background   A hybrid coupler (Figure 1) combines send (transmit) and receive signals so they can be conveyed on a single pair of wires. The combining process of a hybrid coupler is designed to prevent the transmit signal from appearing at the receive port, which could cause oscillations. At one time, hybrid transformers were used to provide the two-wire to four-wire conversion required for telephone circuits; in the late 1970s however, they were replaced with active circuits (such as operational amplifiers). Transformer hybrids are still used, especially when it is difficult or inconvenient to power active circuits.

The four-wire part of the circuit is shown on the left and right sides of Figure 1 for send (transmit) and receive, respectively. The two-wire line (which carries both signals) is shown in the top middle of Figure 1.

Specifications   Figure 1 was redrawn as Figure 2 to accommodate PSpice limitations in modeling multi-winding transformers. In Figure 1, XFMR1 is one TM028 transformer; in Figure 2, it is modeled by transformers TX1 and TX2. Similarly, in Figure 1, XFMR2 is one TM028 transformer; in Figure 2, it is modeled by transformers TX3 and TX4. While this simple way of modeling a transformer with two secondary windings (by connecting the primary windings of two PSpice transformers in series) works for this simulation, it might not work in cases where the mutual inductance between all windings is important.

This lab uses empirical measurements to determine how the transmit signal across the receive load (on the four-wire side of the hybrid) changes with the value of the line and balance resistors. The four ground symbols (Figure 2) are required for simulating the PSpice model and also for measuring the signal levels with the oscilloscope; normally, for better balance, two-wire lines would be left ungrounded.

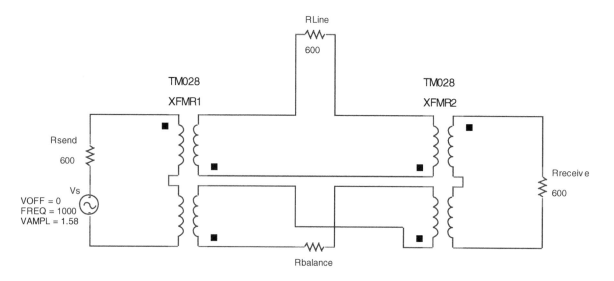

Figure 1: Basic diagram of a two-transformer hybrid coupler.

Extra credit will be awarded for (1) modeling and simulating your design in PSpice, (2) generating waveforms that show how the transmit signal level across load resistor $R_{receive}$ changes in accordance with the Line and Balance resistances, and (3) comparing the PSpice simulation results with the measured results.

Materials

The equipment and components required to perform this experiment are:
- ANDY board
- digital multimeter
- Oscilloscope
- 2 ea TM028 transformers
- 3 ea 150 Ω resistors
- 3 ea 270 Ω resistors
- 3 ea 330 Ω resistors
- 1 ea 1 kΩ trim pot

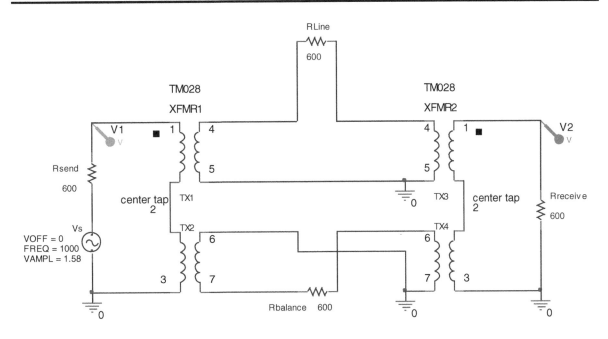

Figure 2: Configuration of hybrid coupler for testing and PSpice simulation.

Procedure

Part A: Circuit Design

1. Build the combining hybrid coupler in Figure 2, using one 270 Ω resistor in series with one 330 Ω resistor to make each 600 Ω resistor. As an alternative, two 1200 Ω resistors can be connected in parallel to make each 600 Ω resistor. Since transformers are passive, they do not require any power. However, power is still needed for the sine wave oscillator and for the op amp attenuators (which feed the oscilloscope) on the ANDY board. Be sure to use the 1k Ω trim pot for $R_{balance}$ which should be connected so that as the pot is turned clockwise the resistance between the two wired terminals increases. Be sure to short the unused terminal to the wiper (see Section 3.11).

2. Connect the Channel 1 input to the oscilloscope 10× attenuator to pin 1 of XFMR1 and adjust the sine wave oscillator for 1 kHz at 1.1 volts peak (2.2 volts peak-to-peak). This sets the voltage level V_1 at .775 volts RMS, which is 0 dBm relative to 600 Ω.

3. Connect the Channel 2 input to the oscilloscope 1× attenuator to pin 1 of XFMR2. This measures the voltage level V_2 across load resistor $R_{receive}$.

Procedure

Part B: Circuit Measurements

15. With a 600 Ω resistor at R_{Line}, adjust the resistance of the $R_{balance}$ trim pot to minimize the voltage V_2 across load resistor $R_{receive}$. Take a screen snapshot of the oscilloscope display and record the voltage for V_2 in Table 1. Remove

the R$_{balance}$ trim pot from the circuit, measure its resistance with your digital meter, and record the R$_{balance}$ resistance measurement in Table 1. Include a copy of Table 1 in your lab report and on the validation sheet. Be sure to reinstall the R$_{balance}$ trim pot in the circuit after you have measured its resistance, being careful not to change its setting.

16. Leaving the R$_{balance}$ trim pot at the same setting as in step 4, change R$_{Line}$ from 600 Ω to 150 Ω. Take a screen snapshot of the oscilloscope display and record the voltage for V$_2$ in Table 1 in your lab report and on the validation sheet.

17. Repeat step 4, leaving the 150 Ω resistor in place of R$_{Line}$. Take a screen snapshot of the oscilloscope display when you find the R$_{balance}$ trim pot setting for minimum received signal level V$_2$. Record this voltage for V$_2$. Remove the R$_{balance}$ trim pot from the circuit and measure its resistance with your digital meter. Record your measurements in Table 1 in your lab report and on the validation sheet.

Table 1: Results.

Measurements (subject to validation)					PSpice Results(Extra Credit)		
R$_{Line}$ Ω	R$_{balance}$ Ω	V$_2$ (p-to-p)	V$_2$/2.2	20 log$_{10}$(V$_2$/2.2) dB	V$_2$ (p-to-p)	V$_2$/2.2	20 log$_{10}$(V$_2$/2.2) dB
600							
150	"						
150							

Note: The " in the R$_{balance}$ column means that the trim pot is left at its previous setting.

Procedure

Part C: PSpice Simulation and Analysis (Extra Credit)

7. Use PSpice to simulate and test your circuit. You will have to model XFMR1 (in Figure 1) as transformers TX1 and TX2 (combined in Figure 2). Similarly, you will have to model XFMR2 (in Figure 1) as transformers TX3 and TX4 (combined in Figure 2). In PSpice, double-clicking on each transformer brings up another screen where you can enter additional parameters. To model these transformers in PSpice, enter 0.1 as the inductance (in Henrys) for the primary winding, 0.1 as the inductance in Henrys for the secondary winding, and 1 as their coupling coefficient. Enter these three parameters for TX1, TX2, TX3, and TX4.

8. Use 600 Ω for R$_{Line.}$ Use the same resistance for R$_{balance}$ that you recorded in step 4. A fixed value resistor should be used to model the R$_{balance}$ trim pot because it is difficult to model a potentiometer in PSpice. Put a PSpice voltage probe on pin 1 of both transformers. Set Vs for 1.58 peak volts to

allow for the voltage drop across R_{send}. This should result in 1.1 volts peak (2.2 volts peak-to-peak) at pin 1 of XFMR1.

9. Recommended PSpice simulation settings: Analysis tab > Analysis type: Time Domain (Transient) > Run to time: 10m seconds > Start saving data after: 5m seconds > Maximum step size: 10u seconds. Run a new simulation each time you change a resistance.

10. Take a screenshot of your simulation results and record the V_2 voltage across $R_{receive}$ in Table 1 in your lab report and on your validation sheet. If V_2 is much smaller than V_1, it will display a flat horizontal line at 0 volts; if this happens, temporarily remove the PSpice voltage probe at V_1 and rerun the simulation to more accurately measure V_2.

11. Repeat step 10 after changing R_{Line} to 150 Ω but leaving $R_{balance}$ the same as it was in step 6.

12. Repeat step 10 leaving R_{Line} at 150 Ω but after changing $R_{balance}$ to the measurement you recorded in step 6.

Lab Report

4. The lab report may be written in a format of your own choosing. Be sure to include your screenshots from steps 4 and 5 along with the measurements section of Table 1 filled in.

5. The dB figures in Table 1 show the relative signal levels between V_2 and V_1. The absolute value is the isolation between the send and receive sides of the four-wire interface. What is the relationship between the line and balance resistances for maximum isolation? Include the answer to this question in your lab report.

6. **Extra Credit:** Include your PSpice circuit diagram and screenshots from steps 10 – 12 and complete the PSpice section of Table 1.

7. Discuss the physical significance of this circuit. What does it accomplish and why is it important?

Validation Demonstrate the measurements of step 6 on your ANDY board to your instructor for verification of your results in the measurements section of Table 1.

Last Revision 1/05/2009

Experiment 33: Passive Filters

Developers   WC Headley, SL Karty and RW Hendricks

Objectives   The objectives of this experiment are: (1) to measure the transfer function of a highpass filter and a bandpass filter; (2) to compare the experimental results with simple circuit theory; and (3) to create the Bode plot for each filter using the experimental data.

Estimated Time for Completion

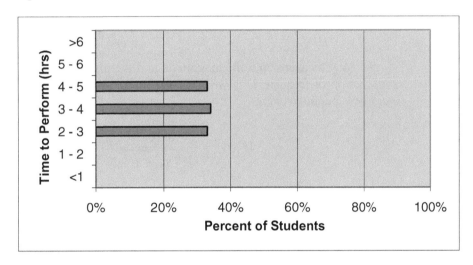

Preparation   Read the sections in your textbook that cover transfer functions, passive filters, the decibel scale, and Bode plots.

Background   A filter is a circuit that passes signals of desired frequencies and attenuates signals of other (undesired) frequencies. Lowpass filters pass frequencies below a critical frequency called the corner (or cutoff) frequency and attenuate frequencies above the corner frequency. Highpass filters pass frequencies above the corner frequency and attenuate frequencies below it. A bandpass filter is a combination of a lowpass and a highpass filter that will pass only frequencies within a given desired band. Finally, a bandstop filter is a combination of a lowpass and a high pass filter that will pass all frequencies except those within a prescribed band.

Simple passive filters are commonly built from resistors, capacitors, and inductors. A highpass and a bandpass filter are illustrated in Figures 1 (a) and (b) respectively. The theoretical analysis of these circuits is well-covered in standard texts; the student is referred therein for a derivation of the equations. The important parameters of these filters are their transfer functions, the corner (or cutoff) frequency for the high pass filter, and the corner and center frequencies for the bandpass filter.

The complex transfer function is defined as $H(\omega) \equiv V_o / V_{in}$. The transfer function for the highpass filter shown in Figure 1(a) is given by

$$H(\omega) = \frac{j\omega RC}{1 + j\omega RC} \tag{1}$$

while the transfer function for the bandpass filter in Figure 1(b) is

$$H(\omega) = \frac{R}{R + j(\omega L - \frac{1}{\omega C})} \tag{2}$$

We may measure both the magnitude and the phase of the transfer function as a function of frequency, as will be done in this experiment. For the highpass filter, these parameters are

$$|H(\omega)| = \frac{\omega RC}{\sqrt{1 + \omega^2 R^2 C^2}}$$
$$\phi = \tan^{-1}\left[\frac{1}{\omega RC}\right] \tag{3}$$

while for the bandpass filter these parameters are

$$|H(\omega)| = \frac{\omega RC}{\sqrt{\omega^2 R^2 C^2 + (\omega^2 LC - 1)^2}}$$
$$\phi = \tan^{-1}\left[\frac{1 - \omega^2 LC}{\omega RC}\right] \tag{4}$$

In electric circuit analysis, it is common to present the gain and attenuation of signals in units of decibels (dB) which are defined by

$$G_{dB} = 20 \log_{10}\left[\frac{V_o}{V_{in}}\right] \tag{5}$$

where V_{in} and V_o are the input and output signal of the filter, respectively. Thus, the gain may also be represented by

$$G_{dB} = 20 \log_{10}|H(\omega)| \tag{6}$$

The cutoff frequency, ω_c, is defined to be the frequency at which the filter attenuates the signal by -3dB. Thus, we see that a -3 dB gain is an attenuation of the output by $1/\sqrt{2}$. This is commonly referred to as the 3 dB point of the filter. For the highpass filter, we may show that $\omega_c = 1/RC$ by setting $|H(\omega)| = 1/\sqrt{2}$ and solving for ω. Similarly, the center frequency of the band-pass filter, which

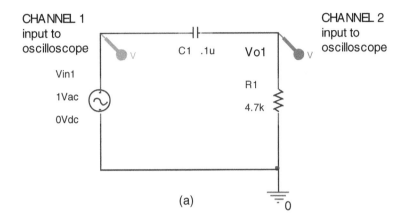

(a)

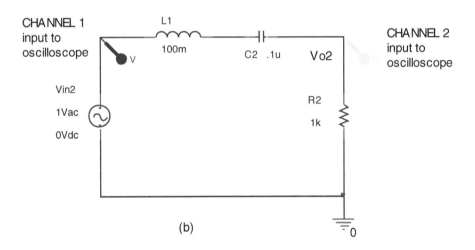

(b)

Figure 1: Circuit diagram for (a) a highpass passive filter and (b) a bandpass passive filter.

is the frequency at which the transfer function is a maximum, may be shown to be $\omega_o = 1/\sqrt{LC}$.

A convenient way to visually display the performance of a filter is to plot the gain (in dB) versus the $\log_{10}$ of the frequency of the signal. It is shown in standard textbooks that Bode plots are made up of straight line segments that are joined at the corner frequencies. The slope of the Bode plot is the exponent of the frequency dependence for a given frequency range. In this experiment, you will determine the Bode plot for the filters shown in Figure 1.

Experiment 33

References   *Boyce, JC, (1988). <u>Operational Amplifiers and Linear Integrated Circuits</u> (2E). Boston: PWS-Kent. p184 ff. and p213 ff.

*Hanselman, D., and B. Littlefield, (2005). <u>Mastering MATLAB 7</u>. Upper Saddle River, NJ: Pearson Prentice Hall.

Stinson, C., and M. Dodge, (2007). <u>Microsoft Office Excel 2007 Inside Out</u>, Redmond, WA: Microsoft Press.

Materials   The equipment and components required to perform this experiment are:
- 1 ea ANDY breadboard
- 1 ea dual trace oscilloscope
- 1 ea 1 kΩ resistor
- 1 ea 4.7 kΩ resistor
- 1 ea 0.1 µF capacitor
- 1 ea 100 mH inductor

Procedure   **Analysis:**

1. Calculate the cutoff frequency and the center frequency for the highpass and bandpass filters shown in Figures 1(a) and (b), respectively. Give the answers in terms of both ω and f.

2. Choose a scientific graphing program (e.g., Excel, MATLAB) and plot the magnitude and phase Bode plots for each filter from 70 Hz to 3 kHz. Do not plot any data points; show only a line through them. Save these graphs for use in steps 9 and 13. A MATLAB program that serves as a template for preparing this plot is given in Appendix D.2. We have found the references by Hanselman and Littlefield (2005) and by Stinson and Dodge (2004) to be excellent sources of information for MATLAB and Excel, respectively. The program may be downloaded from the text website at **http://www.lab-in-a-box.net**.

   Fill in Table 1 with the magnitude and phase calculations for both filters from 70 Hz to 3 kHz. Add additional rows for the frequencies given in steps 8 and 12.

Table 1: Magnitude and phase for Bode plots of highpass and bandpass filters (calculated).

Frequency (Hz)	Calculated Magnitude Highpass Filter (volts)	dB = 20 log previous column	Calculated Phase (degrees) Highpass Filter	Calculated Magnitude Bandpass Filter (volts)	dB = 20 log previous column	Calculated Phase (degrees) Bandpass Filter
70						
3,000						

Table 2: Magnitude and phase for Bode plots of highpass and bandbass filters (measured).

Frequency (Hz)	Measured Magnitude Highpass Filter (volts)	dB = 20 log previous column	Measured Phase (degrees) Highpass Filter	Measured Magnitude Bandpass Filter (volts)	dB = 20 log previous column	Measured Phase (degrees) Bandpass Filter
70						
3,000						

Graph coordinates for Excel: your Bode plot of magnitude should have a y-axis starting at 0 dB at the top and decreasing as you go down the page, with a logarithmic x-axis for frequency. The Bode plot of phase should have a degree scale on it's y-axis and the same logarithmic x-axis for frequency as the magnitude plot. The two graphs should be on the same page, with the magnitude plot above the phase plot, so the frequency axes are aligned with each other.

3. **Extra Credit:** Derive the equations given above for the transfer function, its magnitude, and the phase angle for both filters.

Measurements:

4. Construct the highpass circuit shown in Figure 1(a).

5. Connect the oscilloscope inputs with the green waveform (Channel 1) measuring the function generator output and the red waveform (Channel 2) measuring the filter output.

6. Set the frequency of the sine wave function generator to its lowest value ($\approx$ 70 Hz) and set the amplitude of the function generator to 1.0 V.

7. Measure the magnitude and phase of the output voltage. Fill in Table 2 with your magnitude and phase measurements for both filters from 0 Hz to 3 kHz. Add additional rows for the frequencies in steps 8 and 12. The formula for the phase angle (in degrees) is $\phi = \Delta t \cdot f \cdot 360^o$.

8. Increase the frequency of the function generator in the sequence 125, 250, 500, 1000, 1500, 2000, 2500, and 3000 Hz, repeating the measurements at each step. Show screenshots of your oscilloscope data. Provide representative screenshots of some of the measurements.

9. Enter your data on the Bode plots for the highpass filter created in step 2. Show only the data points; do not connect them with a line. Include an electronic copy of your graphs in your report.

10. Using your experimental data, find the cutoff frequency, ω_c. Calculate the percent difference between your experimental value and the theoretical

value. Include one oscilloscope screenshot at the highpass filter cutoff frequency.

11. Construct the bandpass circuit shown in Figure 1(b).

12. Repeat the measurements of the magnitude and phase angle for the transfer function in the sequence 125, 250, 500, 750, 1000, 1250, 1500, 1600, 1700, 2000, 2250, 2500, 2750, 3000 Hz . You may need to take more data points near the center frequency as the transfer function is very sensitive in this region. While observing the signals on the oscilloscope, adjust your frequency to maximize the output signal. Provide all measurements and two screenshots from the center of the bandpass region, one screenshot with the scope in its oscilloscope mode and one screenshot in its spectrum analyzer mode (to show frequency versus amplitude).

13. Enter your data on the Bode plots for the bandpass filter created in step 2. Show only the data points; do not connect them with a line. Print out (or save an electronic copy of) your graphs for inclusion in your lab notebook. For Excel, use the same graph coordinates as in step 2.

14. Using your experimental data, find the center frequency, ω_o. Calculate the percent difference between your experimental value and the theoretical value.

Last Revision   1/05/2009

Experiment 34: An Active Filter

Developers WC Headley, RF Cooper, SL Karty and RW Hendricks

Objectives The objective of this experiment is to build an active bandpass filter that has gain greater than unity in the bandpass window.

Estimated Time for Completion

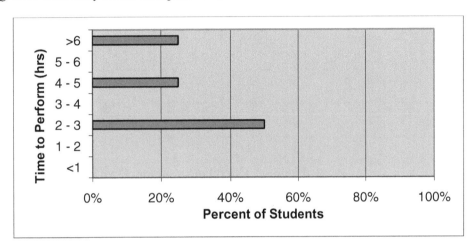

Preparation Read the sections in your text that describe active filters.

Background There are many ways to design active filters as discussed in all introductory circuits texts. Boyce (1988) also has an excellent discussion. The active bandpass filter shown in Figure 1 uses a single op amp in combination with resistors and capacitors to create an active bandpass filter with gain. This bandpass filter circuit is extremely useful because, unlike the passive filter developed in Experiment 33, the center frequency can be changed by varying a resistor instead of changing the values of the capacitors. For this filter, the center frequency is given by:

$$\omega_0 = \sqrt{\frac{R_1 + R_3}{C^2 R_1 R_2 R_3}} \tag{1}$$

The center frequency can be changed by varying the variable resistor R_3. Increasing R_3 decreases the center frequency while decreasing R_3 increases the center frequency. The bandwidth is given by:

$$\Delta \omega = \frac{2}{C R_2} \tag{2}$$

The bandwidth is the range of frequencies between the lower and upper cutoff frequencies. Notice that it is independent of the variable resistor R_3 so the center

271

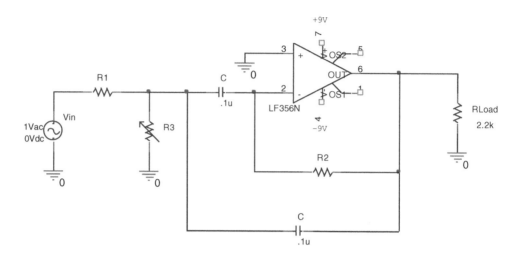

Figure 1: Circuit diagram for active bandpass filter.

frequency may be changed without changing the bandwidth. The gain at the center frequency of the bandpass filter is given by:

$$A_V = \frac{-R_2}{2R_1} \tag{3}$$

Note that in some texts, these filters may be created using three cascaded op amps—one for a lowpass filter, one for a highpass filter, and one for gain. The advantage of the circuit shown in Figure 1 is that it requires only one op amp.

References

*Boyce, JC, (1988). <u>Operational Amplifiers and Linear Integrated Circuits</u> (2E). Boston: PWS-Kent. p 213 ff.

*Hanselman, D., and B. Littlefield, (2005). <u>Mastering MATLAB 7</u>. Upper Saddle River, NJ: Pearson Prentice Hall.

Stinson, C., and M. Dodge, (2007). <u>Microsoft Office Excel 2007 Inside Out</u>, Redmond, WA: Microsoft Press.

Materials

The equipment and components required to perform this experiment are:
- 1 ea ANDY Breadboard
- 1 ea dual trace oscilloscope
- PSpice software
- 1 ea LF356N operational amplifier
- 1 ea 2.2 kΩ resistor
- various resistors *(to be determined)*
- 1 ea trim pot *(to be determined)*
- 2 ea 0.1 µF capacitor

Procedure **Analysis:**

1. Design the bandpass filter in Figure 1 to have a center frequency of 1.0 kHz, a bandwidth of 200 Hz, and a voltage gain of -5 at the center frequency. (Note: The values of the capacitors and the load resistor have already been given to you and are determined by the components available in your parts kit.)

2. Using the results from step 1, choose resistors from your kit to use for R_1 and R_2. You may want to put two or more resistors in series to get close to your design values. Also, choose the trim pot with the smallest range that contains the value you calculated for R_3. For greater sensitivity, you may want to put a smaller trim pot in series with a resistor such that the trim pot, when set near its midpoint, plus the fixed resistor sum to R_3.

3. Using your choice of scientific graphing program (e.g., Excel, MATLAB), plot the magnitude and phase Bode plots for the filter from 60 Hz to 3 kHz. Do not plot any data points; show only a line through them. Save these graphs for use in steps 13. We have found the references by Hanselman and Littlefield (2005) and by Stinson and Dodge (2004) to be excellent sources of information for MATLAB and Excel, respectively. A MATLAB program that serves as a template for preparing this plot is given in Appendix D.2. The program may be downloaded from the text website found at **http://www.lab-in-a-box.net**.

4. **Extra Credit:** Derive Eqs (1) through (3).

PSpice Analysis:

5. Construct the circuit of Figure 1 in PSpice.

6. Set R_1 and R_2 equal to the values determined in step 2.

7. Set R_3 equal to the value calculated in step 1.

8. Using the AC sweep analysis, plot the frequency response.

9. Using the plot of the frequency response, find the center frequency, gain, and bandwidth of the circuit. Calculate the percent deviation of each parameter from the design criteria given in step 1. Explain any discrepancies.

10. Cut and paste a copy of the frequency response plot to your notebook.

Measurements:

11. Construct the circuit in Figure 1, setting the trim pot to the value of R_3 measured in step 1. Set the frequency of the function generator to its lowest value and set its amplitude to 1.0 V.

12. Gradually increase the frequency of the circuit to 4 kHz. Determine the amplitude, gain, frequency, and phase of the output for at least 10 frequencies. Use the graphs created in step 3 as guidance for frequencies at which to acquire data.

13. Plot the data acquired in step 12 on the graphs created in step 3. Plot only the data points.

14. Do the data acquired in step 12 agree with the analytical results created in step 3 and the PSpice results of step 8? Explain any discrepancies.

15. Set the frequency of the function generator to its lowest value and check that its amplitude is still 1.0 V. Gradually increase the frequency of the circuit until the output reaches a maximum. Determine the amplitude, gain, frequency, and phase of the output at this point.

16. Calculate the percent deviation of the measured gain and center frequency from the design criteria given in step 1. Describe two ways to experimentally find the center frequency of a bandpass filter. Explain the relationship between the gain and the phase of the output.

17. Set the upper and lower voltage cursors at the -3 dB point from the signal maximum.

18. Decrease the input signal frequency from the center frequency until the maximum output signal just touches the upper and lower cursors. Record the frequency.

19. Repeat step 18 but increase the input signal frequency from the center frequency. Record the frequency at which the output signal again just touches the cursors.

20. Compute the bandwidth of the filter and compute the percent deviation of the bandwidth from both the design criteria of 200 Hz given in step 1 and the PSpice value determined in step 9. Explain any discrepancies. What happens when R_3 is varied?

Last Revision   1/05/2009

Experiment 35: Sweeping Passive Filters

Developers   RW Hendricks and SL Karty

Objectives   The objective of this experiment is to use a spectrum analyzer to display the characteristics of two simple passive filters and to compare the results to model simulations.

Estimated Time for Completion

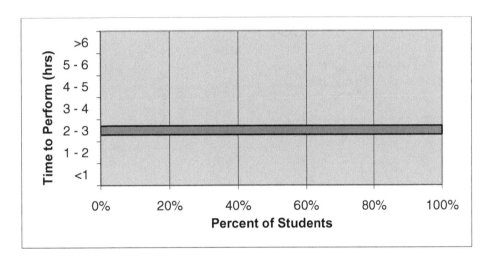

Preparation   Perform Experiment 33 (Passive Filters).

Background   Passive filters (e.g., Figure 1) are ideal to study because of their simplicity. This lab uses the sweep generator and white noise generator in version 1.30 of the Zeitnitz oscilloscope program or using a file posted at **www.lab-in-a-box.net** for use with the arbitrary function generator option of the Velleman scope. These features are used along with the spectrum analyzer to display the characteristics of a band pass filter and a band reject filter (Figure 1).

The Zeitnitz software has two independent signal generators, one for each output channel, making it possible for one channel to be sweeping a tone while the other channel produces white noise. Only one channel will be used in this experiment, first to sweep a tone and then to produce white noise. The spectrum analyzer can display either of two input channels (one at a time). Because the signal generators and the spectrum analyzer can operate simultaneously, the sound card's line output can be plugged back into its line input to display one of the signal generator's outputs. Connecting a filter between the sound card's line output and its line input enables the spectrum analyzer to display the characteristics of the filter with either the sweep generator or the white noise generator.

Using the spectrum analyzer with the sweep or white noise generator to display a filter's shape may minimize the number of phase measurements required. Phase measurements are not required in this experiment; however,

275

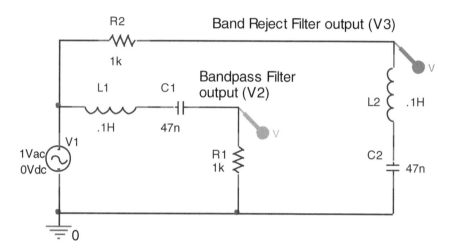

Figure 1: Circuit diagram for a bandpass filter and a band reject filter connected to the same signal generator. The 1k Ω resistor R2 minimizes any interaction between the filters.

when they are required, they will need to be taken manually at each frequency using the oscilloscope (as in Experiment 33).

Both the bandpass and the band reject filters are connected to the same signal generator so that both filters can be swept at the same time using PSpice. The 1kΩ resistor R_2 from the signal generator to the band reject filter minimizes any interaction between the filters. The filters must be swept separately when using the Zeitnitz spectrum analyzer because only one of its spectrum analyzer inputs is active at any time.

Specifications   Connecting a filter between the sound card's line output and line input, and using either the Zeitnitz sweep generator or white noise generator will display the filter's amplitude versus frequency characteristics on the spectrum analyzer.

The spectrum analyzer display may be somewhat unstable if the oscillator is sweeping too quickly; using the spectrum analyzer's peak hold function (a checkbox on the Zeitnitz spectrum analyzer front panel) will make the display easier to read.

The spectral display may not begin until 1,500 Hz (even with a start-sweep frequency of 1,000) if the sweep rate is 2 seconds or faster. Using slower sweep rates will prevent this problem and will provide better resolution.

Materials   The equipment and components required to perform this experiment are:
- ANDY board
- digital multimeter

- Zeitnitz oscilloscope program version 1.30 or later
- 2 ea 47 nF capacitors
- 2 ea 1 kΩ resistors
- 2 ea 100 mH coils

Procedure

Part A: PSpice Simulation and Analysis

1. Model your filter circuits (Figure 1) in PSpice. You can sweep both filters at the same time by placing one PSpice voltage test probe at the output of each filter. Recommended PSpice Simulation Settings are: Analysis type – AC/Sweep/Noise, AC Sweep Type – Logarithmic Decade, Start Frequency 300, End Frequency 10000, Points/Decade 100. Remember to include the internal resistance (approximately 100 Ω) of the inductor in your model!

2. Take a screenshot of your simulation results and include it with your report. Use the cursor to find the frequencies and amplitudes for filling in the Modeled Frequency columns in Tables 1 and 2.[†]

Procedure

Part B: Circuit Design

3. Build the filter circuits in Figure 1. Because these filters are passive, they do not require power. However, power is still needed for the op amp attenuators (which feed the Zeitnitz oscilloscope) on the ANDY board.

4. Connect the output of the bandpass filter (V_2 in Figure 1) to the $1\times$ attenuator of the Channel 1 input to the Zeitnitz oscilloscope/spectrum analyzer.

5. Plug a second stereo cable into the audio output of the sound card. Be sure to connect the ground wire (the "fat" black wire) to the same ground node as the ground from the input signal cable.

6. Connect the Channel 1 output from the Zeitnitz signal generator (the red wire) to the common input to the two filters. Use two cables, one plugged into your sound card's line input and one plugged into your sound card's line output for the sweep generator output. Connect the other end of the output wire to the junction of L_1 and R_2 in Figure 1. Do not connect the Channel 2 output (the thinner black wire) and be sure that it is not shorted to any component. **Note:** This connection serves as the only input to the circuit (denoted by V_1 in Figure 1). <u>Do not</u> connect the output of the ANDY board's built-in function generator! It is unused in this experiment.

7. Select the Zeitnitz Signal Generator tab. Check the Zeitnitz signal generator sweep box and set it for a sine wave of approximately 0.5 volts, 5 second sweep (or longer), starting at 200 Hz and ending at 11,000 Hz. Be sure to connect both stereo cables to the sound card.

[†] MS Word files for Tables 1 and 2 may be found on the text website at **http://www.lab-in-a-box.net**

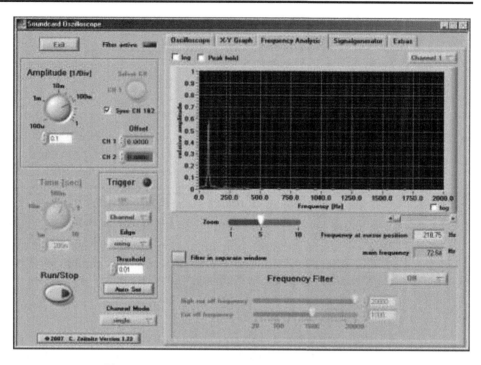

Figure 2: Spectrum analyzer display of a signal.

8. Select the Zeitnitz spectrum analyzer mode by pressing the Frequency Analysis tab. Check the spectrum analyzer "Peak hold" box and the "log" box (above the "Frequency at cursor position" box). If the signal generator sweep box is unchecked, you should see a stationary peaked response (maximum) similar to Figure 2 when the signal generator is tuned to the filter's resonant frequency. The waveform will become wider when the signal is swept. Be sure that the signal generator sweep box is checked before continuing.

Procedure

Part C: Circuit Measurements

9. Connect the Channel 1 Zeitnitz input to the bandpass filter's output (V_2 in Figure 1). Adjust the spectrum analyzer amplitude control for a peak relative amplitude of 1 on the display. Try to adjust the waveform for maximum deflection, as close to the zero at the bottom of the screen as possible while keeping the maximum value at 1. It may be necessary to slightly change the signal generator output because it interacts with the spectrum analyzer amplitude control. Take a screenshot of the Zeitnitz spectrum analyzer display and include it in your lab report.

10. Using the spectrum analyzer cursor, determine center frequency of the filter and the frequencies (both below and above the center frequency) for the relative amplitudes listed in Table 1. Enter your data in the table and include it in your lab report.

11. Move the Channel 1 Zeitnitz input to the band reject filter output (V_3 in Figure 1). It may be necessary to slightly change the signal generator output and the spectrum analyzer amplitude control for maximum deflection as in step 9. Try to adjust the center of the dip as close to zero as possible, while keeping the maximum value at 1. Conduct another sweep and take a screen snapshot of the display to include in your lab report.

12. Make similar measurements to those described in Step 10, record your data in Table 2, and include it in your lab report.

13. Uncheck the signal generator sweep box. Change the Zeitnitz signal generator from sine to white noise and increase the signal generator output to approximately 1 volt. Be sure that the signal generator sweep box is unchecked before continuing. Follow the same procedure as in step 11 for adjusting the display deflection. Take a screen snapshot of the display to include in your lab report. Explain your observations.

14. Move the Channel 1 Zeitnitz input to the bandpass filter output. Follow the same procedure as in step 9 for adjusting the display deflection. Take a screenshot of the display to include in your lab report. Explain your observations.

Lab Report   The lab report may be written in a format of your own choosing. Be sure to include Tables 1 and 2, your screenshots from steps 2, 9, 11, 13, 14, and explain your observations in steps 13 and 14.

Validation   Demonstrate taking the measurements on your ANDY board in steps 13 and 14 to your instructor for verification.

Last Revision   1/05/2008

Experiment 36: Impedance Transmission Parameters

Developers   RW Hendricks and SL Karty

Objectives   The objective of this experiment is to build a two-port network and measure its z impedance transmission parameters.

Estimated Time for Completion

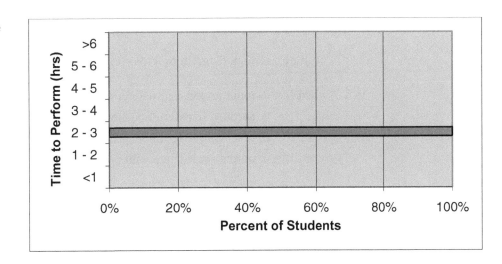

Preparation   Read the sections in your text that describe two-port networks. Download and read Apex Application Note 13 which contains schematic diagrams (Figures 7 and 8) for single op amp voltage-to-current converter circuits. Download Carter (2001) and save it for reference. Perform Experiment 12.

Background   A two-port network is a four-terminal circuit with paired terminals forming an input port and an output port. A port is a terminal pair where energy is supplied or extracted. The two-port network assumes that the net current entering each terminal pair is zero, so the current exiting each port's lower terminal is the same as the current entering each port's upper terminal (Figure 1).

The impedance parameters express V_1 and V_2 in terms of I_1 and I_2. They are given by the z_{ij} in Eqs (1) below.

$$\left. \begin{array}{l} V_1 = z_{11}I_1 + z_{12}I_2 \\ V_2 = z_{21}I_1 + z_{22}I_2 \end{array} \right\} \tag{1}$$

These parameters may be obtained from the following four equations which are derived by setting I_1 or I_2 to zero. They show how the four z_{ij} parameters may be obtained by applying a current at one port (with the other port open) and measuring the resulting voltages at both ports. The first and second equations are

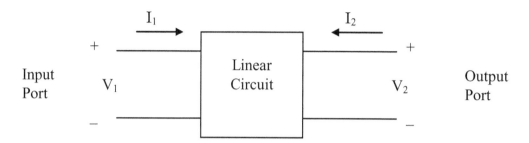

Figure 1. Block diagram of a two-port network.

$z_{11} = V_1/I_1$ when $I_2 = 0$, input impedance with open output port

$z_{21} = V_2/I_1$ when $I_2 = 0$, forward transfer impedance with open output port

$z_{12} = V_1/I_2$ when $I_1 = 0$, reverse transfer impedance with open input port

$z_{22} = V_2/I_2$ when $I_1 = 0$, output impedance with open input port

for driving the input port while the output port is open while third and fourth equations are for driving the output port while the input is open. All four z parameters are impedances and are measured in ohms.

Figure 2 shows the linear circuit that will be used in this experiment which contains a resistor, an inductor, and a capacitor. Linear circuits may also contain dependent sources.

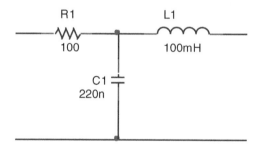

Figure 2. Schematic diagram of a two-port network.

Figure 3 shows a two-port reciprocal network. A two-port network is reciprocal when the open-circuit voltage measured at one port (the voltage is the result of a current injected at the second port) remains the same when the two ports are switched. If a two-port network is reciprocal, then $z_{12} = z_{21}$. Circuits containing only resistors, capacitors, and inductors are always reciprocal. Adding dependent sources would make the network nonreciprocal. If a two-port network is symmetric (not shown), then $z_{11} = z_{22}$.

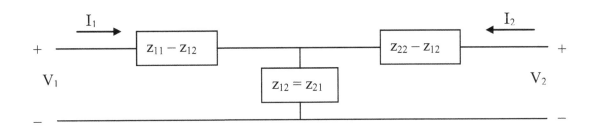

Figure 3. Block diagram of a two-port reciprocal network.

In this experiment, you will build the current injector created in Experiment 12 and then will measure the z-parameters of the circuit shown in Figure 2. The experimental results will be compared with those predicted by theory.

References
Apex Microtechnology (2007). "Application Note 13: Voltage to Current Conversion." 18 December 2008
< http://www.cirrus.com/en/pubs/appNote/Apex_AN13U_C.pdf >

*Carter, B., and T.R. Brown, (2001). <u>Handbook of Operational Amplifier Applications</u>. Application Report SBOA092A. 18 December 2008
<http://focus.ti.com/lit/an/sboa092a/sboa092a.pdf>.

Overview
In Part A, you will use PSpice to model a two-port reciprocal network and determine its z parameters. In Part B, the network, along with a voltage-controlled current source (Figure 4) which will be used to provide I_1 or I_2, will be built on the ANDY board. The circuit in Figure 4, which is identical to the one studied in Experiment 12 under DC conditions, uses the function generator on the ANDY board to input an AC signal into an op amp configured as a current source. In Figure 4, the current gain is –1 mA/volt. The terminals shown connected to the load (Figure 4) can be connected to take the place of the current source in Figures 5b, 6b, 7b, and 8b below.

Materials
The equipment and components required to perform this experiment are:
- ANDY board
- digital multimeter
- Zeitnitz oscilloscope program version 1.30
- 1 ea LM741 or LF356 op amp
- 1 ea 100 Ω resistor
- 4 ea 1k Ω resistors
- 1 ea 220 nF capacitor
- 1 ea 100 mH inductor

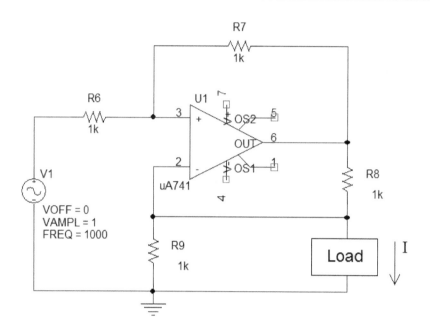

Figure 4. Schematic diagram of an op amp circuit that supplies output current to a load in linear correspondence to the input voltage. (See Experiment 12 for details.)

Procedure

Part A: PSpice Simulation and Analysis

1. Model your network (Figures 5a, 6a, 7a, and 8a) in PSpice. Resistors R2 through R5 have been added to Figures 5a, 6a, 7a, and 8a to reduce the V_1 and V_2 voltage levels (divided by 1,000) so they can be graphed with I_1 and I_2. Recommended PSpice settings are: Analysis tab; Analysis type: Time Domain (Transient); Options: General Settings; Run to time .003 seconds; Start saving data after 0.001 seconds; Maximum step size: 0.00001 seconds.

2. Position the PSpice current source (I_1 or I_2) and the voltage and current probes as shown in Figures 5a, 6a, 7a, and 8a. Run the simulation. Take a screen snapshot of your simulation results for each figure and include it in your report. Use the cursors to make amplitude and phase measurements to calculate z_{11} (Figure 5a), z_{21} (Figure 6a), z_{12} (Figure 7a), and z_{22} (Figure 8a). Be sure to move the voltage probes to the positions indicated in each figure before taking each measurement. Also be sure to move the current source I_1 to the right side of the network being tested (and re-label it as I_2) before taking the measurements for Figures 7a and 8a. Use the formula $\varphi = \Delta t(f)360°$ to convert PSpice time measurements into phase readings and record the phase and the magnitude in Table 1.

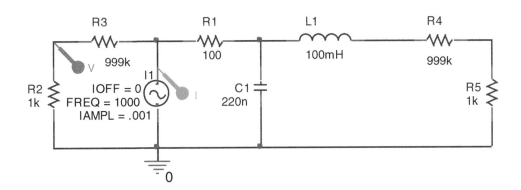

Figure 5a. PSpice: Schematic diagram of a two-port reciprocal network with voltage dividers and current source input. Resistors R2 through R5 are used only in the PSpice simulation, not in the circuit being built and tested (Figure 5b). This circuit shows the setup for measuring z_{11}.

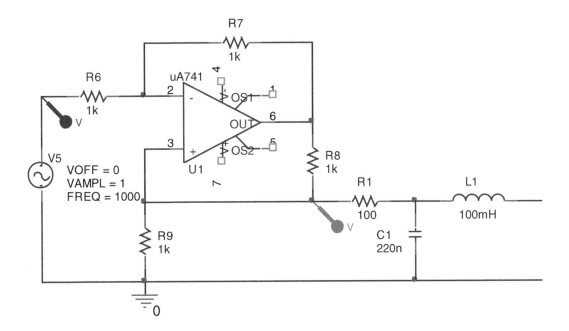

Figure 5b. This network will be built and tested in Part B. Figure 5b is the same as Figure 5a except that the voltage dividers have been removed and the PSpice current source has been replaced by the current source in Figure 4.

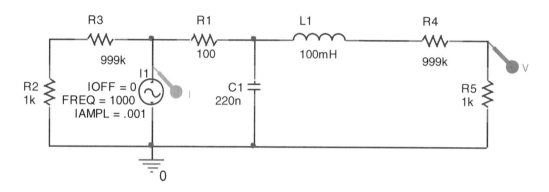

Figure 6a. PSpice: Schematic diagram of a two-port reciprocal network with voltage dividers and current source input. This circuit shows the setup for measuring z_{21}.

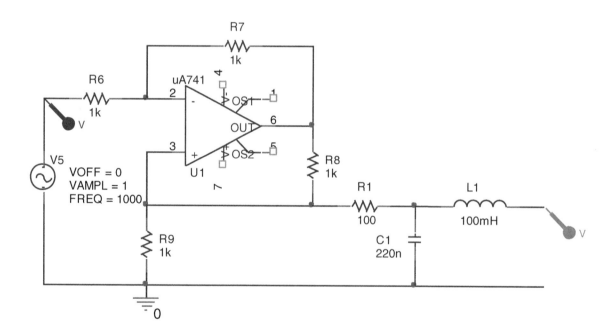

Figure 6b. This version of Figure 6a will be built and tested in Part B.

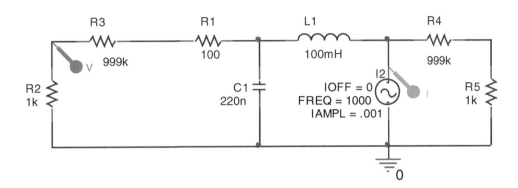

Figure 7a. PSpice: Schematic diagram of a two-port reciprocal network
with voltage dividers and current source input. This circuit
shows the setup for measuring z_{12}.

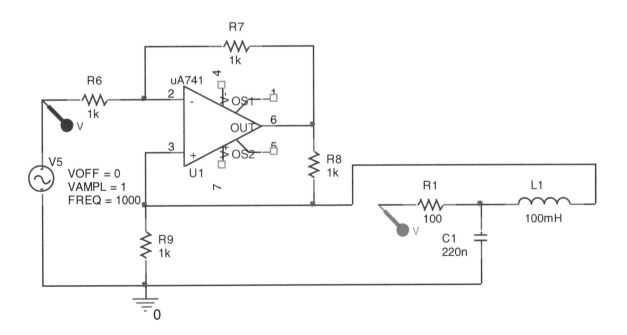

Figure 7b. This version of Figure 7a will be built and tested in Part B.

287

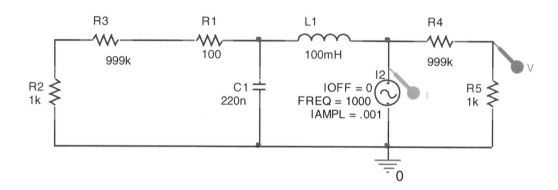

Figure 8a. PSpice: Schematic diagram of a two-port reciprocal network with voltage dividers and current source input. This circuit shows the setup for measuring z_{22}.

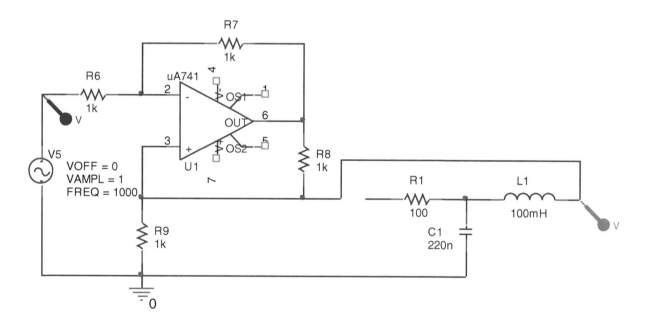

Figure 8b. This version of Figure 8a will be built and tested in Part B.

Part B: Circuit Measurements

3. Build the network in Figures 4 and 5b on your ANDY board. Be sure to connect +9 VDC and –9 VDC to the op amp in Figure 4. Do not build Figure 5a with R2 through R5; these resistors are used only in the simulations (for reducing the V_1 and V_2 voltage levels so they can be graphed with I_1 and I_2). Set the ANDY board function generator for a 1 kHz sine wave output at 1 volt peak. Other voltage levels up to 7 volts may also be used. Use the Zeitnitz oscilloscope to repeat the measurements from Part A on the circuit you built. Use the formula $\varphi = \Delta t(f)360°$ to convert the Zeitnitz time measurements into phase readings and record the phase and the magnitude in Table 2. Calculate z_{11} (Figure 5b), z_{21} (Figure 6b), z_{12} (Figure 7b), and z_{22} (Figure 8b) and enter them in Table 2. Take screenshots of the oscilloscope displays for Figures 5b, 6b, 7b, and 8b and include them in your report.

Part C: Analysis

4. Calculate the percentage differences in the z parameter results (z_{11}, z_{21}, z_{12}, and z_{22}) between Tables 1 and 2, enter them in Table 3, and include the table in your lab report.

5. Explain any discrepancies between your modeled and your measured results.

Lab Report The lab report may be written in a format of your own choosing. Be sure to include Tables 1, 2, and 3, and your screenshots from steps 2 and 3.

Validation Demonstrate taking the necessary measurements required in Figure 8b for step 3 of Table 2 (z_{22}) to your instructor.

Latest Revision 1/05/2009

Table 1. Impedance Parameters (modeled in PSpice).

With $I_2 = 0$, $z_{11} = V_1 / I_1$ & $z_{21} = V_2 / I_1$		With $I_1 = 0$, $z_{12} = V_1 / I_2$ & $z_{22} = V_2 / I_2$	
Figure 5a	Figure 6a	Figure 7a	Figure 8a
$V_1 =$	$V_2 =$	$V_1 =$	$V_2 =$
$I_1 = 1$ ma	$I_1 = 1$ ma	$I_2 = 1$ ma	$I_2 = 1$ ma
$\Theta =$	$\Theta =$	$\Theta =$	$\Theta =$
$z_{11} =$	$z_{21} =$	$z_{12} =$	$z_{22} =$

Table 2. Impedance Parameters (measured with Zeitnitz oscilloscope).

With $I_2 = 0$, $z_{11} = V_1 / I_1$ & $z_{21} = V_2 / I_1$		With $I_1 = 0$, $z_{12} = V_1 / I_2$ & $z_{22} = V_2 / I_2$	
Figure 5b	Figure 6b	Figure 7b	Figure 8b
$V_1 =$	$V_2 =$	$V_1 =$	$V_2 =$
$I_1 =$ ma	$I_1 =$ ma	$I_2 =$ ma	$I_2 =$ ma
$\Theta =$	$\Theta =$	$\Theta =$	$\Theta =$
$z_{11} =$	$z_{21} =$	$z_{12} =$	$z_{22} =$

Table 3. Percentage differences between modeled and measured z parameters.

Parameter	z_{11}	z_{21}	z_{12}	z_{22}
Modeled				
Measured				

Experiment 37: Electromagnetic Interference

Developers   WC Headley, RW Hendricks, SL Karty and DA Class

Objectives   The objective of this experiment is to examine some sources of electromagnetic interference (EMI). The battery charger for a laptop PC is once such source. Other common sources such as fluorescent lights and line noise on the 120V mains are also examined.

Estimated Time for Completion

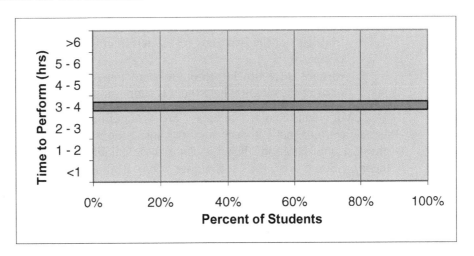

Preparation   Read the sections in your textbook which discuss an instrumentation amplifier. In addition, the dot markings on a coupling transformer must be known in order to perform this experiment. Complete Experiment 30 prior to starting this experiment.

Background   EMI (electromagnetic interference) has become a major problem in all application areas of electronics. Since the sizes of electronic circuits are constantly being reduced through miniaturization and integration, the various circuit elements, parts, and conductors are also in closer proximity with respect to one another. Stray capacitances, inductances and magnetic coupling could therefore lead to unintentional interferences between different circuits or subcircuits, leading to noise problems. Noise can be transmitted from one circuit into another by:

1. conduction current flow,
2. magnetic coupling (a changing magnetic field that couples with a conductor),
3. electric coupling giving rise to 'stray' or 'parasitic' capacitances (from the energy stored in an electric field), or
4. electromagnetic radiation (where a part of a circuit acts like an antenna).

As the frequencies of digital circuits increase, so must the wavelengths of radiation that can cause interference decrease. In radio frequencies, the quarter wavelength may reach the same order of magnitude as the physical dimensions in a circuit. Circuits can then no longer be analyzed using traditional circuit theory with lumped elements.

Under such circumstances when frequencies are high enough, strange things begin to happen. For instance:

1. a conductor trace on a printed circuit board can start acting like an antenna to either receive or transmit a signal,
2. a resistor can start exhibiting the properties of an inductor,
3. the current flows more on the surface of the conductor,
4. transmission line effects occur; there could be a delay between current transients at the two ends of a 2-terminal component, or resonances can occur;, or
5. currents start flowing through small impedances appearing in physical parts of the circuit where there is supposed to be good galvanic isolation.

EMI and noise issues are therefore better understood by using electromagnetic theory and the interactions of EM fields in the actual physical configuration, than by using the available circuit diagram and circuit theory. Some of the techniques for dealing with noise, EMI, and EMC (electromagnetic compatibility) problems are: shielding, grounding, balancing, filtering, impedance matching/mismatching, isolation, separation and orientation, frequency or time domain cancellation schemes, and enclosure design, among others.

Every electronic product being sold must comply with certain EMI/EMC standards and specifications which are regulated in the US by the Federal Communications Commission (FCC) and in Europe by the German Association for Electrical, Electronic and Information Technologies (the VDE; see Wikipedia, 2008). Manufacturers of everything from a pocket calculator to a battleship are therefore required by law to perform tests on all their products and equipment to make sure that they meet these specifications and, if a problem is found, that solutions are designed into their systems to prevent interferences.

These effects are, of course, difficult to observe in simple experiments such as those developed in Lab-in-a-Box. In this experiment, we go out of our way to create severe noise that may be more easily observed by creating a long line (an antenna) and wrapping it around a 120-V AC power line.

Although it would be easier to just build a simple amplifier circuit with an op amp and examine the output, in this experiment we will prepare for the common-mode noise rejection experiment (Experiment 38) by building an instrumentation amplifier and then looking only at the output from one stage of the amplifier in this experiment. This procedure will allow us to go on to Experiment 38, the common mode rejection ratio (CMRR) experiment using the same amplifier circuit and similar noise sources.

A generalized instrumentation amplifier is shown in Figure 1. When $R_1 = R_2 = R_3 = R_4 = R_5 = R_6 = R$, the gain of this amplifier is

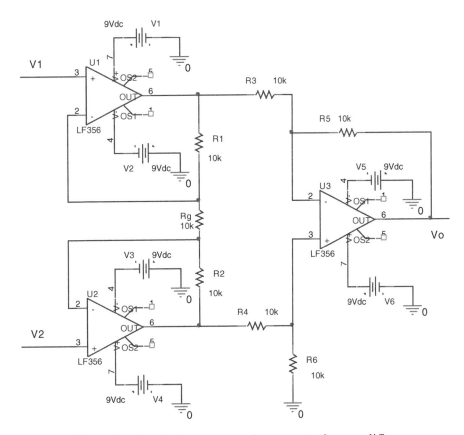

Figure 1: A basic three op amp instrumentation amplifier.

$$v_o = \left(1 + \frac{2R}{R_G}\right)(v_2 - v_1) \tag{1}$$

Thus, for this circuit, any signal that is common to both inputs, $v1$ and v_2, will be rejected by the circuit. This feature, known as common mode rejection, is the subject of Experiment 38. In this experiment, we will investigate various sources of noise signals that can interfere with the desired signal and then in the next experiment we will show how the instrumentation amplifier reduces these nose signals significantly.

The instrumentation amplifier to be built is illustrated in Figure 2. For this circuit and the given component values, the output signal is given by

$$v_o = \left(1 + \frac{20,000}{R_G}\right)(v_2 - v_1) \tag{2}$$

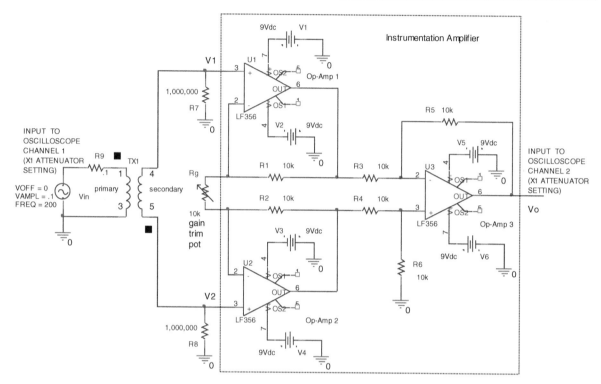

Figure 2: Circuit diagram of the instrumentation amplifier used for an EMI
experiment. R9 is added only to this drawing (not to the
circuit being built) for PSpice simulation. Correct phasing of
input transformer TX1 terminals is shown.

where R_G is the resistance of the gain trim pot. This circuit will be discussed in
more detail in Experiment 38. For the purposes of this experiment, all signals
will be measured from the output of op amp 1.

References

Kitchin, C, and L Counts (2006). A Designer's Guide to Instrumentation
Amplifiers (3/E), Norwood, MA: Analog Devices, Inc. (available free at
http://www.analog.com).

Ott, HW, (1988). Noise Reduction Techniques in Electronic Systems (2E), New
York: John Wiley and Sons.

Wikipedia (2008). 16 November 2008 <http://en.wikipedia.org/
wiki/Verband_der_Elektrotechnik%2C_Elektronik_und_Informationstechnik>.

Materials

The equipment and components required to perform this experiment are:
- 1 ea ANDY board
- 1 ea dual trace oscilloscope
- 1 ea power cord from laptop to wall outlet
- 1 ea TM028 1:1 transformer
- 3 ea LF356 op amps

- 6 ea 10 kΩ resistors
- 2 ea 1MΩ resistors
- 1 ea 10 kΩ trim pot

Procedure

Analysis (Extra Credit):

1. Provide a detailed derivation of Eq (1) based on the circuit of Figure 1.

Measurements:

Part A: Build and test instrument amplifier

2. Construct the instrumentation amplifier shown inside the dotted box in Figure 2 and connect the 10 kΩ trim pot across the inverting pins of the two input op amps (op amp 1 and op amp 2). It is suggested that you start the circuit in column 20 of the breadboard in order to leave space for the transformer circuit.

3. Install the transformer circuit on the breadboard and connect the function generator across the primary side as shown in Figure 2.

4. Using two short pieces of wire, connect the secondary side of the transformer (you may use either coil) to the non-inverting inputs of op amp 1 and op amp 2. Be sure to use the 1:1 terminals of the transformer as identified in Experiment 30.

5. Connect the function generator output to the x1 attenuator of Channel 1 and the output of op amp 3 to the x1 attenuator of Channel 2.

6. Set the function generator to 0.2 V peak-to-peak and the frequency to 200 Hz.

7. Adjust the trim pot to produce the minimum output at op amp 3. Refer to Eq(2).

8. Verify that op amp 3 output is in phase with the function generator. If it is not, reverse the two op amp inputs from the transformer secondary.

9. Verify that the gain is 3.0 (i.e., that the red signal is 3 times greater than the green signal). Provide a screenshot for your lab notebook.

10. Verify that the gain increases as the trim pot is adjusted. On completion, set the gain to 3.

Part B: System Noise:

11. Remove the two short wires between the transformer and the op amp inputs. Leave both 1 MΩ resistors connected.

12. Remove the wires to the inputs of the Channel 1 and Channel 2 attenuators so that there is no input to either channel. Do not leave wires hanging off of the scope inputs; remove them. The attenuator inputs for channels 1 and 2 will remain open through step 16. Do not remove the wires going to the

sound card. We are measuring the noise from the power source that passes through the op amps of the attenuators. Leave the cable going from the attenuator circuit into the sound card connected because this connection is required in all the following steps.

13. Turn the oscilloscope amplitude knob to its lowest setting (fully CCW).

14. Observe the noise carefully. There should be little or no periodicity of the signal. This is essentially "white" nose in which all frequencies are equally represented.

15. Verify that essentially all frequencies are represented equally in the noise by switching from the oscilloscope view to "Frequency Analysis" for the spectrum analyzer view. Record a screen image for your lab notebook. Upon completion of this step, change Zeitnitz from its spectrum analyzer mode back to its oscilloscope mode. This returns Zeitnitz to the same configuration that was used through step 14.

16. On the "Oscilloscope" screen, measure the peak-to-peak noise voltage of the oscilloscope attenuator and calibration circuit using the scope cursors. On completion, do not move the scope cursors.

17. Connect the scope inputs for both Channel 1 and Channel 2 to the output of op amp 3.

18. Observe the noise level without adjusting the scope cursors. Verify that the noise is essentially the same as was observed in step 15. Show a screenshot with the voltage markers measuring the maximum and minimum voltages.

19. On completion of steps 16 and 17, do not remove the oscilloscope connections.

Part C: Antenna Noise

20. Cut two pieces of wire, of two different colors, each at least 1 m long and twist the wires around each other a few times. Do not twist the ends together.

21. Connect one end of each of the twisted wires to each input of the instrumentation amplifier (input of op amp 1 and op amp 2). These will serve as antennas replacing the two short wires removed from the V1 and V2 op amp inputs in step 11 (Figure 2). Do not connect the opposite ends of these longer wires to the secondary of the input transformer until Experiment 38.

22. Coil the twisted wires around the power cord from your laptop. Be sure to wrap the twisted wires around the 120 V power cord and NOT around the low voltage cable to the computer. Be sure that the two remote ends of the wires do not touch each other. Record a screenshot of the output.

23. Compare the noise at the output of op amp 3 to the system noise observed in step 18. Record your observations of both amplitude and frequency of the noise.

24. Press the "Frequency Analysis" button and examine the distribution of frequencies in the noise. You should see a large 60 Hz component.

25. Press the "Filter in Separate Window" button and return to the Oscilloscope screen. Using the low pass filter, reduce the cut-off frequency slowly and observe the noise. The higher frequency components should gradually be removed and you should ultimately end up with a clean 60 Hz signal. This 60 Hz signal is induced from the power supply. Record a screenshot of the "clean" 60 Hz noise for your lab notebook.

26. Turn off the filters of the oscilloscope.

27. Remove the input to Channel 1 from the output of op amp 3 and connect it to the output of op-amp 1. Similarly, connect the input to Channel 2 to the output of op amp 2.

28. Using your fingers, touch the open lead to the antenna connected to op amp 1. Be sure to touch only the wire connected to op amp 1; do not touch the wire connected to op amp 2. Observe the noise signal and record a screenshot for your notebook.

29. While continuing to touch the open lead of the antenna, touch the power transformer to your PC. (This is the black box between the power cord that plugs into the wall and the smaller wire that plugs into your PC.) Also touch the transformer for the ANDY board. (This is the black box you plug into the wall to provide power to the ANDY board. Record your observations. Use screenshots, if desired.

30. Unwrap the antenna wire from the PC power cord and place it near the power cord. Move the antenna wire around in space. Observe the noise. Record your observations.

31. Repeat step 28 while touching the lead to op amp 2. Record your observations. Compare your results with those obtained in step 28.

32. Repeat step 28 while simultaneously touching both antenna leads. Record your observations. Compare your results with those obtained in step 28.

33. Find at least one other source of noise that can be measured. (A purely resistive load such as a toaster or an incandescent light would be interesting.)

34. Repeat the noise measurements of steps 21 through 33 for these new sources of noise.

35. Describe your observations of noise.

36. **Note: Save this circuit for use in Experiment 38**.

Last Revision   12/17/2008

Experiment 38: Noise and the Instrumentation Amplifier

Developers   WC Headley, SL Karty, and RW Hendricks

Objectives   The objective of this experiment is to illustrate the elimination of common mode noise by an instrumentation amplifier and to demonstrate its common mode rejection ratio (CMRR).

Estimated Time for Completion

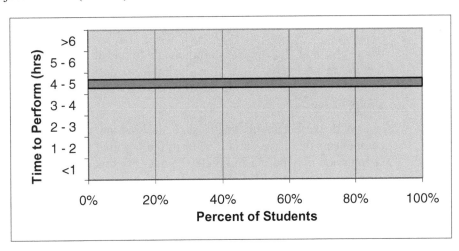

Preparation   Read the sections in your text on an instrumentation amplifier. Also, complete Experiment 37.

Background   In Experiment 37, the student was introduced to the generation of electronic noise. In that experiment a large noise signal was generated by deliberately making an antenna and placing it close to a known source of EMI. Noise levels in the environment are generally much less than those created in Experiment 37. These effects are, of course, difficult to observe in simple experiments such as those developed in Lab-in-a-Box. Nevertheless, in this experiment we examine how such noise can be significantly reduced using an instrumentation amplifier (IA) with a high common mode rejection ratio (CMRR). Unfortunately, of the several introductory electric circuits texts listed in Table 1 of the Preface, only Nilsson and Reidel (2005) discuss CMRR. Thus, in this section, we develop an elementary theory of CMRR for an instrumentation amplifier.

The inputs v_1 and v_2 to a general amplifier circuit such as the one to be considered here can be described in terms of the common mode and the differential mode inputs, v_{cm} and v_{dm}, which are defined as (Nilsson and Reidel 2005):

$$v_{cm} = \frac{v_1 + v_2}{2} \tag{1}$$

and

299

$$v_{dm} = v_2 - v_1 \tag{2}$$

respectively. Here, v_1 and v_2 are the differential mode input signals. From these definitions, it is seen that if there is a signal (usually noise) that is common to the two inputs, then it is cancelled in the differential mode signal but remains in the common mode signal. We will show in the paragraphs below that the output signal, v_o, can be expressed in the form

$$v_o = A_{cm} v_{cm} + A_{dm} v_{dm} \tag{3}$$

where A_{cm} and A_{dm} are the common mode and differential mode amplification factors, respectively. Thus, it is desirable to design an amplifier such that the common mode amplification factor is zero. In this case, the common mode signal is suppressed.

With perfect components, such designs are possible. However, with real components that have variations from the nominal values (see Experiment 2) the suppression may not be complete. To quantify this effect, we define the common mode rejection ratio (CMRR) as

$$\text{CMRR} = \left| \frac{A_{dm}}{A_{cm}} \right| \tag{4}$$

From this definition, the CMRR is infinite if the common mode amplification factor is zero. This is the goal to which we aspire. In the following paragraphs, we will derive the amplification factors and the CMRR for an instrumentation amplifier and apply the results to the instrumentation amplifier built in Experiment 37.

Consider the circuit in Figure 1. This is a generalization of the instrumentation amplifier constructed in Experiment 37. We specify each resistor separately as we are ultimately interested in the effect of a deviation of each resistor from its specified value on the common mode and differential mode gains and the CMRR. For this amplifier, it is seen that $v_a=v_1$ and $v_b=v_2$. Using a nodal analysis, it can be shown that

$$A_{dm} = \frac{R_1 R_7 (R_4 + 2R_5) + R_2 (2R_3 (R_6 + R_7) + R_4 (R_6 + 2R_7) + 2R_5 R_7)}{2R_1 R_4 (R_6 + R_7)} \tag{5}$$

and

$$A_{cm} = \frac{R_1 R_7 - R_2 R_6}{R_1 (R_6 + R_7)} \tag{6}$$

Clearly, if $R_6 = R_1$ and $R_7 = R_2$, then $A_{cm} = 0$ and

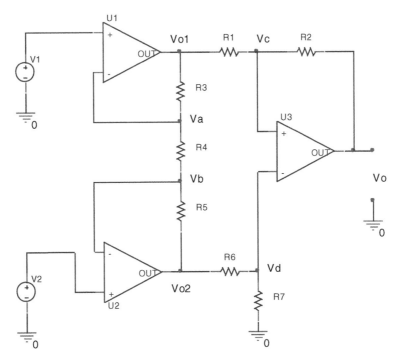

Figure 1: A general instrumentation amplifier.

$$A_{dm} = \frac{R_2}{R_1}\left(1 + \frac{2R_3}{R_4}\right) \tag{7}$$

For the IA used in Experiment 37, we have set $R_1 = R_2 = R_3 = 10$ kΩ and R4 is a 10 kΩ trim pot. In this case, $3 \le A_{dm} \le 200$ as the trim pot is varied from it maximum value of 10 kΩ to a lower level of 100 Ω.

If we now assume that each resistor R_i deviates from its nominal value by some small amount ε_i, and if we assume the nominal values of resistors $R_5 = R_3$, $R_6 = R_1$, and $R_7 = R_2$, then substitution into Eqs (5), (6) and into Eq (4), yield, after keeping only first order terms,

$$\text{CMRR} \approx \frac{R_2(R_1 + R_2)(2R_3 + R_4)}{R_4\left|R_1(\varepsilon_2 - \varepsilon_7) + R_2(\varepsilon_6 - \varepsilon_1)\right|} \tag{8}$$

It is interesting to note that in this approximation the errors in resistors R_3 and R_5 do not appear. We also see that it is important to select resistors R_1 and R_6 and resistors R_2 and R_7 to be as closely matched pairs as possible.

301

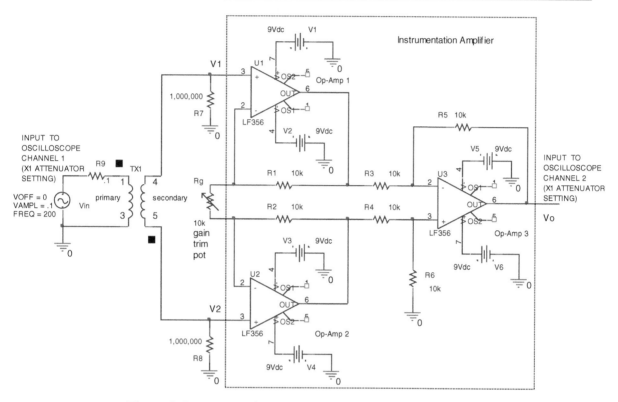

Figure 2: Instrumentation amplifier circuit diagram for CMRR experiment. R9 is added only to this drawing (not to the circuit being built) for PSpice simulation. Correct phasing of input transformer (TX1) terminals is shown.

As a worst case scenario, for the IA shown in Figure 2 (the device built in Experiment 37), if by random chance the errors on the four resistors were $\varepsilon = \varepsilon_1 = \varepsilon_2 = -\varepsilon_6 = -\varepsilon_7$, and if the magnitude of the error were 100 Ω (1%), then the lowest CMRR would be ≈ 150.

There are several manufacturers of monolithic IC instrumentation amplifiers, data for which are easily found by a search of Google. The Analog Devices AD621 is one of many examples (Analog Devices 2006). Manufacturing control of the precision resistors is excellent thus allowing the production of inexpensive devices with superior performance. The Analog Devices website even includes interactive design web pages to assist engineers in selecting the correct device for an application.

References   Kitchin, C., and L. Counts, (2006). <u>A Designer's Guide to Instrumentation Amplifiers</u> (3/E), Norwood, MA: Analog Devices, Inc. (available free at http://www.analog.com).

Nilsson, J.W., and S.A. Reidel (2005). Electric Circuits (7E). Upper Saddle River: Prentice Hall.

Materials

The equipment and components required to perform this experiment are:

- 1 ea ANDY board
- 1 ea dual trace oscilloscope
- 1 ea power cord from laptop to wall outlet
- 1 ea TM028 1:1 transformer
- 3 ea LF356 op amps
- 6 ea 10 kΩ resistors
- 2 ea 1MΩ resistors
- 1 ea 10 kΩ trim pot

Procedure

Measurements:

1. Verify that the instrumentation amplifier shown inside the dotted box in Figure 2 and which was built in Experiment 37 is operating correctly. Be sure the transformer is installed and connected to the function generator correctly. Follow the steps under part A of the Procedure in Experiment 37. Note: To verify the initial setup, temporarily reconnect V1 (the input to op amp U1) and V2 (the input to op amp U2) to the input transformer's secondary winding (Figure 2) using the original short wires from Experiment 37. Connect the channel 1 oscilloscope input to the function generator output. Connect the channel 2 oscilloscope input to the V_o output from U3. Set the function generator for a 0.2 V peak-to-peak output signal with a frequency of 200 Hz. Set the gain to 3 by adjusting the gain trim pot Rg for 0.6 V peak-to-peak at V_o. Verify that op amp 3 output is in phase with the function generator. If it is not, reverse the two op amp inputs from the transformer secondary. Note which op amp input is connected to which transformer terminal; this will be important in step 3. Remove the short wires connecting the secondary winding of the input transformer to the op amp inputs, but leave both 1 MegΩ resistors connected to the op amp inputs. Disconnect both oscilloscope inputs in preparation for step 2.

2. Connect Channel 1 of the oscilloscope to the output of op amp 1 and connect Channel 2 to the output of op amp 2.

3. Take two long pieces of wire (about 1 m is adequate) and wrap them several times around the power cord to your PC. If you have a laptop PC, be sure that you use the 120V AC side of the cord (the side nearest the wall plug) rather than the DC side (the side nearest your computer). Connect one end of one wire to one terminal of the secondary side of the transformer and the other end to the input of op amp 1. Connect one end of the second wire to the other terminal of the secondary side of the transformer and the other end of that wire to the input of op amp 2. Be sure that the long wire from each transformer terminal is connected to the same op amp that the short wires were disconnected from. The only difference between the configuration at

the end of step 1 and at the end of this step is that the wires connecting the secondary of the input transformer to the op amp inputs are replaced with longer wires. The longer wires act as antennas to pick up and couple the same 60 Hz interference into the U1 and U2 op amp inputs. **Note: Input lines are not intended to be "antennas" for picking up AC hum, except in this experiment.**

4. Be sure that the function generator is still set to the values in step 1.

5. Observe that the waveforms consist of high frequency waves riding on top of a lower frequency wave. To better see this, turn the oscilloscope trigger off. Also adjust the time scale to show many periods of the lower frequency wave. You are observing the sum of the desired 200 Hz signal with a 60 Hz noise component superimposed. The ratio of these signals will be determined by the amount of coupling between the antennas and the power cord and the magnitude of the function generator signal. When done, be sure to return the trigger to the "Auto" setting.

6. Go to the Frequency Analysis tab of the oscilloscope. Set the displayed channel to Channel 1. Set the zoom to 5 and move the horizontal slider all the way to the left. You should observe two major peaks and a few smaller harmonics.

7. Record a screenshot for your notebook.

8. Determine the frequencies of the two largest peaks. Label the source of each signal as either noise or the function generator.

9. Check the frequency analysis of Channel 2. Are the values the same as for Channel 1?

10. Return to the Oscilloscope window.

11. Connect the oscilloscope to show the output of the function generator on Channel 1 and the output of the instrumentation amplifier (output of op amp 3) on Channel 2.

12. Does the output of the circuit look noise-free? Compare with the observations of step 5.

13. Check the gain of the circuit.

14. Go to the frequency analysis tab and select Channel 2. You should now observe that the common mode noise is gone.

15. **Extra Credit Question**: Operating with high input signal levels reduces the common-mode voltage range of an instrumentation amplifier. What else might cause the same problem?

Last Revision: 9/28/2008

Acknowledgements

W e are indebted to Professor Rich Christie of the University of Washington for bringing the concept of Lab-in-a-Box to our attention in the spring of 2004, for providing draft write-ups of their experiments for our consideration, and for introducing us to Sol Kaye at Electronix Express. The entire development of our implementation of Lab-in-a-Box has sprung from these conversations.

Robert Lineberry of our Technical Services Group played a critical role in making our implementation of Lab-in-a-Box possible. Working with a team of faculty members and instructors, and interfacing between Virginia Tech and Electronix Express, Bob supervised the design and testing of several prototypes of the RSR/VT Analog and Digital (ANDY) board that we use in all but one of the experiments described in this book. Sol Kaye worked with his team at Electronix Express, including Robert Wichiciel, in the US and with his suppliers in Taiwan to prepare all engineering and circuit drawings of the board and to produce several prototypes during the spring of 2005. Five hundred boards, as well as all supporting materials, were ready for use in four different Virginia Tech courses during the fall semester of 2005.

We are especially indebted to Dr. Christian Zeitnitz of the Bergische Universität Wuppertal for making his PC Oscilloscope available to our students at no cost. His enthusiasm and support of this project are greatly appreciated. We also wish to thank Dr. Mark W. Lund for making the information on AWG sizes and current capacities available from the Powerstream website, Mr. Syd Levine of AnaLog Services for the information on the preferred resistor series and the decade values table from their website, Mr. Gene Hankins of Action Electronics for the lovely resistor color code chart, and Mr. Robert Endl for the information on capacitor digit multipliers, tolerance codes, and temperature range and stability codes from the CapSite 2008 website. We are also indebted to Bob Lineberry for allowing the use of the material in Section 3.4 on Circuit Breadboarding and Wiring that he prepared for our digital electronics courses. By presenting this information as common to all of our courses, it is possible to assure uniformity in teaching good laboratory practices regardless of the order in which the courses are taken.

We wish to thank the faculty and staff of The Bradley Department of Electrical and Computer Engineering at Virginia Tech for their enthusiastic support of this project. Professors William Baumann and Nathanial Davis IV played critical roles in both the conceptual design and implementation of the experiments, while Rick Cooper, Bob Lineberry, Dennis Newman, and Jason Thweatt assisted in the design of the ANDY board to meet the needs of the four courses in which it is used. Bill Shumate was instrumental in finding the Zeitnitz PC Oscilloscope package while Bob Lineberry found the Behringer sound card. Bill and Bob also provided many of the photographs and line drawings. Dr. Leslie Pendleton, Director of Undergraduate Advising for the department, brought together the original team of students who developed the first experiments. Finally, Rick Cooper and Bob Lineberry have been invaluable in providing expertise to help debug and test experiments, especially when things did not go quite as anticipated. Professor Allen MacKenzie and Dr. Tom Staley made valuable contributions to the ideas expressed in Chapter 2. Finally, Professor Hardus Odendaal provided much of the material for the Background of Experiment 37.

Of course, we could not have created Lab-in-a-Box without the enthusiastic support of the many students who have helped us develop the experiments presented here. Some of these students were employed as summer interns, while many participated by enrolling in Independent Research projects during the ensuing semesters. Among these are Megan Green, Joe Hartwell, William C. Headley, Sam Karty, Ka Ming Lai, Dan Moore, Carl Shek, James B. Webb, and Alex Young. Their respective names appear under the heading "Developers" in the introduction to each experiment and a brief bio of each is given in the section on "Meet the Developers" at the end of the book.

Several undergraduate students, some of whom had already completed their introductory circuits course and some who were taking it as we were developing this text, donated time an effort to test our experiments and provided feedback on our design and write-ups. Among these are Alrue Brumskine, Al Fayez, Michael Fong, James Isom, Theresa Nelson, Eric Roback, John White, and Alex Young. We also thank the many students in ECE 2004 and ECE 3004 who brought many inconsistencies and problems to our attention. Two of our graduate teaching assistants, David Kleppinger (2004/2005) and David Class (2005/2006), carefully tested all of the experiments yet again during their tenures working with us.

As the concept of Lab-in-a-Box is becoming more widely known, we are to receiving comments and suggestions from faculty members outside the local Virginia Tech community. In preparation for adoption of Lab-in-a-Box at Piedmont Virginia Community College, Craig Lorie reviewed the entire manuscript and offered numerous suggestions and corrections. All of these comments are greatly appreciated.

Finally, we wish thank the National Science Foundation and our Program Managers, Ms. Sue Kemnitzer and Dr. Russell L. Pimmel of the Division of Undergraduate Education (DUE) for financial support under Departmental Level Review (DLR) grant 03-43160 and Combined Curriculum and Laboratory Innovation (CCLI) Phase 2 grant 08-17102, and for accompanying Research Experience for Undergraduates (REU) funds, all of which made this work possible.

About the Authors

Robert W. Hendricks is now the Associate Department Head of the Materials Science and Engineering Department at Virginia Tech. He teaches courses in introductory materials science and electric circuits and advanced courses in nuclear materials and semiconductor wafer fabrication. He also teaches and performs research in the areas of microelectronics and semiconductor processing and packaging. He has special interests in pedagogy and in assessment methodologies.

On first arriving in Blacksburg, Hendricks was a professor in the Materials Science and Engineering Department (1986–2001) and was jointly appointed as professor in that department and in the Bradley Department of Electrical and Computer Engineering (1997–2001). He joined the ECE Department full time in 2001. He returned to his joint appointment between the ECE and MSE Departments and began his current position in 2007.

Prior to joining the faculty at Virginia Tech, Dr. Hendricks was a product manager and chief scientist at Technology for Energy Corporation in Knoxville, Tennessee (1981–1986), and was a member of the technical staff (1964–1970), a senior staff member (1970–1981), and co-founder and associate director of the National Center for Small-Angle Scattering Research (1978–1981) at Oak Ridge National Laboratory.

Dr. Hendricks earned a BMetE degree (1959) and a PhD in Materials Science (1964), both from Cornell University, and an MBA (1985) from the University of Tennessee. He has published over 120 papers in the reviewed literature, is the co-inventor of four patents, and has been the principal investigator on over $3 million of sponsored research.

Prof. Hendricks has been recognized by the College of Engineering three times for his innovations in engineering education. In 1996 he received the Dean's Award for Outstanding Service for his work in developing the MSE Writing and Communications Program. In 2001 he was recognized with a second Dean's Award for Outstanding Service for his work in developing the Minor in Microelectronic Engineering, a joint effort between the ECE, MSE, and Physics Departments. And, in 2006 he received the Dean's Award for Excellence in Teaching for his development of Lab-in-a-Box and for his work in restructuring the circuits and electronics curriculum in the ECE Department.

Dr. Hendricks is a Fellow of the American Association for the Advancement of Science (AAAS), the American Physical Society (APS), and ASM International, is a Senior Member of the Institute of Electrical and Electronics

Engineers (IEEE), and is a member of the Materials Research Society (MRS), and The Metallurgical Society (TMS).

Kathleen Meehan is an associate professor in the Bradley Department of Electrical and Computer Engineering at Virginia Tech where she teaches introductory electronics and other courses on semiconductor materials and device physics. Her interests in engineering pedagogy include the development of multimedia learning materials and other methodologies to address the full range of learning styles.

In addition to her appointment as a faculty member at Virginia Tech in 2002, Dr. Meehan has worked at the University of Denver (1997-1999) and West Virginia University (1999-2002). She conducts research on the synthesis and characterization of nanomaterials for biomedical applications and the design, fabrication, and simulation of optoelectronic and power electronic devices.

Dr. Meehan worked in industry before moving into academia full-time in 1997. She first worked as a Member of Technical Staff at Lytel, Inc. (1985-1987) where she designed, processed, and characterized optoelectronic devices for telecommunications applications. During this time, she also taught at Somerset Community College. In 1987, she joined Polaroid Corporation as the manager of the GaAs Processing group. She became Engineering Manager and acting Director of the Microfabrication Group in 1993, where she oversaw the activities to support several laser printer and digital camera projects. In 1994, she was promoted to Senior Research Group Leader and led a number of research and development projects. During her evenings, she taught a number of graduate courses at Northeastern University. She moved into the field of biophotonics when she left Polaroid, beginning with her employment at Biocontrol Technologies (1995-1997). In addition, she runs a small consulting business, Optoelectronic Solutions, and has been a part of two other high tech start-ups.

Dr. Meehan earned a BSEE degree (1980) from Manhattan College and an MS (1982) and a PhD (1985) in Electrical Engineering from the University of Illinois – Urbana/Champaign. She has published 35 papers, is co-inventor of four patents, and has been principle or co-principle investigator on over $4 million of sponsored research.

Dr. Meehan has collaborated with Dr. Hendricks on numerous curricular activities including her participation on the third edition of this textbook.

Meet the Developers

David A. Class graduated from Virginia Tech in May 2006 Cum Laude with a Bachelors of Science in Electrical Engineering and a minor in Mathematics. He has since enrolled in their Master of Science in Electrical Engineering program with a concentration in Control Systems. In his spare time he likes to read and design in the areas of analog electronics, embedded systems, robotics, and computer vision.

Richard F. Cooper received a BS in Electrical Engineering from Virginia Tech in 1980 and is currently a senior computer systems engineer in The Bradley Department of Electrical and Computer Engineering where he has responsibility for teaching the power systems and the analog electronics design laboratory courses. Prior to joining the ECE Department, he worked for the US Geological Survey (1969–1974) and for the department (1974–1980). Rick has special interest in large-scale computing hardware, power, and analog circuits and is a believer in a strong analytical and theoretical background for electrical engineers.

Megan Courtney Green is a senior in The Bradley Department of Electrical and Computer Engineering at Virginia Tech where she is majoring in Electrical Engineering and minoring in Mathematics. She expects to graduate in May 2007. As an undergraduate, Megan is a member of the Eta Kappa Nu ECE and the Phi Sigma Theta honor societies and has been on the Dean's List in 2005. During the academic year she works as a computer consultant for the Virginia Tech 4Help office which provides campus-wide technical support on all aspects of the use of computers in academia. During the summer of 2006 she was employed as an intern by the KTA Group in Herndon, VA. She has special interests in Biomedical Engineering and plans to continue her studies in this area at the graduate level.

Joseph J. Hartwell is a 2007 graduate of Virginia Tech in Electrical Engineering. He currently works for Virginia Transformer Corporation as an application engineer, costing and pricing substation-class transformers, making presentations to consulting engineering firms, and offering system solutions to utility customers. He also serves in the North Carolina Air National Guard, and has been selected for an officer position in the 245th Civil Engineering Flight after serving 10 years in the Virginia Air National Guard and being deployed to both Iraq and Afghanistan. A native of West Virginia, Joe enjoys going to church, playing guitar and writing music, and riding his Harley when he's not teaching motorcycle safety at one of three community colleges.

William C. Headley is currently a Bradley Fellow at Virginia Tech pursuing his PhD in Electrical Engineering. His current research focus is in signal detection and modulation classification systems. He received his BS in Electrical Engineering from Virginia Tech in the winter of 2006. During the summer of 2005, he worked under an NSF grant helping in the design of the ac circuits laboratories covered in this book.

Andrew Heilesen is a senior in the Bradley Department of Electrical and Computer Engineering at Virginia Tech. His major area of study is Electrical Engineering.

Michael Hutton is a junior in the Bradley Department of Electrical and Computer Engineering at Virginia Tech. His major area of study is Electrical Engineering.

James A. Isom is a junior in the Bradley Department of Electrical and Computer Engineering at Virginia Tech. His major area of study is Electrical Engineering and his minors are Microelectronics Engineering and Spanish. He was selected as a Micron Scholar in 2006 and was a runner-up for the Horton Scholarship. Starting in the fall of 2006, he will be studying the properties of GaN diodes with Professor Louis Guido. James also enjoys playing club water polo at Virginia Tech.

Sam Karty is a senior in the Bradley Department of Electrical and Computer Engineering at Virginia Tech. He will graduate in May 2008. He has an amateur radio license and is the author of an article, "The Dangers of Cathode Keying: Ham Radio and Electrical Safety," published in *QST* Magazine. When he's not working with AC circuits, he enjoys reading science fiction.

Ka-ming Lai graduated from Virginia Tech in 2005 where he was an Honors student in the Electrical and Computer Engineering Department.

Robert B. Lineberry received a BS in Physics from Virginia Polytechnic Institute and State University in 1976 and is a computer systems engineer with The Bradley Department of Electrical and Computer Engineering at Virginia Tech. Prior to joining the ECE department, he consulted for computer research and development firms near Washington, DC (1976-1984). He has special interests in computer security and analog and digital design. He is the co-author of the DevHC11 software package (1998-2003) and is the co-designer of the RSR/VT Analog and Digital (ANDY) board (2004-2005), on which most of the experiments in this book are based. In 2006, Mr. Lineberry received the Dean's Award as "Technical Employee of the Year" in the College of Engineering at Virginia Tech.

Daniel R. Moore graduated from Virginia Tech in 2006 with a degree in Electrical Engineering and is currently employed by ADM Micro in Roanoke Virginia doing embedded systems design to create utilities optimizing hardware. He has special interests in digital control systems, PIC programming, embedded systems design, PCB layout, and automotive control systems.

Carl Shek is currently attending Virginia Polytechnic Institute and State University and expects to graduate May 2009 with a Bachelor of Science in Computer Engineering. During the summer of 2008, he worked as a research assistant, developing tutorials for PSpice, MATLAB, and Lab-in-a-Box. He is pursuing a career in embedded systems with the experience and knowledge he has gained at Virginia Tech.

William D. Shumate received an Associates degree in Electronics and Instrumentation from New River Community College in Pulaski, VA in 1966 and is currently a Computer Systems Engineer in the Bradley Department of Electrical and Computer Engineering at Virginia Tech. Prior to joining the ECE Department in 1980, he was with Hercules Inc. in Radford, VA (1967–1974), Los Alamos National Laboratory, Los Alamos NM (1974–1977), and the

Virginia Tech Geophysics Department (1978–1980). He has special interest in archery, photography, and music.

Robert Smith was an electrical engineering student in the Bradley Department of Electrical and Computer Engineering at Virginia Tech. He graduated in 2010.

J. Braxton Webb enrolled at Virginia Polytechnic Institute and State University (Virginia Tech) in 2001. During his undergraduate career he was one of the first students involved in the development of Lab-in-a-Box. James enrolled in Virginia Tech's B.S./M.S. program offered to select students and began his Masters education in conjunction with the completion of his undergraduate studies. In May of 2005, he graduated magna cum laude with a B.S. in Electrical Engineering and a minor in Music. In June of 2005, he began work with the Virginia Tech Configurable Computing Laboratory (CCM Lab). In August of 2006, James completed his graduate education and received his M.S in Electrical Engineering. His thesis work is entitled: "Methods for Securing the Integrity of FPGA Configurations". James is currently employed by JDSU Corporation, Test and Measurement Telecom Field Service Division, Germantown, Maryland as a hardware research and design engineer. His work includes systems that utilize FPGAs.

Alexander Young attends Virginia Polytechnic Institute and State University, where he is working towards a Bachelor of Science in Electrical Engineering, and hopes to graduate in May 2007. Previously, he has worked as a video, data and telephone technician as well as manager of a wilderness outfitting store. Alex enjoys sports and outdoor activities. In 2001 he summited Mt. Shasta in northern California and Mt. Adams in Washington. Currently, Alex is training for his first triathlon.

Appendix A: Parts List

Students will need the following components to perform the Lab-in-a-Box experiments described in this text.

1. 1 ea RSR/VT Analog & Digital Trainer (ANDY board) (purchase from Electronix Express as part number 32VPTABRD)

2. 1 ea Model MY-64 Digital Multimeter or approved equal (purchase from Electronix Express as part number 01VPTMY64).

3. 1 ea Behringer Model UCA202 external sound card (purchase from Electronix Express as part number 32VPTUCA202).

4. 1 ea Model TK1 Toolkit (purchase from Electronix Express as part number 32VPTTK1) consisting of:

   a. 1 ea wire stripper/cutter
   b. 1 ea 3/16 inch screwdriver
   c. 1 ea Philips head screwdriver
   d. 1 ea 5-inch curved SS clamps
   e. 1 ea needle nose pliers

5. 1 ea Parts and Components kit consisting of the items shown in Table A.1 (purchase from Electronix Express as part number 32VPT20743074).

6. 1 ea Model WK1 Wire kit consisting of six spools of colored wire (purchase from Electronix Express as part number 32VPTWK1).

7. 1 ea Model RK1 Resistor Kit (purchase from Electronix Express as part number 32VPTRK1-1/2W). The kit includes 5 ea of 73 different resistors with resistances varying in a sequence from 1 Ω to 1 MΩ (see Table A.2).

In addition to the above required components, several optional items are recommended, including such items as professional wire strippers, plastic parts boxes, etc.

Table A.1: Parts and Components Kit[†]

1. 5 ea 200 Ω, 510 Ω, 1.1 kΩ, 2.0 kΩ, 2.4 kΩ, 3.0 kΩ, 3.6 kΩ, and 200 kΩ 1/2W carbon film resistors (5% tolerance)
2. 10 ea 10 kΩ 1/2W carbon film resistors (5% tolerance)
3. 10 ea 1.0 MΩ 1/2W carbon film resistors (5% tolerance)
4. 4 ea 0.001, 0.0022, 0.0047, 0.01, 0.022, 0.047, 0.1, 0.22, 0.47, 1.0, 2.2, and 4.7 µF 100 V Mylar film capacitors (±10%)
5. 8 ea 100 µF 50 V, electrolytic capacitors
6. 10 ea 0.1 µF 100 V, Mylar film capacitors
7. 2 ea 470 pF 50 V, ceramic disk capacitors
8. 4 ea 1 mH, 10 mH, and 100 mH inductors
9. 3 ea 100 Ω cermet potentiometers
10. 3 ea 1 kΩ cermet potentiometers
11. 3 ea 10 kΩ cermet potentiometers
12. 3 ea 100 kΩ cermet potentiometers
13. 8 ea red LEDs
14. 8 ea yellow LEDs
15. 8 ea green LEDs
16. 2 ea bipolar LEDs
17. 2 ea LED bar graphs with 10 discrete LEDs (DIP)
18. 2 ea CdS photocells
19. 3 ea LM324 op amps (quad general purpose)
20. 10 ea LF356 op amps (JFET input, low noise)
21. 5 ea LM741CN op amps
22. 3 ea LM555D timers
23. 1 ea 8 Ω 0.2W stereo speaker
24. 2 ea 3.5 mm stereo cable
25. 1 ea 3.5 mm cable adapter (3.5 mm stereo jack to 2 RCA plugs)
26. 2ea TM028 audio transformers
27. 3 ea SPDT slide switches (breadboard compatible)
28. 1 ea resistor color code chart
29. 5 ea 200 mA fast-acting fuses for MY-64 DMM
30. 1 ea 9V alkaline battery for MY-64 DMM

[†] Available from Electronix Express as part number 32VPT20043004.

Table A.2: Contents of Model 32VPTRK1 Resistor Kit

1/2W Resistor Kit containing 5 each of 73 standard 5% carbon film resistors in the series:

1.0, 1.2, 1.5, 1.8, 2.2, 2.7, 3.3, 3.9, 4.7, 5.6, 6.8, 8.2, 10, 12, 15, 18, 22, 27, 33, 39, 47, 56, 68, 82, 100, 120, 150, 180, 220, 270, 330, 390, 470, 560, 680, 820, 1K, 1.2K, 1.5K, 1.8K, 2.2K, 2.7K, 3.3K, 3.9K, 4.7K, 5.6K, 6.8K, 8.2K, 10K, 12K, 15K, 18K, 22K, 27K, 33K, 39K, 47K, 56K, 68K, 82K, 100K, 120K, 150K, 180K, 220K, 270K, 330K, 390K, 470K, 560K, 680K, 820K, 1M

Appendix B: Recommended Bibliography

The following texts are classics in their field and are highly recommended by the authors for inclusion in the student's personal reference library.

Booth, W.C., G.G. Colomb, and J.M. Williams, (2008). The Craft of Research (3/E). Chicago: Univ. Chicago Press.

Boyce, JC, (1988). Operational Amplifiers and Linear Integrated Circuits (2E). Boston: PWS-Kent. p284.

Bransford, J.D., A.L. Brown, and R.R. Cocking, (2000). How People Learn: Brain, Mind, Experience, and School, Washington, DC: National Academy Press.

Carter, B., and T.R. Brown, (2001). Handbook of Operational Amplifier Applications. Application Report SBOA092A. 18 December 2008 <http://focus.ti.com/lit/an/sboa092a/sboa092a.pdf>.

The Chicago Manual of Style (15/E), (2003). Chicago: Univ. Chicago Press.

Fischbech, H.J., and K.H. Fischbeck, (1987). Formulas, Facts and Constants for Students and Professionals in Engineering, Chemistry, and Physics (2/E). Berlin: Springer-Verlag.

Gibaldi, J., (2003). MLA Handbook for Writers of Research Papers (6/E). New York: Modern Language Association of America.

Glantz, S.A., (2005). Primer of Biostatistics (6E), New York: McGraw-Hill.

Grant, J., (2007). Corrupted Science: Fraud, ideology and politics in science. Surrey, UK: AAPPL Press.

Hanselman, D., and B. Littlefield (2005). Mastering MATLAB 7, Upper Saddle River, NJ: Prentice-Hall.

Huff, D., (1993). How to Lie with Statistics. New York: W.W. Norton Company.

Hunt, B.R., R.L. Lipsman, J.M.Rosenberg, K.R. Coombes, J.E. Osborn, and G.J. Stuck, (2006). A Guide to MATLAB for Beginners and Experienced Users 2/E. Cambridge: Cambridge University Press.

Kane, T.S., (1988). The New Oxford Guide to Writing. Oxford: Oxford Univ. Press.

Newton, R.G., (1997). The Truth of Science. Cambridge, MA: Harvard.

Polkinghorne, J., (1998). Science and Theology: An Introduction. Minneapolis: SPCK/Fortress Press.

Sagan, C., (1996). The Demon-Haunted World. New York: Ballantine.

Strumpf, M. and A. Douglas, (2004). The Grammar Bible. New York: Henry Holt.

Strunk, W. and E.B. White, (2000). <u>The Elements of Style</u> (4/E). Needham, MA: Allyn & Bacon.

Tarutz, J.A., (1992). <u>Technical Editing: The Practical Guide for Editors and Writers</u>. Reading, MA: Addison-Wesley.

Tufte, E.R., (1983). <u>The Visual Display of Quantitative Information</u>. Cheshire, CT: Graphics Press.

Turabian, K.L., (2007). <u>A Manual for Writers of Term Papers, Theses and Dissertations</u> (7/E).Chicago: Univ. Chicago Press.

Valiela, I., (2001). <u>Doing Science</u>. New York: Oxford Univ. Press.

Wainer, H., (1997). <u>Visual Revelations</u>. New York: Copernicus (Springer-Verlag).

Wilson, E.B., (1990). <u>An Introduction to Scientific Research</u>. New York: Dover.

Appendix C: Elements of Statistical Analysis of Data

In the following sections, we introduce you to some elementary statistical concepts that are important for properly analyzing and interpreting data acquired in the experiments presented in this book. We start with the mean, variance, and standard error of a set of measurements, and then illustrate how one can use these data to determine if data from two different sets of measurements come from the same sample population. Next, we illustrate how to determine confidence limits for measured data. An experimental measurement without an accompanying confidence limit is nearly worthless. Invariably, if an experimentally determined confidence limit is not provided, the reader will subconsciously provide one based on experience. This can potentially lead to serious misinterpretation of the data and could possibly be dangerous for the user. Next, we will learn the rudiments of how to perform a simple hypothesis test. We wish to determine whether or not the experimental data meet expectations. We then introduce the concept of linear least squares, a method by which we can fit an analytical expression to observed data. Then we examine how one can determine the standard errors of the least squares fitted parameters. Finally, we introduce the concept of the propagation of errors so that you may estimate the standard errors of parameters that are not observed directly, but are derived from observed data.

It is not our purpose to give a detailed discussion or derivation of the concepts presented here. Rather, we present only on outline of the concepts and then try to integrate each concept into the various experiments so that you will be able to learn, and appreciate the power of, these concepts by example rather than from a theoretical discourse. Of course, the references by Mandel (1964), Glantz (2005), or Montgomery and Runger (2006), or many other standard statistics texts should be referenced for further details. These references are given in Section 2.3 of the text.

Sample Mean and Variance

It is important to know if the components you are using come from a sample that is representative of the nominal value of the component. To determine if this is the case, we must measure the mean value of the sample, its variance, and then must determine if this sample is "close enough" to the nominal value. You will learn the details of such calculations in your statistics course. The mean, the variance, and the standard error of a set of measured values (of, for example, the resistances of a batch of resistors) are, respectively

$$\overline{X} = \frac{\sum_{i=1}^{n} X_i}{n} \tag{1}$$

$$s^2 = \frac{\sum_{i=1}^{n}\left(X_i - \overline{X}\right)^2}{n-1} \tag{2}$$

$$s = \sqrt{s^2} \tag{3}$$

Here, n is the number of components in the sample. The values of $\bar{X}$, s^2, and s are the mean, the variance, and the standard deviation of the population of the measured components. Note that the denominator of Eq (2) is $n-1$. This is known as the unbiased estimate of the variance. Some computer programs compute the biased variance of the data in which the denominator of Eq (2) is n rather than $n-1$. If the sample size is small, significant errors can be made by computing the wrong variance.

Central Limit Theorem

Let us measure the mean value of a very large population of components (e.g., resistors or capacitors) many times, each time using a sample size of n for each measurement. A fundamental theorem of statistics known as the *central limit theorem*, states that the distribution formed by the averages of independent samples of the population, all of size n, will tend to be Gaussian or normal regardless of the distribution of the original population. This is important for our study of resistors and capacitors in Experiment 2 because their manufacturing processes do not necessarily yield a normal distribution of resistor or capacitor values.

Confidence Limits

If we take a sample size n of components from this larger population (say an entire production run) of components, then the standard error of the mean of this sample will be given by

$$s_{\bar{X}} = s / \sqrt{n} \tag{4}$$

If μ is the mean of the population of components and if $\sigma_{\bar{X}}$ is the standard error of the mean of this population, then it can be shown that the distribution of the variable Z, which is given by

$$Z = \frac{\bar{X} - \mu}{\sigma_{\bar{X}}} \tag{5}$$

follows a standard normal distribution. However, the variance of the population, $\sigma_{\bar{X}}^2$, is generally not known. If we use $s_{\bar{X}}^2$ as a best estimate of $\sigma_{\bar{X}}^2$, then it is found that the variable

$$Z = \frac{\bar{X} - \mu}{s_{\bar{X}}} \tag{6}$$

follows a t-distribution with $\nu = n-1$ degrees of freedom. As $\nu \to \infty$, the t-distribution becomes a normal or Gaussian distribution. A table of values of the t-statistic for various percentage points is given in Table C.1. In this table, α is the area under the t-distribution from $t_{\alpha,\nu}$ to infinity or from $-t_{\alpha,\nu}$ to minus infinity.

The probability P that a given mean $\overline{X}$ determined from a sample of size n of the population deviates from the population mean μ by an amount $t_{\alpha,v}$ is given by

$$P(\overline{X} > t_{\alpha,v}) = \alpha \tag{7}$$

Similarly, on the lower side

$$P(\overline{X}_n < -t_{\alpha,v}) = \alpha \tag{8}$$

From Eqs (7) and (8), we may determine the confidence interval for our estimate of the population mean as

$$\overline{X} - t_{\alpha/2,v} \cdot s_{\overline{X}} < \mu < \overline{X} + t_{\alpha/2,v} \cdot s_{\overline{X}} \tag{9}$$

Notice that to have 95% confidence that μ lies between the limits given in Eq (9), we must use $t_{\alpha/2,v}$ to account for the 2.5% probability that it lies above the given range and 2.5% probability that it lies below.

Hypothesis Tests

We may also use the t-statistic to test hypotheses. For example, in Experiment 2, two important hypotheses we wish to test are (1) does the nominal value of a resistor properly describe the mean values of the actual resistors as manufactured? and (2) are two different samples of devices from the same population? The first test is important for determining if a sample of n resistors has a mean described by the nominal value of the resistors (i.e., are the resistors truly 10 kΩ resistors as marked by the color codes), while the second test is important for determining whether two different collections of resistors come from the same population. In the first case, we calculate the t-statistic as

$$t = \frac{\overline{X} - X_{\mathrm{nom}}}{s_{\overline{X}}} \tag{10}$$

where X_{nom} is the nominal value of the component's value to which we wish to compare our sample of components. If the value of t is larger than the value of $t_{\alpha/2,v}$ obtained from Table C.1, then we may conclude that the nominal value of the resistor is does not described the sample distribution at the 1- α confidence level.

If we wish to compare two distributions, such as two different groups of components that may have been collected from two different manufacturing runs, we must compute the t-statistic

$$t = \frac{\overline{X}_1 - \overline{X}_2}{\sqrt{s_{\overline{X}_1}^2 + s_{\overline{X}_2}^2}} \tag{11}$$

If we want to determine, for example, if the mean of sample 1 is larger than the mean of sample 2, then the t-statistic is compared with the value of $t_{\alpha,v}$ found in the table where the degrees of freedom is now $v = 2n - 2$. A similar argument can be made to determine if the mean of sample 1 is less than the mean of sample 2. On the other hand, if we wish to determine only if the mean of sample 1 is different from the mean of sample 2, then we must compare the t-statistic with

$t_{\alpha/2,v}$ If the sample sizes are not equal, then the denominator of Eq (11) must be replaced by the pooled estimate of the variance and Eq (11) becomes

$$t = \frac{\overline{X}_{n,1} - \overline{X}_{n,2}}{\sqrt{\dfrac{s^2}{n_1} + \dfrac{s^2}{n_2}}} \tag{12}$$

where

$$s^2 = \frac{(n_1 - 1)s_1^2 + (n_2 - 1)s_2^2}{n_1 + n_2 - 2} \tag{13}$$

is the pooled estimate of the variances and the degrees of freedom is $v = n_1 + n_2 - 2$.

Method of Least Squares

If one gathers data in which a dependent variable is measured while one or more independent variables are changed (e.g., when the current though a device is measured as the voltage across the device is varied), it is generally observed that the dependent (measured) results are scattered to a greater or lesser degree around the expected theoretical curve that relates the dependent and independent variables. The question arises as to what is the best analytical representation of a curve through the measured data. As is shown in standard statistical texts such as those by Miller and Freund (1977), Mandel (1964), Glantz (2005), or Montgomery and Runger (2006), perhaps the most widely accepted mathematical model is the method of least squares. In this method, the coefficients of the relationship between the independent variables and the dependent variable are found such that the sum of the squares of the deviations of the observed data from the analytical expression is minimized. There are several variants of this method: a simple linear least squares in which the relationship between the dependent variable and a single independent variable is a straight line; a non-linear least squares in which the relationship between the dependent variable and a single independent variable is a non-linear relationship; and a multivariable linear least squares in which the relationships between the dependent variable and multiple independent variables are each linear. In this text, only the first method will be used. The reader is referred to the cited texts for information concerning the latter two methods.

In the method of linear least squares, we wish to find the coefficients (a,b) that will minimize the sum of the squares of the deviation of n measured data points from the straight line $y = a + bx$. It can be shown (Miller and Freund, 1977) that (a, b) are given by the solution to the normal equations

$$\sum_{i=1}^{n} y_i = an + b \sum_{i-1}^{n} x_i \tag{14}$$

and

$$\sum_{i=1}^{n} x_i y_i = a \sum_{i=1}^{n} x_i + b \sum_{i=1}^{n} x_i^2 \tag{15}$$

Most scientific calculating programs such as Excel and MATLAB have built-in functions to compute (a, b). If you cannot find the necessary built-in functions for your graphing program, the parameters are easily computed in a spreadsheet from Eqs (14) and (15).

Least Squares Confidence Intervals

Of particular importance, one also wishes to know the confidence intervals for (a, b). These are, respectively, given by the expressions

$$-t_{\alpha/2} \cdot s_e \sqrt{\frac{S_{xx} + (n\bar{x})^2}{nS_{xx}}} \leq a \leq t_{\alpha/2} \cdot s_e \sqrt{\frac{S_{xx} + (n\bar{x})^2}{nS_{xx}}} \tag{16}$$

and

$$-t_{\alpha/2} \cdot s_e \sqrt{\frac{n}{S_{xx}}} \leq b \leq t_{\alpha/2} \cdot s_e \sqrt{\frac{n}{S_{xx}}} \tag{17}$$

In Eqs (16) and (17), the variable $t_{\alpha/2}$ is the t-variable described above and given in Appendix C, while the computed variables are given by

$$s_e^2 = \frac{S_{xx} S_{yy} - \left(S_{xy}\right)^2}{n(n-2) S_{xx}} \tag{18}$$

where

$$S_{xx} = n \sum_{i-1}^{n} x_i^2 - \left(\sum_{i=1}^{n} x_i\right)^2$$

$$S_{yy} = n \sum_{i-1}^{n} y_i^2 - \left(\sum_{i=1}^{n} y_i\right)^2 \tag{19}$$

$$S_{xy} = n \sum_{i-1}^{n} x_i y_i - \left(\sum_{i=1}^{n} x_i\right)\left(\sum_{i=1}^{n} y_i\right)$$

When one determines the least squares coefficients (a,b), one should always compute their confidence intervals using the methodology described above. We note that neither Excel nor MATLAB have such built-in capabilities, and the computations required in Eqs (16) through (19) must be programmed by the user.

Important Note: If the confidence interval for either of the variables (a,b) includes zero within its range, then that coefficient is not statistically significantly different from zero for the level of confidence selected.

Linearization Of Equations

If one has a model for a circuit that one wishes to verify experimentally, the discussion above is fine provided the model is linear. What should one do if the relationship is non-linear? For example, what if one wishes to determine the non-ideality factor, n, of a diode from the expression

$$I = I_o e^{\frac{eV}{nkT}} \tag{20}$$

By measuring the current, I, through the device by varying the applied voltage, V, at fixed absolute temperature, how should one proceed, especially if one also wishes to determine the confidence interval for n?

A simple way to accomplish this is by linearizing Eq (20) by taking the natural logarithm of each side of the equation. In this case, Eq (20) transforms to

$$\ln(I) = \frac{eV}{nkT} + \ln(I_o) \tag{21}$$

Then, if one sets

$$\begin{aligned} y_i &= \ln\left(I_i\right) \\ x_i &= V_i \end{aligned} \tag{22}$$

and uses Eqs (14) and (15) to find (a,b), then we find that

$$\begin{aligned} a &= \ln\left(I_o\right) \\ b &= \frac{e}{nkT} \end{aligned} \tag{23}$$

The value of n is easily found from the equation for b.

Propagation of Errors

Finally, we discuss the propagation of errors when one has a situation in which the desired variable is not directly measured, but is a derived value, as in the case of the non-ideality factor described above. For this discussion, consider a variable X which is a function of several independent variables x_i as given by $X = X(x_1, x_2, \ldots x_n)$. It can then be shown (Mandel, 1964) that

$$\sigma_X^2 = \left(\frac{\partial X}{\partial x_1}\right)^2 \sigma_{x_1}^2 + \left(\frac{\partial X}{\partial x_2}\right)^2 \sigma_{x_2}^2 + \cdots + \left(\frac{\partial X}{\partial x_1}\frac{\partial X}{\partial x_2}\right) \cdot \text{cov}(x_1, x_2) + \cdots \quad (24)$$

where $\sigma_{x_i}^2$ is the variance of x_i and $\text{cov}(x_i, x_j)$ is the covariance between variables (x_i, x_j).

As an example, let us estimate the standard error of the non-ideality factor as described above. By linearizing Eq (20) as described above, and solving the second expression of Eq (23) for n, we can find, from Eq (24), that if the temperature is held constant

$$\sigma_n^2 = \left(\frac{\partial n}{\partial b}\right)^2 \sigma_b^2 = \left(\frac{-e}{b^2 kT}\right)^2 \sigma_b^2 = n^2 \frac{\sigma_b^2}{b^2} \quad (25)$$

Thus, we can find the estimated variance and standard error of the non-ideality factor by using the estimated variance of the slope of the linearized equation as determined in the previous section.

Table C.1 Percentage points of Student's t-test distribution[†]

v	90%	95%	97.5%	99%	99.5%	99.75%	99.9%	99.95%
1	3.078	6.314	12.71	31.82	63.66	127.3	318.3	636.6
2	1.886	2.920	4.303	6.965	9.925	14.09	22.33	31.60
3	1.638	2.353	3.182	4.541	5.841	7.453	10.21	12.92
4	1.533	2.132	2.776	3.747	4.604	5.598	7.173	8.610
5	1.476	2.015	2.571	3.365	4.032	4.773	5.893	6.869
6	1.440	1.943	2.447	3.143	3.707	4.317	5.208	5.959
7	1.415	1.895	2.365	2.998	3.499	4.029	4.785	5.408
8	1.397	1.860	2.306	2.896	3.355	3.833	4.501	5.041
9	1.383	1.833	2.262	2.821	3.250	3.690	4.297	4.781
10	1.372	1.812	2.228	2.764	3.169	3.581	4.144	4.587
11	1.363	1.796	2.201	2.718	3.106	3.497	4.025	4.437
12	1.356	1.782	2.179	2.681	3.055	3.428	3.930	4.318
13	1.350	1.771	2.160	2.650	3.012	3.372	3.852	4.221
14	1.345	1.761	2.145	2.624	2.977	3.326	3.787	4.140
15	1.341	1.753	2.131	2.602	2.947	3.286	3.733	4.073
16	1.337	1.746	2.120	2.583	2.921	3.252	3.686	4.015
17	1.333	1.740	2.110	2.567	2.898	3.222	3.646	3.965
18	1.330	1.734	2.101	2.552	2.878	3.197	3.610	3.922
19	1.328	1.729	2.093	2.539	2.861	3.174	3.579	3.883
20	1.325	1.725	2.086	2.528	2.845	3.153	3.552	3.850
30	1.310	1.697	2.042	2.457	2.750	3.030	3.385	3.646
40	1.303	1.684	2.021	2.423	2.704	2.971	3.307	3.551
50	1.299	1.676	2.009	2.403	2.678	2.937	3.261	3.496
60	1.296	1.671	2.000	2.390	2.660	2.915	3.232	3.460
80	1.292	1.664	1.990	2.374	2.639	2.887	3.195	3.416
100	1.290	1.660	1.984	2.364	2.626	2.871	3.174	3.390
∞	1.282	1.645	1.960	2.326	2.576	2.807	3.090	3.291

[†]Table adapted from <http://en.wikipedia.org/wiki/student%27s_t-distribution> The table selected values for distributions with v degrees of freedom for the 90%, 95%, … 99.95% confidence intervals ($\alpha = 0.10, 0.05, …0.0005$, respectively.)

Notes

The data in Table C.1 are "one-sided." This means that for the entry 1.833 under $v = 9$ and 95% (a sample size of 10 with 9 degrees of freedom and 95% confidence limit or $\alpha = 0.05$), then $P(t < 1.833) = 0.95$. It also means $P(t > -1.833) = 0.95$. Thus, $P(-1.833 < t < 1.833) = 0.90$.

Example

Consider a sample of 21 ea 1 kΩ, 5% tolerance resistors. We determine that the mean resistance is 984 Ω with a standard deviation of 17.2 Ω. No single measurement is observed below 950 Ω or above 1050 Ω. The resistors are color-coded as (brown, black, red, gold). Are these resistors properly color-coded?

Answer: At the 95% confidence level, $t_{v,\,\alpha/2} = t_{20,\,0.025} = 2.086$. Thus, the population mean, μ, is thus expected to lie between

$$\overline{X} - t_{v,\,\alpha/2} \cdot \frac{s}{\sqrt{n}} < \mu < \overline{X} + t_{v,\,\alpha/2} \cdot \frac{s}{\sqrt{n}}$$

Substituting values, we find

$$984 - 2.086 \cdot \frac{17.2}{\sqrt{21}} < \mu < 984 + 2.086 \cdot \frac{17.2}{\sqrt{21}}\ \Omega.$$

or

$$976 < \mu < 992$$

Thus, although all the resistors are within the tolerance of a 5%, 1 kΩ resistor, this sample of resistors comes from a population that is statistically significantly different (at the 95% confidence level) from the nominal value of 1 kΩ. Examination of Table 11 in Section 3.8 shows that the nearest resistor below 1 kΩ in the E24 (5%) series is 910 Ω. None of the resistors fall within its 5% tolerance band of [864; 956] Ω. Thus, the resistors cannot be classified as 910 Ω, 5% resistors. Further, consider the possibility that they could be 953 Ω, 2% resistors from the E48 series. These resistors must have all of their values lying in the range [934; 972] which is clearly not the case. Thus, this sample of resistors is correctly color-coded.

This result has implications for circuit modeling using PSpice. If the circuit calls for nominal 1 kΩ, 5% resistors and the analysis is being performed prior to purchase of a given lot of resistors, then in a sensitivity or Monte Carlo analysis, these are the values that must be used. However, if the analysis is being performed post-purchase of the resistors described in this example, then it would be appropriate to use a 984 Ω, 1% resistor $(7.8/984 \cdot 100\% \approx 1\%)$ for an analysis at the 95% confidence level.

Appendix D: MATLAB Codes

D.1 Experiment 27–complexpowerlab.m

```
% complexpowerlab.m
% Version 1.3
% Updated Wednesday, March 22, 2006

clear
clc

A = input('\nInput current magnitude in milliAmps: ');
B = input('Input current phase in degrees: ');
D = input('Input instantaneous maximum power in milliWatts: ');
C = input('Input instantaneous minimum power in milliWatts: ');
E = input('Input the frequency of the function generator in Hertz: ');

% Calculations based on current and phase angle:    These calculations assume a Voltage of 1 Volt at 0
degrees phase angle
ApparentPower1=abs(.5*A*1*exp(j*B));        %This is equation 38
AveragePower1=abs(.5*A*1*cos(B*pi/180));      %This is equation 37
ReactivePower1=abs(.5*A*1*sin(B*pi/180));     %This is equation 42
PowerFactor1=cos(B*pi/180);
%%%%%%%%%%%%%%%%%%%%%%%%%%%%%%%%%%%%%%%%%%%%%%%%%%%%%%%%%%%%%%%%%%

% Calculations based on max and min power
ApparentPower2=.5*(D-C);            %These are a consequence of equation 41, and can be seen
AveragePower2=.5*(D+C);             %graphically in Figure 11.2 of Alexander and Sadiku
PowerFactor2=AveragePower2/ApparentPower2;   %PF is a ratio of real power to apparent power
ReactivePower2=sqrt(ApparentPower2*ApparentPower2-AveragePower2*AveragePower2);   %Comes
from solving equation 43
%%%%%%%%%%%%%%%%%%%%%%%%%%%%%%%%%%%%%%%%%%%%%%%%%%%%%%%%%%%%%%%%%%

% Graph of the voltage, current and power waveforms
t=0:.00001:(2/E);
Voltage=A*cos(2*pi*E*t);
Current=A*cos(2*pi*E*t + B*pi/180);
Apparent=.5*max(Current)*cos(0-B*pi/180)+.5*max(Current)*cos(2*pi*2*E*t+0+B*pi/180);
figure;
subplot(2,1,1);
hold on;
plot(t,Apparent,'b');
plot(t,Voltage,'g');
plot(t,Current,'r');
axis tight;
grid on;
plot(t,Apparent,'blue');
legend('Power','Voltage','Current');
xlabel('Time (ms)');
ylabel('Magnitude');
title('Voltage and Current Creating Real and Reactive Power');
```

```
hold off

% Explanation of the 3 waveforms
subplot(2,1,2);
axis off;
text(0,1,'This graph shows the positions of the voltage, current and power waveforms over');
text(0,.85,'time. The voltage should actually be 1 volt, but has been scaled down to illustrate');
text(0,.7,'phase shifting. If the voltage and current waveforms were in phase, then the power');
text(0,.55,'factor would be 1 (unity) The waveforms are not identical, and therefore we have');
text(0,.4,'reactive power loss. Also note that the frequency of the power waveform is twice');
text(0,.25,'that of the voltage and current waveforms.');
%%%%%%%%%%%%%%%%%%%%%%%%%%%%%%%%%%%%%%%%%%%%%%%%%%%%%%%%%%%%%%%%

% Graph of the power waveform
figure;
subplot(2,1,1);
hold on;
plot(t,Apparent,'blue');
axis tight
grid on;
AverageLine=.5*(max(Apparent)+min(Apparent));
plot(t,AverageLine,'red');
xlabel('Time (ms)');
ylabel('Power in milliWatts');
title('The Power Waveform');
legend('Power','Average Power');

% Explanation of the power waveform
subplot(2,1,2);
axis off;
text(0,1,'This graph shows the power waveform over time. The amplitude of which is');
text(0,.85,'Apparent Power (S). Any value below the X-Axis is called Reactive Power (Q),');
text(0,.7,'and simply means that the storage device (such as an inductor or capacitor)');
text(0,.55,'is actually supplying power to the power supply. The device is supplying')
text(0,.4,'this power for the duration of time that the waveform is below the X-Axis.');
text(0,.25,'In addition, the Average Power (P) line shown in red falls as well. Thus we');
text(0,.1,'can see how important that maintaining unity power factor is for AC systems');

% Required Lab Values
hold off;
figure(2);
fprintf('\nApparent Power Based on Current Magnitude and Phase is: %f', ApparentPower1);
fprintf(' milliVA \nAverage Power Based on Current Magnitude and Phase is: %f', AveragePower1);
fprintf(' milliWatts \nReactive Power Based on Current Magnitude and Phase is: %f', ReactivePower1);
fprintf(' milliVARS \nPower Factor Based on Current Magnitude and Phase is: %f', PowerFactor1);
fprintf('\n\nApparent Power Based on Instantaneous Power is: %f', ApparentPower2);
fprintf(' milliVA \nAverage Power Based on Instantaneous Power is: %f', AveragePower2);
fprintf(' milliWatts \nReactive Power Based on Instantaneous Power is: %f', ReactivePower2);
fprintf(' milliVARS \nPower Factor Based on Instantaneous Power is: %f', PowerFactor2);
fprintf('\n\n');
```

```
% Percent Deviation Calculations
EApparentPower = input('Please input your expected Apparent power in milliVA: ');
EAveragePower = input('Please input your expected Average power in milliWatts: ');
EReactivePower = input('Please input your expected Reactive power in milliVARS: ');

InternalApparentDeviation=(100*abs(ApparentPower1-ApparentPower2)/ApparentPower2);
InternalAverageDeviation=(100*abs(AveragePower1-AveragePower2)/AveragePower2);
InternalReactiveDeviation=(100*abs(ReactivePower1-ReactivePower2)/ReactivePower2);

ExternalApparentDeviation=(100*abs(ApparentPower1-EApparentPower)/EApparentPower);
ExternalAverageDeviation=(100*abs(AveragePower1-EAveragePower)/EAveragePower);
ExternalReactiveDeviation=(100*abs(ReactivePower1-EReactivePower)/EReactivePower);


if(InternalApparentDeviation<15)
    fprintf('\nApparent power derived from p(t) and from the current magnitude and phase are within
acceptable (+/-15 percent) margins');
else
    fprintf('\nApparent power derived from p(t) and from the current magnitude and phase are NOT within
acceptable (+/-15 percent) margins');
end
if(InternalAverageDeviation<15)
    fprintf('\nAverage power derived from p(t) and from the current magnitude and phase are within
acceptable (+/-15 percent) margins');
else
    fprintf('\nAverage power derived from p(t) and from the current magnitude and phase are NOT within
acceptable (+/-15 percent) margins');
end
if(InternalReactiveDeviation<25)
    fprintf('\nReactive power derived from p(t) and from the current magnitude and phase are within
acceptable (+/-25 percent) margins');
else
    fprintf('\nReactive power derived from p(t) and from the current magnitude and phase are NOT within
acceptable (+/-25 percent) margins');
end

if(ExternalApparentDeviation<15)
    fprintf('\n\nApparent power derived from the current magnitude and phase and your analytical results are
within acceptable (+/-15 percent) margins');
else
    fprintf('\n\nApparent power derived from the current magnitude and phase and your analytical results are
NOT within acceptable (+/-15 percent) margins');
end
if(ExternalAverageDeviation<15)
    fprintf('\nAverage power derived from the current magnitude and phase and your analytical results are
within acceptable (+/-15 percent) margins');
else
    fprintf('\nAverage power derived from the current magnitude and phase and your analytical results are
NOT within acceptable (+/-15 percent) margins');
```

```
end
if(ExternalReactiveDeviation<15)
    fprintf('\nReactive power derived from the current magnitude and phase and your analytical results are
within acceptable (+/-15 percent) margins');
else
    fprintf('\nReactive power derived from the current magnitude and phase and your analytical results are
NOT within acceptable (+/-15 percent) margins');
end

fprintf('\n\nPercent deviation for Apparent Power in this circuit is: %f', ExternalApparentDeviation);
fprintf(' Percent \nPercent deviation for Average Power in this circuit is: %f', ExternalAverageDeviation);
fprintf(' Percent \nPercent deviation for Reactive Power in this circuit is: %f', ExternalReactiveDeviation);
fprintf(' Percent\n');
```

D.2 Experiment 34–networkfunction.m

```
%networkfunction.m - Plot the Bode plot of a network function
%      Based on Dorf and Svoboda, Introduction to Electric Circuits (7e),
%      Hoboken: John Wiley (2006). p.631
%
%      Version 1.0 11/01/2006
%
clear
clc
%
%-------------------------------------------------------------------
%      Create a list of logarithmically spaced frequencies
%-------------------------------------------------------------------
wmin=10;          % starting frequency, rad/s
wmax=100000;      % ending frequency, rad/s
w=logspace(log10(wmin),log10(wmax));
%-------------------------------------------------------------------
%      Enter values of the parameters that describe the network function
%-------------------------------------------------------------------
K=10;             % constant
z=1000;           % zero
p1=100; p2=10000; % poles
%-------------------------------------------------------------------
%      Calculate the value of the network function at each frequency
%      Calculate the magnitude and angle of the network function
%-------------------------------------------------------------------
for k=1:length(w)
    H(k)=K*(1+j*w(k)/z)/((1+j*w(k)/p1)*(1+j*w(k)/p2));
    mag(k)=abs(H(k));
    phase(k)=180*angle(H(k))/pi;
end
%-------------------------------------------------------------------
%      Enter Experimental Data as magnitude (Hdata), phase (Pdata), and
%      frequency (Fdata) in Hz.
%-------------------------------------------------------------------
    Hdata=[9, 5, 2, 1, 1, 0.5, 0.15];
    Pdata=[-25, -50, -55, -38, -40, -70, -85 ];
    Fdata=[10, 30, 100, 300, 1000, 3000, 10000];
%-------------------------------------------------------------------
%      Plot the analytical Bode plot with experimental data points
%-------------------------------------------------------------------
set(gcf, 'Color', [1,1,1]);    % set the background color to white
subplot(2,1,1), semilogx(w/(2*pi), 20*log10(mag), 'k', Fdata,
20*log10(Hdata),'ko')
axis([ 1,100000, -20, 20]);    % scale the y-axis of H
xlabel( 'Frequency (Hz)' ), ylabel( 'Gain (dB)' )
title( 'Bode plot', 'Fontsize', 12, 'Fontweight', 'bold'  )
subplot(2,1,2), semilogx(w/(2*pi), phase, 'k', Fdata, Pdata, 'ko')
axis([1, 100000, -90, 0]);     % scale the y-axis of the phase angle
xlabel( 'Frequency (Hz)' ), ylabel( 'Phase (degrees)' )
```

Appendix E: Derived SI Units

Table E.1 Derived SI units with special names

Quantity	Units	Symbol	Basic units
force	newton	N	$kg \cdot m/s^2 = J/m$
energy	joule	J	$kg \cdot m^2/s^2 = N \cdot m$
power	watt	W	$kg \cdot m^2/s^3 = J/s$
pressure	pascal	Pa	$kg/s^2 \cdot m = N/m^2$
temperature	degree Celsius	°C	$= K - 273.15$
electric charge	coulomb	C	$= A \cdot s$
electric potential difference (voltage)	volt	V	$kg \cdot m^2/s^3 \cdot A = J/A \cdot s = W/A$
electric resistance	ohm	Ω	$kg \cdot m^2/s^3 \cdot A^2 = V/A$
electric conductance	siemens	S	$s^3 \cdot A^2 / kg \cdot m^2 = A/V = 1/\Omega$
electric capacitance	farad	F	$A^2 \cdot s^4/kg \cdot m^2 = A \cdot s/V = C^2/N \cdot m$
electric inductance	henry	H	$kg \cdot m^2/s^2 \cdot A^2 = V \cdot s/A$
magnetic flux	weber	Wb	$kg \cdot m^2/s^2 \cdot A = V \cdot s$
magnetic flux density	tesla	T	$kg/s^2 \cdot A = V \cdot s/m^2 = Wb/m^2$
luminous flux	lumen	lm	$= cd \cdot sr$
illumination	lux	lx	$cd \cdot sr/m^2 = lm/m^2$
frequency	hertz	Hz	$cycles/s = s^{-1}$

(Based on data in Table 2.1.3 of Fischbech and Fischbeck, (1987).
<u>Formulas, Facts and Constants</u> (2/E). Berlin: Springer-Verlag . p111.)

Appendix F: Derived SI Units

Table F.1 SI and PSpice unit prefixes

Exponent	Prefix	SI Symbol	PSpice Symbol[*]
10^{12}	tera-	T	T
10^{9}	giga-	G	G
10^{6}	mega-	M	MEG
10^{3}	kilo-	K or k	K
10^{-3}	milli-	m	M
10^{-6}	micro-	μ	U
10^{-9}	nano-	n	N
10^{-12}	pico-	p	P
10^{-15}	femto	f	F

* The prefixes used in PSpice are case-insensitive, which is why the prefix for mega and milli must be spelt differently.

Photo Credits

Photo	Page	Source
Figure 1	2	WD Shumate
Figure 2	3	Electronix Express
Figure 4	36	Electronix Express
Figure 5	39	RB Lineberry
Figure 6	39	RB Lineberry
Figure 8	41	RB Lineberry
Figure 9	41	RB Lineberry
Figure 10	41	RB Lineberry
Figure 11	42	RB Lineberry
Figure 12	42	RB Lineberry
Figure 13	44	Electronix Express
Figure 14	44	JB Webb
Figure 15	45	JB Webb
Figure 16(a)	46	JB Webb
Figure 16(b)	46	WD Shumate
Figure 19	58	WD Shumate
Figure 21	62	Coil Winding Specialists
Figure 22	64	WD Shumate
Figure 24	65	WD Shumate
Figure 26	66	WD Shumate
Figure 27	69	STMicroelectronics
Figure 28	69	National Semiconductor
Figure 31	72	WD Shumate

The quotation on page v is from R. Feynman, The Character of Physical Law, Cambridge, MA: The MIT Press (1965), p127.